ORATOR PUBLISHING
51 Cheap Street,
Sherborne,
Dorset DT9 3AX
www.junglenomics.com

First published 2019

Hardback ISBN - 978-1-9164823-0-2
paperback ISBN - 978-1-9164823-1-9
mobi ISBN - 978-1-9164823-2-6
epub ISBN - 978-1-9164823-3-3

Printed and bound in the United Kingdom by
www.spiffingcovers.com

Cover design and layout by www.spiffingcovers.com

Junglenomics

Nature's solutions to the world environment crisis:
a new paradigm for the 21ˢᵗ century and beyond

Simon M Lamb

Orator
Publishing

Preface

*"You never change things by fighting the
existing reality. To change something, build a
new model that makes the existing model obsolete"*
Buckminster Fuller (1895-1983) –
philosopher, futurist and global thinker

For millions of years ecosystems have kept a fine balance between competitors for the Earth's resources so that no single organism has been able to monopolise them. But for the first time in the long history of Life on Earth that balance has been disturbed. The culprit is human economic activity in the form of markets, and despite efforts to address it the resulting environmental fallout remains severe and ongoing, with potential consequences that hardly bear contemplation. Yet although today's conflict between economics and Nature is so intense that it may seem irreconcilable, this book describes how we can in fact reconcile them. We can do so by emulating the very thing we are at odds with – natural ecosystems.

First base in this is to approach the problem dispassionately: markets may be responsible for the steep decline in the health of the world's natural environments and their precious cargo of biodiversity, but intrinsically they are neither good nor evil: they are only the manifestation in economics of a fundamental force within *all* living things – an irresistible drive to colonise resources. I'm going to explore how this understanding can show us the way to harness those same markets to stop and even reverse the precipitous environmental decline that threatens our well-being – some say our very survival – and to exist benignly alongside our fellow species for the long-term future.

I would like to begin, not as you might expect at the Industrial Revolution and the great explosion of markets that followed, but at the very birth of the economic world some 15,000 years ago. Why? Because understanding the historical factors that have brought us to this dangerous place is essential for identifying the most effective ways to turn things around.

A fresh approach is much needed. Nations have gathered more than 20 times to discuss rescuing the world's environments, and almost every time they have declared reams of good intentions. A pretty clear picture of what needs to be done has emerged – a must-do list that stretches from carbon reduction, to rainforest protection, to ocean governance, to pollution eradication, to food security. Yet despite all the talk and promises, to many people's immense frustration, little of substance has been achieved and the environmental slide has continued largely unchecked.

Encouragingly though, the subject has at last taken centre stage and minds have been fully concentrated on it. The result is that the much-fanfared "COP21" meeting in Paris late in 2015 was well attended. It succeeded in setting by far the most ambitious targets yet through a raft of voluntary pledges by 196 nations. Enthusiasm for the resulting accord was not in short supply; it was hailed as "monumental" and "a turning point". Yet if we have learned anything from the many previous meetings, it is that promises are cheap. Even if it is a turning point, the Paris Accord is still only the beginning of the story – the first step on a long and difficult journey towards a sustainable relationship with the natural world. With targets now set, the challenge is no longer *what* to aim for, but *how* to get it done. *Implementation* is the new watchword.

However, the world is a complex place with innumerable competing economic and political interests that frequently clash, undermining even the best and most organised of plans. So how can nations turn their enthusiasm and good intentions into reality? How can they tame the powerful market forces that have caused our excesses and yet still develop and grow their economies in order to bring people out of poverty? This is now the greatest challenge facing the world. For if world leaders cannot bring their pledges to fruition soon then all their talk and planning will once again be wasted, and the world will continue on a path towards a future that is unworthy of mankind's extraordinary intelligence and ability.

Carbon-generated climate change is seen as the biggest environmental issue, but it is by no means the only one. Biodiversity, the oceans, pollution, poverty – these too are vital global issues that equally deserve our immediate attention. It is therefore time to harness the ardour and momentum gained in Paris to do much more than reduce carbon emissions, and to fundamentally revise our entire interface with the natural world.

Despite much doomsaying that it is already too late, I believe there is still time to achieve the ultimate goal of reconciling our economic needs with those of the natural world, but only if nations thoroughly review their thinking and go about it in the right way.

So what is the right way?

Junglenomics describes how to turn these ambitions into reality. It does so by viewing them through the lens of science – the science of evolution, of ecology and of anthropology. I call the resulting economic paradigm "Ecosystem Economics" – or *Junglenomics* – because it owes its inspiration to the workings of Nature and the organisation of its ecosystems. The guidance it provides is much more than a quick fix: it is a blueprint for our entire future relationship with the planet.

If the mass of scientific evidence is to be believed, it is no exaggeration to say that we are approaching the "last chance saloon", which means that unless the world gets its act together quickly it faces an era of despair and decline. But I will argue that with Nature's guidance, it is not too late to create an era of hope and rejuvenation.

This book shows how we can all play our part in a 21st-century environmental renaissance. By better understanding ourselves and our place in Nature, *Junglenomics* shows how our generation can do something heroic to rescue our declining planet, both for ourselves and for our children, far into the future.

Why You Should Read this Book

Like so many of you, I have spent my life witnessing the decline of the natural environment of this spectacularly beautiful planet with a deep sense of frustration at the seeming inability of mankind to protect the world on which he depends for his very survival. This wilful neglect has gone unchecked for so long that it is even changing the climate, creating an existential threat to humankind.

At the same time, I have always believed passionately in science and in the inimitable workings of evolution. Charles Darwin – a fellow free-thinker from another century who achieved heights of revelation I could only dream of – has been my idol. If scientific discoveries have led us to this place, can science not show us the way out, I asked myself? So some twenty years ago I began to investigate why this extraordinary dichotomy should exist, to enquire what underlying evolutionary reasons could bring the most intelligent entity on the planet to rush so unremittingly towards his own decline and possible destruction in the full knowledge of what he is doing. I began to view it as a phenomenon - one that, like all other things in the Universe, must have a rational, scientific explanation.

It was a fascinating and absorbing journey. Over the years my studies brought me to the writings of inspiring scientists, thinkers and authors such as Dawkins, Lewin, Morgan, Attenborough, Leakey, Carson, Gould, Wills, Wilson, Sacks, Jones, Stern, West-Eberhard, Rattray-Taylor, Sahlins and others, as well as countless papers and articles, and through this I developed a revealing perspective on the conflicts of the human-planetary interface. A powerful certainty came to me – one that not only greatly surprised, but also deeply inspired me. It came not all at once, but in stages, elusive at times, until one day I at last fully grasped the truth - that the only possible way out of our great 21st century quandary comes not from mankind - *but from Nature.*

This book is therefore not some fiendishly cunning plan of my own to save the world – to rescue humanity from its own suicidal tendencies – far from it. It is Nature's. It has been developed over billions of years, producing all the great wonders of Life that so amaze us, including of course ourselves. *Junglenomics* is merely an instrument to explain how Nature's blueprint can – indeed must - be applied to the economic world without delay to guide it to safer waters, just as it nears the reefs.

So why should you read this book? Because it contains a new and important truth about our economic world and a science-based manifesto for change at a time of great need for it. Why should you believe this? Because I come to this greatest issue of our time not only with many years of private study and thought, but also armed with a lifetime of experience in business and investment markets, a close affinity with the natural world and the cycle of the seasons, an unswerving belief in Darwin and in the ubiquity of natural processes, and a passion for the subject that is absolute and unconditional. I wholeheartedly share Jane Goodall's belief that *"every individual has a role to play. Every individual makes a difference"*. This is why I have spent two decades searching for answers to the two most pressing questions of our age: why despite our great intelligence do we, the human race, destroy the natural world? And how can we re-establish our presence within the ancient natural rhythms of life on Earth?

As I think, and therefore write, in plain English, this book is largely free from what Alex Evans called *"the arid jargon... owned by a priesthood of experts"* [1]. Yet it is not simplistic. I harbour no illusions that there's a magic pill to solve the world's environmental problems. Yet neither is it complex, for I will show that there is a clearly recognisable thread running through our history and current affairs that if traced leads to certain logical conclusions, hard on the heels of which come clear solutions. I will bring together all the chief conservation issues under one banner, with one encompassing solution – Ecosystem Economics – *Junglenomics*.

This book is for all those who, like me, care deeply enough about our planet that they are prepared to spend precious time understanding the underlying nature of our problems in order to find solutions to them. That way they can add informed voices to the clamour for fundamental change* that must soon come if dire environmental consequences are to be avoided (*this is now beginning, thanks mainly to Greta Thunberg); that way can the many forces of conservation also unite to help the world move into the new age of human relationships with the natural world that is so urgently needed.

I believe it is for each one of us in every country to impress on those that control national economic levers the urgent need to adopt Nature's ecosystem strategies to rapidly reform all environmentally destructive markets, so that together we can help usher in a brighter, safer future for this precious, irreplaceable Earth. Yet the only way this book can succeed in its ambitions is if you the reader help to spread its message. So I very much hope that you – wherever you may live in the world, for we are all in this together - will review it kindly and recommend it widely. It would be amazing if you would adopt it as your own, so please sign up on the website - www.junglenomics.com - and receive a copy of the summarised *Manifesto for a Planet-Saving Economic Revolution.*

Acknowledgements

Particular thanks go to Myles Archibald for his close interest and encouragement, the convivial lunches and the well-judged 'nudging' that helped me sort a labyrinth of ideas into some kind of order. Thanks are due also to Martin Toseland, Mark Lucas, Howard Herzog, Pavan Sukhdev, Nick Hanley, Humphrey Walwyn, Lisa Genasci, Julia Hailes, Toby Green, Debbie Elliott, and the many people and organisations all over the world who lent me their illustrations and provided information and encouragement. Thanks also to James, Richard and Gabriel at SpiffingCovers for their outstanding work and help in producing this book and the website, and to Angela and Andrea for their scrupulous editing.

Above all though, nothing would have been possible without the loving support, help, encouragement, not to mention considerable forbearance over so many years, of my wonderful wife and companion Kristina.

To Chris, Jamie, Ant, Tom, George, Ollie, Cameron, Sophie and Charlie
and the generations to follow

CONTENTS

PART 1
The Economic Avatar

Chapter 1
The Economic Ecosystem

"Here hills and vales, the woodland and the plain,
Here earth and water seem to strive again;
Not chaos-like together crushed and bruised,
But, as the world, harmoniously confused:
Where order in variety we see,
And where, though all things differ, all agree."
Alexander Pope – "Windsor Forest"

Albert Einstein is lauded as one of the greatest brains of the 20th century – perhaps *the* greatest. His name has become synonymous with extraordinary insights about space, time, matter, gravity and light. And as one would expect of a man of such genius, during his lifetime he articulated a number of profound thoughts, and these live on to guide and inspire us. One such thought has been the primary inspiration for this book. He wrote: *"Look deep into nature, and then you will understand everything better."*

This book is all about looking deep into Nature in order to better understand, and from there to find answers to, the major environmental crises of our era. These answers, it turns out, are hidden in plain sight – within the ecosystems that are everywhere about us.

I said in the preface to this book that markets are to blame for our environmental problems, and this is undoubtedly true. But if markets are to be manipulated into protecting and enhancing the natural world rather than destroying it (which is one of the central themes of this book), it is essential to understand their true nature and discover what drives them – not the superficial economic tides that are often spoken about, but the deeper forces that underlie all behavioural phenomena on our planet.

Thus, to explain the rationale for *Junglenomics* – the ecosystem approach to conservation – as a solution to the decline of the natural world, in this first chapter I'm going to ask you to embark on a brief journey back in time with me. After all, we need to take into account the evolutionary context in which our current destructive behaviour has been incubated. Like all other living things, we humans evolved within ecosystems, the very same ecosystems that we are now destroying. But in the hubris of success we have lost our way, forgotten our roots and denied our true identity as but a single cog in a vibrant worldwide ecosystem.

It's a massive problem. So great is the likelihood for economic conflict with the natural environment today that almost any economic niche that isn't engineered to be systemically benign has potential malfunction – even dysfunction – built into it. To put this right involves first viewing ourselves and our behaviour from an ecosystemic viewpoint. As conservationist Douglas P Wheeler wrote: *"To halt the decline of an ecosystem, it is necessary to think like an ecosystem."*

But before turning the clock back, I believe it is important to set any preconceived ideas about who and what is to blame for our environmental problems to zero. Why? This is best explained with another quote from Einstein: *"We cannot solve our problems with the same thinking we used when we created them."*

So, to borrow from IT jargon, in order to decipher the "source code" of our problems and see how to reset our relationship with the natural world, we first need to shut down our minds and then reboot in "safe mode", liberated from the "cookies" – the entrenched prejudices – that bias our thinking and prevent us from gaining a clear vision of our true place in the world and recognising our route to safety.

One such preconception concerns a subject about which a great deal has been said and written, yet in truth remains little understood. Ask almost anyone what is to blame for the natural world's decline and they will name "greed" as the prime suspect. They may well be right in essence, but what exactly is this "greed" and where does it come from? Some see such greed as intrinsic to human nature, others an acquired societal trait, others again a sickness of the capitalist system.

Yet all these miss the mark. The truth is far more interesting. For while individual avarice is an ugly trait, which may fall into any of these categories, the so-called "greed" to which we attribute environmental over-exploitation is of an entirely different order and has origins that long precede mankind's brief existence. It's important to realise that this fault (if that is what it is) is not unique to us – it is universal. This is because the capturing of resources to provide food, water and shelter is indispensable for survival; it is an integral element of Life, a vibrant, natural process that takes place around us all of the time. It drives not only humans but *all* living creatures – microbes, fungi, plants, insects, fish and mammals alike, to colonise and profit from life-sustaining resources. From ocean to garden pond, from desert to swamp, from jungle to meadow, in our homes, even in our bodies, hordes of organisms dedicate themselves to obtaining and holding niches in which to live and forage. Our planet is truly a maelstrom of resource colonisation; indeed, it is one of the chief activities of living organisms, and has been so since the beginnings of Life on Earth more than three billion years ago.

In point of fact, so vital is it to Life that this "resource hunger", as I prefer to call it, ranks alongside the imperatives to survive and to reproduce and, as such, represents nothing less than a *third primary imperative of Life*. It also lies at the heart of the evolutionary process, causing profound consequences in the form and behaviour of every species as they adapt to capture new resources. Yet remarkably it is almost entirely overlooked by science.*

Resource hunger has likewise been of huge relevance to the evolution of our own species and it remains central to our lives today because, as one of the most successful colonisers of all time, we owe not only our own evolution but also the runaway success of our economic world to its powerful influence. That success has given us an unprecedented dominance

*Author's Note: There is a considerable body of empirical evidence to support these assertions; however, I am reserving them for another book (The Engine of Evolution). Nevertheless, the circumstantial evidence for the rampant drive of Life to colonise new resources is amply illustrated by the very fact that living organisms are present in every place on Earth in which life-sustaining resources are found. I therefore ask for an acceptance that Life's colonising imperative is a truism and recognition that consequently it is also a powerful force in human motivation.

over the natural world, enabling and encouraging our resource hunger to become excessive to the point of self-destruction.

The core reason for our ill treatment of the natural environment thus lies deep in the substrata of the behaviour of all life forms, not just ours, way beneath the exigencies of the everyday struggle for survival, ecological and economic alike. Understanding this is important because it reveals that the gene-driven, colonising forces behind our environmental misdemeanours are too entrenched and powerful to be curtailed by the uncoordinated and piecemeal assortment of economic, ecological and political instruments that we currently deploy to control them. Despite many worthy intentions, because there is no holistic vision in place our decision makers continue to react to environmental events as they happen rather than pre-empting them. One moment the focus is rainforests, the next climate change, the next vehicle emissions, the next oceanic plastics, as if each were a new, separate and surprising development. The result is the ongoing, widespread failure to control events that is so vividly illustrated by the dismal environmental news stream we have to endure on an almost daily basis.

Therefore, the big question for us is how do we go about neutralising the effects that our resource hunger has on the natural world? The moral approach has been tried; it hasn't worked. The legal approach has also been tried; that too has largely failed – hardly surprising when you consider the power of the forces ranged against these attempts. The truth is that Nature holds the answers we need: as Edward O Wilson wrote: *"Nature holds the key to our aesthetic, intellectual, cognitive and even spiritual satisfaction."* One could add "economic satisfaction" to this list, since conserving Nature also holds the key to our future prosperity. We can't of course expect Nature to bail us out directly – it doesn't care a jot about our predicament – but we can take it upon ourselves to try to build similar harmony in our economic world by employing Nature's proven template.

The world's current environmental problems are thus rooted in our past – not the recent past which economists usually concern themselves with, but in that deeper history that is the preserve of anthropologists and archaeologists. To launch this much-needed environmental renaissance, we therefore first need to trace the origins and development of our current resource hunger, beginning with the events that propelled us out of the hunter-gatherer continuum into an alien economic dimension that gave us dominance over so much of the natural world.

The farming revolution and the natural environment

Consider the contrast between our pre-economics existence as nomadic hunter-gatherers, living entirely off the land, owning almost nothing, leaving little or no lasting trace of our passing, and us now in our modern economic guise. It's a startling change in lifestyle for any creature to have undergone in just a few thousand years, which is a tiny blip in evolutionary time. Thanks mostly to the development of hunting weapons and the mastery of fire, the success of the hunter-gatherers was so complete in terms of what was possible for them that they had reached a plateau of achievement. Having adopted the mantle of top predator, they could climb no higher; so there they settled for tens of thousands of years, enjoying Nature's cornucopia as fully adapted and highly skilled wild foragers who neither desired nor required further invention or innovation.

In those ancient times, generation after generation followed each other and little changed, and what did change could take millennia. Hunter-gatherers had become highly successful and influential in the ecosystems they were a part of. It is true that they probably caused the extinction of most megafauna in Eurasia, and later in Australasia and the Americas, because their prey had not benefited from millions of years of co-evolution with them; yet they still existed as an integral part of the revised ecosystems, able to exploit them without diminishing their viability. Their resource hunger was moderate simply because they had little or no use for surplus. Frequently on the move, they had no use for anything they couldn't easily carry with them.

And so it might have remained to this day if something truly extraordinary hadn't taken place. No one alive then could possibly have foreseen the astonishing effects of what was to happen next, for it is near impossible to exaggerate the cultural and psychological gulf that existed between our hunter-gatherer ancestors and their farming successors. So great was this gulf that although they were unchanged genetically, to all intents and purposes the farmers' new way of life turned them into a separate species.

The sea change in our ancestors' behaviour started innocently enough. It began some 15-20,000 years ago, when somewhere a band of hunter-gatherers decided to start experimenting with their local environment. Fire had long been their best friend, and suddenly they found a new use for it. Perhaps tired of having to travel great distances to hunt game, they realised that with a little work they could entice that game to come to them. To do so they began to light fires to alter the landscape, creating a mosaic of grassy clearings to attract prey species such as antelope, bison and aurochs and to encourage the growth of useful plants.

Not particularly dramatic in itself, you might think, this judicious new use of fire. But its eventual consequences were to be Earth-changing – literally. For in this simple act of landscape alteration, our ancestors had struck on a novel realisation that would change their way of living and thinking forever. That realisation was that if you were clever enough, much more could be wrung from the environment than it would naturally provide for you. Instead of being at Nature's behest, they saw that they could take their fate into their own hands.

Over time these foragers' methods became more sophisticated and widespread, and by around 10,000 years ago, merely modifying the landscape had developed into farming much as we know it today – growing crops and rearing domesticated animals. That's quite a leap of course: domesticating wild animals and growing and storing food crops is a long way from landscape alteration with fire and axe. But once the environment-altering mindset was born, it was only a matter of time.

Once farming was discovered, there was no going back. Yet when drought and floods did their worst, and parasites and diseases struck, agriculture proved anything but reliable. Ever oscillating between feast and famine, from here on there was nowhere for farming folk to go but onwards; if agriculture was to support larger than natural populations in the long term, then the pressure was on to improve farming methods, and this could only be achieved by increasing farming knowledge and expertise – and by putting ever more wild land under the plough. A substantial proportion of modern Europe's field systems were created from about 4,500 years ago by clearing huge tracts of forest and scrub, involving an exceptional commitment of time and labour.

The correlation that developed between rising populations and rising food productivity was to have grave consequences for the natural world. Gradually, swathes of the world's surface became clothed in many-coloured crops where far fewer wild species could survive. The upshot is that a planet that would once have sustained only a few million people is today able to support billions; but in so doing we humans have "un-wilded" vast areas of land, elbowing innumerable other species out of the way in the process.

This much is history. But although it was a game changer, it was not farming itself, but the extensive baggage that came with it, that was to make us who we are today. If we look carefully at that baggage, we can get closer to understanding the difficulty we now have in controlling our resource hunger.

Surplus junkies

Had the old hunter-gatherer mindset persisted, our farming ancestors might have grown and reared only those crops and livestock that they needed to survive. As it happens some did get by with such "subsistence" farming, remaining in limbo between one kind of existence and the next. Many tribal peoples in tropical regions still do so, just as a few hunter-gatherers still persist in something akin to the old ways, albeit altered by interactions with agriculturalists and enforced isolation in agriculturally unproductive regions.

It's easy to say "shoulda, coulda, woulda" in respect of how, if sensitively developed, farming might have kept collateral damage to the environment to a minimum; only it doesn't work like that. Farming was a whole new ball game with new rules and new priorities. Little by little, the practical demands of the farming life began to create some deep psychocultural changes in our ancestors, which we have inherited. The most significant of these changes (in relation to the natural environment) are twofold, each as influential as the other, and each a revealing insight into the development of our modern, ultra-resource-hungry persona.

The first change was the brand new (for us) drive to store *surplus* resources. As hunter-gatherers, we were content with the food we had because we knew we could find more at any time. But the advent of larger, crop and cattle-dependent populations meant that foraging in the wild would no longer serve if agriculture failed, as it frequently did. But more importantly, the seasonal nature of arable farming necessitated the producing of sufficient stores of food to enable both people and livestock to survive the winter months or the dry season.

The outcome was that the priority of the new farming communities was no longer amassing *sufficient* resources to meet their immediate needs as hunter-gatherers, but stockpiling *surplus* – and then more surplus on top of that just in case – a belt and braces strategy that would have saved innumerable lives in difficult times. Natural selection thus favoured farming communities that set aside reserves to meet contingencies, a change in focus that was to have major consequences for the generations that followed (*not just in the northern hemisphere – the giant grain stores of the Incan Empire, upon which much of their success was based, still stand as a monument to the same inclination*).

It isn't that other species do not accumulate surpluses; plenty do – honeybees and squirrels for example. And if like them we had limited our excess production to food alone, less harm might have come of it. But the need or desire for surplus was not limited to food production: it developed into a much broader mindset that came to apply to almost everything. Farming had brought about a profound change in our ancestors' psyche, and as a result their lives began to be trammelled by non-essential, excess property. It is no coincidence that archaeological records after this time reveal the growing appearance of non-utilitarian, non-votive objects in grave goods, in particular objects denoting high status, such as precious jewellery and gold torques (neck rings).

To reinforce this change, the hoarding of large surpluses soon became a mark of success – a bright plumage if you like. The words "rich" and "riches" would probably never have entered hunter-gatherers' vocabulary because their riches were of a different order; but now, the more "wealth" that was accumulated, the greater the social status and power of the owner. This created hierarchies – another concept alien to hunter-gatherers.

This is truer than ever today, for the desire to gather surplus has become one of the hallmarks of our era. What is more, the extent to which surplus can be accumulated has been magnified a millionfold by the economic system. It is claimed, for example, that the average US household contains around 300,000 objects [2], from drawing pins to toasters. And while US children make up just 3.7% of the children on the planet, they own nearly half the world's toys and children's books. However, as we now know all too well, the true cost of much of that wealth is much greater than just its dollar price tag: it is creating a growing toll on the environment both in terms of its manufacture and its disposal.

Property ownership as the source of possessiveness and aggression

The second, deep psychocultural change experienced by our farming ancestors radically altered their attitudes towards each other, and equally significantly, towards the natural environment around them. So influential was this change that it was to single-handedly transform the nature of society and sow the seeds for the great developmental upsurge that followed. Today it is central to modern society and economics worldwide. It is the concept of *ownership*.

Our hunter-gatherer ancestors required little to survive and had minimal possessions, so they had no need to be covetous of resources. In contrast, the time and energy that farmers invested in raising crops and cattle meant that they naturally wanted to reserve exclusive access them – to *own* them. By extension, they also wanted to own the land they raised them on, accruing unprecedented value to it and creating settled, rather than mobile, populations.

So for this new breed of men and women, the nomadic life – migrating through wildernesses at the behest of the seasons, blending into the landscape with all the other animals as their ancestors had done for hundreds of generations – was over. The new reality was that the increased food yields which allowed populations to grow caused a level of dependence on controlling food-producing land from which there could be no turning back.

This fact alone makes what followed inevitable – even an essential trait; for securing territory soon became a major driving force in human society. Acquisitiveness, territorialism, possessiveness, covetousness and ambition – all manifestations of a sharply reawakened resource hunger – now became hallmarks of agrarian societies, replacing the easy-going ways of the foraging life, increasing competition, and leading to violent conflicts between groups. Natural selection now favoured those with the wit and wherewithal to defend property, but also to covet and acquire more of it – to *colonise* it, and to be aggressive in doing so.

Survival and success no longer stemmed from cunning and bushcraft, but from gaining and retaining control over land and its resources. Consequently, for the first time in the known history of mankind, the ownership and control of resources became an overriding priority, which meant that they needed to be defended by ever larger, ever more militaristic groups. Little wonder then that an arms race began, and that it continues to this day.

The world had as a result become a perilous place, and the new property culture was to blame. It had changed our ancestors from being social colonisers, spreading gradually across the globe, into being the most rampant resource colonisers the world has ever seen. This was no ordinary coloniser: *Homo sapiens* were on the road to becoming superbeings – heavily armed, sophisticated and extremely dangerous.

It was a sinister foretaste of things to come. For while the profound change to territorialism among farming communities was undoubtedly a major source of our subsequent success, it is not hard to see how it has contributed to nearly all the major social problems from which the world suffers today. For many in society it bore, and continues to bear, a heavy price – exclusion, deprivation, disease, starvation, criminality, social violence, warfare and all the other contingent sufferings of the human story past and present.

These are the human costs of our success, but the natural world has also paid an extortionate price for our meteoric development. These costs – pollution, environmental degradation, resource stripping and species loss, already running at insupportably high levels, continue to rise. And it is all driven by one thing, resource hunger – the universal drive to acquire and control resources, the *colonising imperative* incarnate. This same force drove wave after wave of colonists to cross the steppes and to sail south from Scandinavia as Vikings, amongst innumerable others. It eventually drove northern peoples – Spanish, English, Dutch, German, Portuguese and others – to explore, colonise and exploit the great continents of Africa, the Americas and Australasia, their resource hunger stoked by fierce national rivalries.

It didn't stop there, though. The invention of farming had turned us into a new breed of land-hungry, surplus hoarders, and it was a combination that was soon to bring about a perfect storm of change that far exceeded anything the world had seen before. And it was all down to one consequence of living in the agrarian world: *specialisation*.

Specialisation and the new economic dimension

Whether they would have wanted to or not, let's face it, hunter-gatherers never would have got a look-in among the new farming communities. Admittedly they have survival skills that are second to none, but each hunter-gatherer is essentially a clever jack of all trades with no incentive to innovate. Not so with farmers, though, because as noted earlier their growing populations provided a fresh incentive to develop new techniques and tools to preserve and improve agricultural yields. Innovation therefore became the domain of individuals who had been released from the daily need to forage, which profoundly altered the structure and organisation of human society.

Economists call this "the division of labour", but it is really all about *specialisation*. It could be said that specialisation was the key to all subsequent economic, political and social advances, so it was an extraordinarily significant development. It gave rise to an unprecedented diversity of occupations within communities. One group became responsible for breeding and tending cattle, another for growing corn, one for making cooking vessels and storage jars (potters were among the first and most important specialists [3]), another for making and repairing implements, and so on.

The consequences would have been felt quickly because when we practise one skill, we tend to get better at it; and we all know what practice makes. People also begin to gravitate towards skills that interest them or for which they have a natural aptitude. This in turn leads to all sorts of new ideas about fresh uses for tools, design innovations and to experimenting with new materials. The invention of bronze, by combining copper and tin, surely didn't happen by chance; someone somewhere was actively looking for better materials out of which to make useful objects – and he was probably already experienced in manufacturing tools and weapons before he began to experiment with metals.

It could be said that one of the most interesting things about the growth of specialist skills triggered by the advent of agriculture was the vast extent of their unrealised potential. How could these peoples have the slightest suspicion that specialisation would lead eventually to the invention of cars, cameras, televisions and computers? How could they possibly grasp that it would one day enable people to walk on the Moon? If ever there was a monumentally important developmental threshold for Life on Earth, let alone for humankind, this was it. It was arguably the greatest threshold since the evolution of refined toolmaking some three million years earlier, and long before that the development of air-breathing lungs. Little did they know that they had entered a truly extraordinary new dimension – the *economic* one.

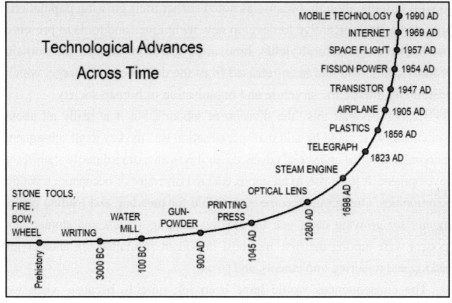

This was a gradual but profound revolution, and it was to change beyond recognition the lives of these peoples' descendants. It was also to unleash the growth of something that, by allowing greater access to resources, stimulated an unprecedented hunger for them; hence it was instrumental in accelerating the rate of damage we now inflict on the natural environment: *technology*.

Technology – the route to riches beyond measure

Specialists didn't only do things better; from this time on they also began to manufacture things better, including the tools of their particular trade. As time went on, each new modification or invention by specialists added to an expanding web of inter-influencing technologies – wheels, ploughs, harnesses, boats and so forth.

Previously, the evolution of technology had been extremely slow. Hundreds of thousands of years had divided significant technological developments, for example from Oldowan to Acheulian hand axes, then tens of thousands of years to spears, blowpipes and arrows. Now, specialisation gradually increased the pace to millennia, then centuries; then by the time of the Romans, perhaps decades, until, after a millennium-long Dark Age hiatus, it began to gather pace again. Nowadays it can be measured in weeks or even days.

The result is that we now find ourselves in the middle of another *Cambrian explosion* (the great era of rapid species evolution some 550 million years ago that led to most of the animal groups alive today), only this is a technological one. Today we are born, live and die quite at home in a womb of vastly diverse technology. Here at the beginning of the 21st century, it is almost second nature to us; no sooner do yet more miracles of invention appear than we regard them as old hat. The pace of change is extraordinary, so much so that in the First World we have become accustomed to living, not rooted in the present and past as our forebears were, but in the future. We live in a buzz of expectation of scientific and technological advance, eager for an anticipated technological utopia. To many it seems to hold a promise of the eventual end of want, war, disease and an unlimited array of fabulous gadgets with which to play. So fast does technology move that new technologies are often out of date even as they hit the showroom shelves. We have become like children who at Christmas rip each present from its wrapper and discard it after a brief inspection, eager for the contents of the next, and the next and the next. And given the conveyor belt of marvellous, tempting technological products on offer, who can blame us?

What's more, this rampant colonisation of the economic dimension is only just beginning. The Internet revolution is still young, financial markets are still evolving new ways to trade, and reports from laboratories and research facilities around the world show that a huge array of technological advances and innovations is on the horizon. According to economist Paul Romer, we consistently fail to grasp how many ideas are still out there awaiting discovery. These possibilities don't just accumulate, they multiply exponentially. The same applies to the colonisation of those possibilities, for economic colonisation isn't simply a one-dimensional spreading out across territory; like biological evolution, it multiplies multidimensionally, creating an ever-expanding web of technological innovation and diversification. Entrepreneurs dog technology's every footstep, ever eager to find and exploit – to *colonise* – the market opportunities it creates as it rolls out before them, a virtual landscape without horizon.

Cultural and environmental consequences accompany these changes. Some are obvious, others too subtle to detect without the benefit of historical hindsight. It doesn't take a genius, for example, to spot the immediate social consequences of the introduction of the mobile phone, the Internet and social media, yet their accumulative, long-term effects on society are much harder to foresee. We can only now fully appreciate the magnitude of the birth of modern science, in that it has turned out to be the greatest developmental threshold in economic history, propelling us into a hyperdrive of complex discovery and invention. Although it is barely 200 years since that point of technological detonation, already barely a corner of the Earth remains untouched or unharmed by it, and there lies the tragedy.

Trade and markets

Developing special skills or making smart new inventions is all very well, but there's a big potential drawback: you can't eat it. The only way to get food is to go to someone who has surplus food and try to barter or do a swap or a trade. Specialists are traders not by choice, but of necessity. They sacrifice *producing* food for *procuring* it, putting their trust in farmers to create enough surplus to feed them and their families: I'll give you these skilfully made pots in return for some meat and milk; this fine plough for a cow and two goats. This must be how it all began.

Little did they know at the time that those early trades between food producers and artisans represented the first steps into unexplored jungle. Where there had been just one human species – the hunter-gatherer – in effect this alternative jungle provided a plethora of niches for increasing numbers of technologically evolving *economic* species to colonise. Potters, weavers, blacksmiths, fletchers, wheelwrights, millers, goldsmiths, saddlers, tanners and so forth all became specialist actors colonising a vibrant, innovative and expanding economic matrix. And the more populated that matrix became, the more dependent upon it were its people. It created a new perspective and a new survival landscape for our ancestors, one based on the development and exchange of goods and services, giving rise to something entirely new – the marketplace, the public arena for "agents" and "traders".

The simple act of swapping one thing for another was the chief catalyst for all subsequent economic development. At every turn the exploiting of trading opportunities gave rise to yet more market opportunities, and so it continues.

This extraordinary phenomenon has steadily graduated towards ever-greater complexity. In the process, it has grown into a seemingly unstoppable colonising juggernaut, hungrily devouring the world's natural resources.

The invention of agriculture brought with it many employment opportunities for our ancestors. This not only radically changed their way of life; it reignited the resource hunger within them as they sought the raw materials they needed. Nevertheless, strange as it may seem, despite these great apparent changes, in the grand scheme of things *nothing had changed at all*. That may sound counter-intuitive, even contradictory, but it's true nonetheless.

To see this, we need to grapple with something that I suspect some people will find a little startling, perhaps even unsettling. This is that we are living, not in some economic otherworld that is the unique product of human genius, but in a system as natural as any that came before. This *economic ecosystem* is driven by the same forces, bound by the same laws and contains the same diversity of species – economic species – as natural ecosystems.

This is the key understanding behind the *Junglenomics* paradigm, and it can help us reforge the link between mankind and the natural world that was broken 15,000 years ago when those first farmers began clearing the primeval wilderness.

The economic jungle

There is of course nothing new about comparing the economic world to a jungle, or in likening its development to Darwinian evolution. Similarities between aspects of the business world and the jungle are so striking that the comparison long ago became a cliché. It's hardly a complimentary analogy though, for when we declare, "It's a jungle out there!" we generally do so to express our distaste at the dog-eat-dog behaviour we so often encounter in business. Perhaps ruthlessness in business disconcerts us because it contrasts with the more considerate customs of social intercourse. Privately though, some of us may get an uneasy feeling that in the cut and thrust of the economic arena, we ourselves may not be in control of the finer points of our own behaviour. Everyone has their price, it is said. Individual conscience is all too easily submerged in the turbid pools of commercial interests; even scientists have been known to prostitute their arts to serve corporate ends or personal ambition.

In this era of globalisation and soaring human populations, the effect of commercial expediency on the environment, on biodiversity and on human health and wealth can be acute and even tragic. At a time when economics and Nature urgently need to be reconciled, it is not comforting to know that the conduct of business often reveals a side that seems to sing to an older, darker tune. So who or what calls this tune?

In describing early economies, I remarked that the agriculture-enabled division of labour in effect made what had been one identifiable species – the hunter-gatherer, *Homo sapiens* – into many species, i.e. economic ones. But I am now going to argue that this is more than just a comparison; in fact the economic diaspora is a parallel phenomenon both propelled and bound by the same natural laws – not least the innate imperative to colonise resources. For when you come to look at economic life in its full context it becomes obvious that it's not just *like* a jungle, it really *is* one, and not just in a pejorative sense: the natural world has transposed into a new dimension.

Of course, the economic world doesn't have trees, snakes, insects and panthers, at least not literally; but it has people like you and me behaving and interacting exactly as if we were their equivalents. Indeed, we behave and interact in economics according to all the same rules and norms as a wild ecosystem. Evolutionary economists have long studied these phenomena. Where classical economics models base themselves on the principles of Newtonian physics, in contrast the "ecological model of competition" views economics as if it were a biological phenomenon; and in it, Darwinian terms such as "evolution", "development" and "survival of the fittest" are therefore writ large [4].

How can we know this?

Most people would probably say that there's nothing very natural about economies; indeed, that they are inherently *un*natural – an artificial construct that we humans invented with only superficial resemblances to natural systems. But they would be fundamentally mistaken, because in reality agriculture and technology and the arrival of commerce neither did nor *could* change any of the principles of Nature that preceded them. To begin with let's not forget that, for all the rapidly increasing sophistication of human development from that era onwards, the game of life still revolved around three fundamental things: survival, regeneration and – to enable these – the colonisation of resources, just as it does today.

This means that each and every one of us is genetically driven, not just to stay alive and reproduce successfully, but to acquire the necessary resources to do so. As we'll see though, because of the way in which things have transpired, our ability to acquire those resources has skyrocketed, as has our desire for them.

Parallels between economic and natural systems

If economies truly are an extension of ecosystems, one should expect to find many working parallels between them – and indeed there are. Firstly, we know that economies are populated by a similar cast of characters to ecosystems. For example, it isn't difficult to see that economies contain both predators and prey: think of ruthless, asset-stripping private equity companies and large businesses that swallow up smaller ones and spit them out in pieces. The same goes for scavengers, which is another way of looking at waste recyclers and bankruptcy auctioneers, for instance, since they too make a living from the leftovers of others.

Then there are parasites: anyone who has been bitten by a mosquito, leech or flea, or has contracted bilharzia, knows that ecosystems are not short of them, and again the same goes for economies: criminals are the parasites of the economic world, feeding on the labours of others. Interdependence and cooperation are everywhere in economies too, as are opportunists, drones, nocturnalists and so forth.

Niches are comprised of similar criteria too: a lawyer, for example, fulfils specific functions that are compatible with survival as a lawyer, and is just as constrained by the defining parameters of lawyership as any hippopotamus is by being a hippopotamus. In both systems, each species or "actor", as economics terms them, becomes established within a viable specialist niche, and each competes for foraging territory, otherwise known as "market share".

Likewise, in both cases, competition is the name of the game, and businesses often encroach on each other's niches much as their wild counterparts do. A phone call from an electricity company offering me a design-and-build service drove this particular point home. Who knows if this will ever prove viable for them, and whose business niche may be rendered less viable by their encroachment? Likewise, large supermarkets frequently try to encroach on the niches of others by selling, for example, books, clothes and electrical goods.

Similarly, the density of numbers varies: some economic fauna need the equivalent of packs, herds or flocks to function – construction companies come to mind – while others, architects, for example, can be viable in just ones or twos. As in Nature, large numbers are not necessarily indicative of success: depending on the nature of their job, workers may earn either a pittance or a fortune just as easily by being a one-man band or by being part of a large corporation.

Again, just as the numerousness of each species found in a habitat is limited by environmental factors, such as the availability of food and rates of predation, so there are limits on the number of each type of economic actor that can be sustained by local market conditions, or micro ecosystems as we may as well call them. A small town may support forty builders, ten doctors and three butchers, but only one funeral director, for example; while a given area of woodland may similarly limit the viable numbers of wolves, squirrels and caribou.

The two systems also develop new networks of niches in the same way. Many thousand years ago, a single species of fish, a *cichlid*, by chance entered a newly formed, fish-vacant lake, Lake Malawi. There the fish soon began to evolve into all the classic niches of any ecosystem – predators, grazers, scavengers and so forth – to colonise all possible resources. As a result, there are now over 530 distinct species. So one could say that we humans are the cichlids of an economic Lake Malawi because business has similarly adapted to and colonised all the archetypal niches, building a market "ecosystem" by exploring and exploiting all available opportunities. Darwin's finches also did this on the Galapagos Islands, evolving specialised features to access the nutrients contained within new foodstuffs, for example more powerful beaks to break open hard-shelled nuts.

The physical and behavioural changes that enabled cichlids to diversify in Lake Malawi, and finches to spread through the Galapagos, evolved to allow them access to untapped resources. In economies, this evolution takes place for exactly the same reason, via new ideas and advancing technology, likewise providing access to untapped resources for economic actors. Therefore, in both systems an inverted pyramid of opportunist species builds on each newly evolved primary species, creating opportunities for the evolution of a whole network of subdependent and interdependent species which together comprise ecosystems, irrespective of whether they are natural or economic.

Take cattle breeding as an economic example. Essentially the breeding of cattle is carried out to supply a section of the food market; but it has also given rise to markets (and hence to the economic actors that exploit them) for glue, hides, fertilisers, herbicides, machinery, buildings, seed, foodstuffs, medicines and much more. Cattle breeding also creates niche work for abattoirs, auctioneers, dealers, truckers, veterinary surgeons, researchers, teaching colleges and so on. And in the next tier of economic evolution, the needs of each of these help to provide niches for others again – equipment for the vet, petrol and repairs for the truckers, advertising for the auctioneers, as well as insurers, bankers, accountants, chiropractors and solicitors for them all. It creates a matrix of economic interdependence indistinguishable from that of ecosystems.

Ecosystems and economic systems also have internal organisation in common; again there is a direct comparison between species and businesses. For example, cost-benefit equations apply to both: each system is only able to survive by operating at a "nutritional" profit: in ecology this profit takes the form of a net gain of energy obtained by foraging, over the energy cost of seeking that forage; here the "profit" is the surplus energy needed for other things, such as defending territory, staying warm, competing for mates and so forth. In economics it is the excess of money spent at work over money earned, ensuring there is cash to take home to buy food and pay bills. Without such profits, the eventual outcome is extinction for the former, and bankruptcy for the latter.

Nothing is forever. Viability, animal and human alike, is under constant revision as its determining factors shift. Even when you have a viable economic niche you still can't afford to be too fragile. To survive you need to have a certain amount of resilience to external shocks [5]. As many have learned to their cost, whole industries – even entire economies – are just as vulnerable to changing circumstances as ecosystems. Like species, over time industries arise and then disappear, their products or services either defunct or superseded by competitors.

Global equivalence

While it is relatively easy to draw parallels between ecological and economic systems at the local, the micro scale, comparison at the macro scale is more complex. In any dynamic system, millions of local events interacting with each other tend to give rise to many kinds of emergent phenomena on the grand scale. In economies, these produce the kind of financial movements that are a prime concern of national governments, multinational businesses and organisations like the International Monetary Fund. They involve debt and cash, inflation and deflation, recession and boom, exchange rates, interest rates and the movement of capital and commodities around the world.

When I first approached this subject I strongly suspected it was the case, but I couldn't say with any certainty that economies and ecologies operated on parallel macroeconomic planes. To resolve this, I searched for an existing study of economics viewed as a natural process. As economics is a human construct, and we are but creatures of Nature, surely its natural origins would have been examined? While I drew a blank in that respect, I was intrigued to find that the reverse comparison has indeed been made, and more than once: *Nature has been examined as if it were an economy.*

Probably one of the first to refer to Nature in this way was Darwin. In 1838, he wrote in his notes: "*One may say there is a force like a hundred thousand wedges trying to force every kind of adapted structure into the gaps in the economy of Nature...*" This is where Robert E Ricklefs got the title of his book, *The Economy of Nature* [6]. Ricklefs' conclusion was broadly that, while market economies are fundamentally governed by successful mathematical equations, so too are ecosystems; only there it isn't money and markets that rule, but chemistry, nutrient flow, genetics and so forth.

Geerat J Vermeij [7] expounded on similar ideas about ecosystems and evolution which he had been working on for decades. He viewed an economy as an organising theory that can be used to analyse the evolution of the biosphere. Most importantly, he saw it as a theory capable of providing a full description of natural, as well as human, systems. Ecosystems, in other words, can be described in the same terms as economies (rather than the other way around, as discussed here).

I warmed to Vermeij's hypothesis immediately. Clearly, he had come to similar conclusions albeit that the emphasis was a mirror image of mine. He too saw that the difference between human and natural economies lay solely in one detail – that humans can manipulate the economic system, through regulation, tax and interest rates for example. But those manipulations still have to be tailored to certain constraining factors – supply, demand, competition, specialisation, cooperation etc., in order to retain profitability. We are ruled by such factors just as surely as wildlife is ruled by its ecological equivalents.

Globalisation represents a major new opportunity for commerce, yet markets, whether local, national or international, still rely on the same fundamental elements of viability (for which read profitability) – supply, demand, efficiency, competition and resilience. Ecosystems too have been undergoing a degree of globalisation, either deliberate or accidental: in addition to exotic flora and escaped pets, international travel aboard planes, ships, cars, trucks and trains has spread many species far and wide, microbes, plants, reptiles and mammals alike, and they can now try to compete in places they previously stood little or no chance of reaching. It is estimated that around 50,000 non-native species have been introduced to the United States alone.

Intriguingly in the context of this book, some ecologists and economists have found close parallels with Nature in that infamous financial meltdown, the credit crunch of 2007-9 [8]. They point out that until a short time before, national markets had operated much more independently: they were more akin to separate ecosystems. Globalisation had altered all that, and economists failed to keep up with the complex changes that accompanied it. Where once national borders acted as firebreaks, preventing or at least restricting the spread of systemic malfunctions, now there was massive international financial connectivity. This allowed local systemic malfunctions (in this case, mislending in the USA) to spread around the world to an unprecedented degree. Now instability and loss of confidence in credit markets in one region can all too easily result in the withdrawal of credit elsewhere in the world [9].

Interestingly, these analysts highlighted the parallels between this kind of malfunction and a natural environment such as a swamp, where sudden imbalances can develop and disrupt ecological balances causing an algal bloom which chokes the swamp. It is particularly intriguing (and of course pertinent to the current discussion) that *ecologists* [10] were among those who contributed to a study published by the Federal Reserve Bank of New York in 2007, just before the credit crunch, warning that while huge sums were being spent on assessing the risks of individual investments, very little attention was being given to systemic risks. Frustratingly for those who took part, little notice was taken of their warning that the loss of diversity caused by globalisation had left the financial system more vulnerable to failure.

Complexity theorists have something to say on the matter too. They modelled how small, local events can have far-reaching and profound consequences where there is connectivity, such as in weather systems. Who hasn't heard of the "butterfly effect"? Globalisation has by definition greatly increased market connectivity, and while that has accelerated healthy economic development it has also created easy pathways for unhealthy development. Theorists speculated how such financial viruses could be prevented from spreading in the future without stifling innovation and financial evolution. They concluded that international connectivity needs to be reduced by developing new financial firebreaks while still allowing considerable freedom locally [(11)].

Once again, the close parallels between ecology and economics had been recognised, this time in the mechanics of a financial crisis. Most interesting for me, though, was that theorists from different disciplines were at last beginning to unite in looking to Nature both for a comparative model and for corrective solutions – the core strategy advocated in this book. Complexity already recognises the homogeny of complex systems of all kinds, yet rarely in the past have economists and ecologists found themselves on the same page [(12)].

The commonality of resource hunger

This catalogue of parallels is described to try to convince you, the reader, of something that I myself have been sure about for a long time: that we truly inhabit an *economic ecosystem*, and this is an essential precursor to justifying the concept of *Junglenomics*.

Yet all of it is of mere academic interest until one comes to recognise the existence of something that overarches both worlds; that the resource-colonising imperative – *resource hunger* – is the core driver in both systems. For resource hunger is not only the engine of evolution and diversity in Nature, and hence of our very existence on this orb; it is also the engine of the economic dimension, and therefore the root cause of our pillaging of the natural environment.

How do I know this? Compare the two: life has colonised an amazing variety of environments, some of which we would term extreme. We now know that not only are scorched deserts, frozen Arctic wastes and oxygen-deficient altitudes home to numerous organisms, but also many astonishing places until recently not dreamed possible: deep inside solid rock, kilometres beneath the Earth's surface, for example, or in the chemical nightmare and boiling temperatures of sea floor volcanic vents; even high up among the clouds. These all provide habitats for organisms that do not merely survive, but flourish in spite of their (to us) extreme conditions, or more accurately – *because* of them. For wherever there is an opportunity in Nature, wherever there is a life-sustaining set of resources available, you can be sure that some resource-hungry entity will always adapt to exploit it.

Exactly the same happens in economies: whatever *can* be exploited by business *will* be exploited, whether it's timber in a forest, fish in the sea, minerals in the ground or the bones of a tiger; *nothing* is beyond its grasp.

Viewed in this way, it becomes clear that resource hunger crossed over from ecosystems to the economic systems within us, secreted in our genes, and that it drives the economic world just as surely and powerfully as it does the natural one.

How could it not, after all? We are but creatures of Nature, like any other. Already adept colonisers before our entry into the economic life, thanks to our unique ability to create complex technology we have since become *hyper*colonisers, surely the most thorough, efficient and diverse exploiters of resources the world has ever seen. It is because we have enjoyed such a free rein to denude our planet of its resources without considering the future consequences that we have found ourselves in a steadily worsening imbalance with the natural world.

Continuity in change

The more one considers it, the clearer it becomes that market economies do indeed imitate Nature – far too much so for coincidence. Indeed, it is impossible to avoid the conclusion that beneath the apparently new and different surface of economic activity, little has changed other than the timescales involved.

At the heart of this understanding lies a simple but vital conclusion: that the principles of Nature – proliferation, colonisation, mutation, natural selection, evolution, competition, resilience, viability, opportunity and so on – *could* neither change nor disappear from our lives. What has actually happened is that they have undergone a systemic transfer, one in which speciation has been replaced by specialisation, and evolution by technological innovation. Albeit a very curious one, the economic world is still just another classic evolutionary scenario out of the same drawer and following the same rules.

So, far from breaking loose from the constraints of the animal kingdom for a new-dimensional adventure in some intellectual and economic otherworld, in reality we never left it at all. We have never ceased to be creatures of Nature, and we remain obedient to its dictates in economics as much as we ever did in all our long evolutionary history.

Unfortunately though, colonising the economic world has come at a price, and in Nature's time-honoured fashion the bill for it is now being presented. For, although for many people the flowering of the economic dimension has been an enormous success, it is fast becoming a hideously costly one. It turns out that in their natural state, ecological and economic systems are not very compatible at all: over-exploitation, environmental pollution and habitat destruction are the triple hallmarks of this economic onslaught on the natural world. I therefore have little doubt that if we are going to prevent the looming ecological and economic crises, we will need strategies founded on a comprehensive awareness of the natural forces that underlie them.

Virtual ecosystems

For my part, making the eco-economic connection was a natural progression from everything I had previously concluded about the colonisation of resources. I wanted to discover the effect of Nature working within economies, and this perspective eventually led me to an inescapable and towering conclusion: that *the parallels between economic and ecological systems go well beyond mere correlation. The two systems are so close in principle, function and effect that to all intents and purposes economies should be regarded as "virtual ecosystems".* Indeed, I have come to regard business occupations as a costume in which we dress up to perform some classical role as actors within the ecosystem of economic life. This costume is more than mere metaphor: it creates an adapted identity in the economic jungle just as surely as do a zebra's stripes or a leopard's spots in the wild. The characteristic ebbs and flows of products and services through markets; the evolution of their complexity of form, function and organisation; the fine balances struck between competing, parasitic and cooperative elements; the identical nature of the underlying motivations – all of these indicate that the patterns of both systems are closely in step and working under the same rules. In reality, economies are only a reiteration of an ancient order, an alternative function of Nature subject to entirely natural laws and protocols.

This realisation on my part underpinned the *virtual ecosystem* concept, but taken to its logical conclusion it goes even further than that; I now saw that it must also have powerful implications for the management of economic policy in relation to the environment. It is my belief that this interpretation of economic life as a natural phenomenon is the Rosetta Stone that will allow us to understand and hence at last properly address our mismanagement of the planet. With predictability of effect being the gold standard in devising economic policy, it could help us find more effective ways to improve our relationship with the natural environment.

This last idea, that we could use our knowledge of natural systems to help run economies that are more in tune with Nature, I find powerful and exciting; for finding effective ways in modern economies to exert control over the more destructive effects of resource hunger is the purpose of this book.

The human dimension – we are not automatons

At this point I am acutely aware that I need to set something straight. I am in no way implying that each and every member of the human race is always a slave to resource hunger in the way that other species are. We are the first organisms on Earth to have an awareness and understanding of ethics and society, and there lies our strength and our potential redemption. Yet we are deeply naïve if we think that, in the theatre of business, our fellow men and women of all nationalities can ever be relied upon to rise above their profound competitive impulses and adhere to some wishful, universal enviro-economic panacea. There is no "ethics pill" for business, and we must remain vigilant against, and collaborate to neutralise, the destructive effects of resource hunger on people and on the natural environment wherever it occurs. After all, no amount of disapproval or enforcement will keep human fingers from the giant sweet shop that is the wealth of the natural world.

The painful fact is that our woeful behaviour towards the natural environment cannot be properly addressed until the ancient currents deep within us, which underlie our resource-hungry actions, are recognised and accommodated within enviro-economic policy. We do not need to remind ourselves that despite our advanced intelligence, we humans are still subject to the greatest power controlling all living organisms – the power of genes. Our behaviour signifies that our genetic impulses are incompatible with the economic theatre we have constructed as such impulses were forged in an earlier time when we were no more powerful than other creatures.

This has profound implications: it means that, while we may feel we enjoy free will as individuals, it is clear that *en masse* we do not; we remain obedient to ancient, gene-inspired urges and instincts that control more of our economic lives than we might care to admit. We have fashioned the key – technology – to a vast smorgasbord of natural resources which we acquire by any means possible, and for which our appetite is never sated. And we have done so because we are hardwired to do so; and that in turn is because as a highly successful strategy it results in greater human populations.

On one level, therefore, it isn't difficult to answer the question, why do we destroy our environment? You have heard of "realpolitik" (a system of politics or principles reflecting practical rather than moral or ideological considerations)? Well, this is "realeconomik". Some people argue that this is all about capitalism gone mad. They say that a revolution is needed to stop the drive for growth and to make big business democratically accountable. Others believe that if we are all intellectually "on board" with green economics, we will solve our problems in the spirit of a common cause. This is patently not the case. The problem is far more deep-rooted and demands sophisticated and comprehensive solutions.

But while I reject these arguments, they are right that essentially this is an economics problem. It is also true that most of this ecological destruction happens for one simple reason – profit. But there is nothing wrong with profit *per se*; it makes the economic world go around and is hence indispensable. However, profit that incorporates environmental damage and a loss of natural capital is a perversion, an illusion of profit because it takes no account of environmental cost. It sells the foundation stones of the natural world which it does not own. It has no right to them. As they help to maintain the integrity of the biosphere upon which we all depend, these foundations are as much common property as the air we breathe.

Yet it is not the business world that should be blamed for this because businesses simply follow the economic cues set out before them as automatically as honeybees seek nectar. Instead it is a failure of the world's markets to recognise and assign value where true value lies – in natural ecosystems and the immensely important services they provide for the planet, and hence for us.

Our huge success and proliferation as a species has meant that we are now exceeding the carrying capacity of our environment; and it's only going to get worse as populations rise. This is happening worldwide and that makes it a global threat to us as well as to other species. Natural cataclysms have happened in the past – the meteor strike that caused the demise of the dinosaurs 65 million years ago, for example; but this time it is *we* who are the trauma, so much so that our activities affect some 83% of the world's land mass and all of its oceans [13] – over 40% of which are affected drastically [14].

Whatever the distant future holds for economic systems, of one thing we can be certain. It is that – if we can avoid destroying ourselves in the meantime – we will inevitably and inexorably continue to develop this new economic dimension tier upon tier, far into the future. But this is not a given. It depends on our urgently finding constructive ways to modify our natural resource-hungry exuberance and excessive lifestyle that threatens the environment that succours us.

Finding ways to modify our economic resource hunger depends on rather more than identifying its source, however. It demands a proper understanding of the way that source – that colonising energy – materialises and exerts its influence on economic life. For that, one must first recognise the true nature and ecosystemic function of the very lifeblood of economic life – the conduit of our resource hunger: *money*. This is the final and key piece of the jigsaw.

Money – the universal resource

"When it's a question of money, everybody is of the same religion." – Voltaire
Heard on a US TV advert – *"Money's on my mind all the time, every day"*

Money. We are forever talking about it, singing about it, writing about it, arguing and fighting about it. For good or evil it infiltrates our lives from cradle to grave. Elections are fought and won largely on the management of it; who doesn't remember Bill Clinton's undying campaign slogan: *"It's the economy, stupid!"*? We are obsessed with money – how to make it, how to borrow it, how to spend it, how to save it, how to invest it.

However, perhaps none of this is surprising as today there's very little we can acquire, apart from love, so the Beatles said, without money. Where once we could forage for food for ourselves, now the division of labour means that most of us must do something else, get paid money for it and then swap some of that money for food. At least food is one of the four basic necessities that money can get us, along with water, shelter and warmth. But things have moved on considerably since those four basics were all anyone aspired to.

I want to explain here how the invention of money and the economic revolution it created sent natural resource exploitation into overdrive, generating whole new categories of resources and propelling us into unexplored wildernesses to prospect for them. Understanding how and why money has taken command of almost every aspect of our lives will show us how to loosen its shackles and find solutions to our over-exploitation of the natural environment.

At the basic level, money operates as a token of exchange for things that satisfy our primary needs: food, water, warmth and shelter. That visit to the supermarket may feel like a mundane chore, but we all know it's essential. Food shopping is but a short step from hand-to-mouth foraging. The food shopper is but a hunter-gatherer once removed; it's just that someone else has done all the hard work. In all other respects, we might as well be plucking berries from bushes as packets from shelves. Moreover, when we buy meat we are in effect trading into a share of someone else's kill.

One can liken money to nutrients coursing through the body of an economy, nourishing the parts through which it flows, feeding and energising it. We tap into this nutritional flow to varying degrees by working and earning. By storing up money instead of spending it, individuals and businesses create resource savings, or "capital" as it is called – in effect a money larder waiting to be spent.

This link between money and resources is entirely dependent on civilisation being stable; otherwise it falls apart. Although it's still a relatively new concept in the span of human history, we are so inured to money that it's hard to imagine the world without it. Perhaps a post-apocalyptic scenario, such as that portrayed in *Mad Max*, is the nearest we can imagine, where populations have been decimated, society has broken down, bands of survivors struggle for domination, and money has lost all meaning. Banknotes are good only for lighting fires or as toilet paper. What then passes for currency between groups is whatever aids survival – perhaps guns and ammunition, alliances, food, shelter and clothing.

What this brings home to us is that money is only useful while it remains fully exchangeable for resources. Here money is "resources-in-waiting" and, as we will see, this realisation is central to understanding how money has taken centre stage in environmental destruction.

It goes like this. As described earlier, our ancestors' adoption of farming brought surplus. The only way to make use of that surplus was through barter, which gradually expanded and increased in sophistication, leading to unforeseen levels of wealth. Yet that was abject poverty in comparison with what was to come. As one could amass only so much agricultural produce, money's predecessors – useful items like obsidian, a raw material widely used for making tools and weapons, then ingots of tradable lead, copper or bronze – were the inevitable outcome.

Eventually precious metals took over, the ultimate resource tokens, and these were to endure for millennia. Little wonder, because unlike their predecessors, coinage of gold, silver and bronze was portable, durable and its value widely recognised. Back in 600 BC when King Croesus of Lydia first stamped his image on coinage, it might have been staters or drachms. Today it could be dollars, pounds, euros or yuan. As coinage developed, money could stand alone as one half of a trade, re-exchangeable at any time for almost anything. You didn't trade stuff much any more; you *bought* stuff.

And now you could hoard wealth as never before, and that's exactly what people began to do, assuaging their conditioned urges to amass surplus on a scale previously unimagined. The wealthy began demanding more and more non-essential stuff, creating markets for exotic objects where before none had existed: animals, animal products, plants, precious stones and minerals were among them.

Wealth and luxury, and their effects on our behaviour towards the environment

As we have seen, because hoarding surplus was a survival strategy in farming it has long since become fully ingrained in us. And because money so easily represented that surplus, it became a major accelerant of it. Where we had been limited in how much grain, cattle, obsidian or arrowheads we could store, we could now indulge our hoarding instincts to the full, like J R R Tolkien's fictional dragon, Smaug, accumulating wealth in unprecedented quantities.

However, and this point is crucial to comprehending the origins of our environmental misconduct, while it made the dramatic growth of the world's major economies eventually possible, at this time money was still only a superior *means of attaining* greater surplus; it was not the creator of surplus in the way that it is today, where money so often makes money. The massive size and power of today's mega-economies actually stems from the way in which we ourselves have chosen to use this stored, surplus-to-survival money. We have chosen not to share it with the needy, but instead to accumulate something else, something unheard of in the long history of the world. It is summed up by a single, meaning-laden word: *luxury*. No other creature can conceive of this.

Compare Man 20,000 years ago in bushcraft mode – nothing saved, nothing wanting – with modern Man owning a mansion, swimming pool and Lamborghini (I'm not talking about the uber-rich here, just the seriously well-off). The difference between Bushcraft Man (hunter-gatherers) and Lamborghini Man is not just about wealth: Bushcraft Man feels wealthy too, just in a different way. The real difference lies in his attitude to surplus. Generally Bushcraft Man can't tolerate it, so he would have been no use whatsoever for building market economies.

Lamborghini Man, on the other hand, is a surplus junky; he's acquisitive by nature and he consumes or hoards far and away beyond his immediate needs. His world is built on what is known as the "economics of scarcity" – the desire for what is not universally obtainable. If scarcity and desire are the twin engines that power capitalist economies, money is surely the fuel in the tank.

Nevertheless, this is not a criticism, for it is what Lamborghini Man does with this money surplus that helps energise economies and employs millions. It helps keep the economic ship afloat. If he allowed his money just to accumulate under the mattress it would go out of circulation and stifle growth; but unless he is a miser, he doesn't do that. Of course he wants money, but he wants luxury goods and services even more. So he spends most of it on houses, staff, plush cars, exclusive holidays, expensive sports, yachts, aircraft and so forth. He also invests it in his children's education, healthcare, pensions and not least on creating yet more layers of wealth-generating enterprises. By doing so, he is helping to maintain, diversify and expand the economic ecosystem within which he lives and thrives. He becomes at the same time both a coloniser and a creator of opportunities for colonisation, exactly like any big beast in the wild.

I have used him as an extreme example, but actually Lamborghini Man personifies all "successful" *Homo economicus* – all active participants in markets who buy and sell stuff with money. He is a reward-conditioned

animal. He may work hard, even obsessively, but with few exceptio.
top of his agenda is the pursuit of pleasure, whatever form it may come
a result, and despite many centuries of austere preachers' best attempts the
world over, the marketplace for luxurious objects and activities has spawned
major industries. It has helped supercharge global economic growth and
development. I don't just mean the ostentatious extravagances of the rich
here – we are all in it together to some degree – but every single unnecessary
thing from roll-ups to fine Cuban cigars; from root beer to Chateau Lafite;
from inflatable rubber rings to luxury yachts. All these things are surplus
to needs; all are luxuries; and unfortunately, many create markets that
encourage environmentally destructive practices.

It is surely this human fixation with personal reward systems that
makes Mankind so interesting. The human penchant for things that
sparkle, for luxurious food and drink, for humour, sport, music, sex, travel,
entertainments, collecting, gadgets, gambling, vacations and a thousand
other amusements, has given rise to a vast new hunting ground teeming
with vibrant and colourful economic niches ranging from archaeology to art,
and from skydiving to barn dancing. The provision of luxury in a thousand
different forms is now a mainstay of the world economy, without which it
would collapse. You could say that the first trade involving the exchange
of a subsistence-related object for something frivolous and non-essential, a
shining shell necklace perhaps, was as momentous an occasion in the human
story as the invention of the wheel.

Our varying idiosyncrasies, tastes, phobias and desires have thus turned
much of the world into a vast playground for the well-off (by which I mean
anyone with enough money to join in), providing limitless fertile territory
for ever more economic colonisation and ever more markets that cause
environmental degradation and destruction.

Money as a focus for resource hunger

In money-based economies, the drive to colonise becomes a surplus
imperative, more commonly known as the "profit motive", which is nothing
less than the chief driving force of the economic world. The resource-
colonising imperative has been diverted away from bartering for goods into
acquiring their economic substitute – money.

But is that really so unexpected? Money is simply a token exchangeable for items we want. There is plenty of evidence that even chimpanzees easily learn to accept reward tokens exchangeable for food just as readily as direct food rewards. Even more remarkable is that, in contrast to food rewards, they have spontaneously saved tokens earned individually before exchanging them for rewards in bulk [15].

This would seem to explain a great deal about the subtle effects money has on us. It isn't completely understood yet, but recent experiments have produced some interesting results which seem to confirm the view that money has become a fully fledged food-foraging substitute. It seems that money taps into brain circuits which evolved to make decisions that are important to our biology. In tests volunteers who went hungry were found to be less likely than replete ones to make charitable donations, for example [16].

Such results have led researchers to conclude that the same brain pathways are used for gaining money as those evolved for obtaining food. In other words, our subconscious minds interchange them. This means that the energy and ingenuity we spent on gathering food (and for agriculturalists, a large surplus of it) are now transferred to gathering money instead. The upshot is that because money is exchangeable for almost anything, in our minds money *has become* the resources we are conditioned by our genes to crave.

Being a matter of survival, the getting of food is and always has been a serious business for all living creatures, and hence a major source of competition and conflict. Likewise, getting *enough* food is just as serious a business. No wonder researchers find that when money is in the frame, many people start to behave differently from social norms – in particular they behave "selfishly and obsessively" [17]. Money even acts as a social substitute, consoling the socially deprived, they say [18]. It also seems to bestow a sense of well-being and security, just as a full larder would have done in the past. Whether we like it or not our lives are inextricably entangled with money, and it exerts a power over us that excites our deepest instincts.

Money is thus the universal resource for us humans because it acts as a token for almost anything we desire to possess, not just food. It is no surprise that our focus is so keenly fixed on it. This status endows it with immense power in the human psyche, provoking most of us to accumulate as much of it as we can, far beyond anything we need for survival. Indeed, it is no exaggeration to say that the getting of money has become the prime and overriding imperative of modern man.

As such it has even overcome our equally deep-rooted instincts to respect the environment that supports us, refocusing our creative technological talents on extracting maximum monetary value from the natural world. I don't only mean in the direct sense of people making money out of cutting down ecologically precious forests and such like, though that is a major part of it; I mean that by converting what were once useless sows' ears, like palladium, tantalum and silicon, into silk purses such as smartphones and computers, money has driven us to exploit a vast range of natural resources in a free-for-all of epic proportions.

All this means something very significant indeed about the reawakened resource-colonising instinct in post-hunter-gatherer humans: *money has hijacked it*. It has refocused the immense power of the colonising imperative simmering in our genes, much as a magnifying glass focuses sunlight into a beam of intense heat. No wonder we are so fond of it.

This understanding of money's pivotal evolutionary role in the human psyche opens a whole new range of approaches for us regarding environmental protection, for it spotlights the very root of the great economic-ecological conflict that plagues our planet and threatens our future. It helps us concentrate on areas that would be most influential in bringing about a much-needed ceasefire between the human race and Nature. Anyone who tells you we can do this by rising above our instincts and tapping into some broadly undefined "better nature" is kidding you, and maybe themselves. A tiny proportion of people would join in. But for the masses in their billions all over the world, it just isn't going to happen. The sooner we accept this incontrovertible fact the sooner we can get on with rescuing our planet.

The power of markets

The same goes in respect of money's channel into the world – markets. Markets are the most powerful force in the modern economic world. They are responsible for almost everything materially good in our lives, from food, water and warmth, to cars, buses and planes, to luxuries large and small; as such, they impinge directly on our well-being, even our state of mind. After all, our contentment is based largely on the degree to which we are able to obtain from markets that which we need or desire. Yet because they are essentially amoral – an impersonal function of supply and demand – markets also have a dark side; they introduce many bad things to the world, including those that degrade and destroy the natural environment. Controlling such destructive markets is the major challenge facing Humankind.

In times past, markets tended to be local to where people lived. Therefore, information about them was easily available, and their effects, beneficial or otherwise, could be experienced first-hand and appropriate adjustments made. But over the past 150 years or so, the ability to judge between good and bad markets has been greatly eroded by the great distances over which they operate. Their remoteness to us has made it difficult to gain information about them. How could we understand the consequences on the environment and animal and plant species of our buying a hardwood door, a fur coat, a sushi lunch, a gas-guzzling car, a can of hairspray, or merely carrying our shopping home in plastic bags?

The answer is that for the most part we couldn't; just as we couldn't fully appreciate the harmful effects of smoke belching from factory chimneys until it was investigated and publicised. Lacking information, consumers have been mostly innocent participants in a feeding frenzy taking place on an unprecedented variety of natural resources all over the world. Our demand for new and exotic objects in shops and stores in the great consumer societies of Europe and North America was so considerable that for a long time we didn't realise the damage that was being done to produce them – until the unholy truth began to leak out.

Today a lot of this has changed. Markets increasingly come with information attached about how the goods they supply are damaging the natural environment and its wildlife and undermining peoples' livelihoods, though still not nearly enough, and sometimes with a cynical attempt to deceive.

Unfortunately, that doesn't mean we can simply close down what we now know to be "bad" markets, because some, especially the energy, food and transport industries, have grown far too big, making themselves indispensable components of modern life and mainstays of prosperity.

So here we stand in the first quarter of the 21st century, dismayed by the damage so many markets are still causing, yet largely powerless to stop them doing so. We are riding a runaway train towards environmental Armageddon. The brakes may be screeching a little, but even with the buffers in sight, markets are still shovelling more coal into the boiler.

It is clear to me that our leaders' failure to control bad markets isn't through lack of effort; it's because they don't have a proper plan, just some "good ideas" and educated guesses. For example, wherever there are bad markets – for hard drugs, wilderness asset-stripping and wild animal parts, for example – they still can't make up their minds how to tackle them, perhaps because they are so big and unmanageable that it's difficult to be sure what will work. Arguments swing back and forth between polar opposites – controlled licensing and outlawing. Indecision regarding rhino horn and elephant ivory markets epitomises this indecision, but they are only headline examples of a far more wide-ranging malaise. Without a full appreciation of the underlying forces at work, sentiment, short-termism and "common sense" tend to gain the upper hand, often with disastrous consequences. Not only animals but people are dying as a consequence.

The avatar economy – the downside of economic versatility

In today's complex, highly stratified market economies, it isn't hard to see where our market-driven, money-lubricated technological advances have led. We have become uniquely able to strip the world of its resources with apparent impunity. This is made all the more extreme because, unlike other creatures, as economic actors we are not linked permanently to any one set of resources. We enjoy unprecedented freedom unavailable elsewhere in Nature. As each resource is exhausted, whether it be timber, fish or tigers, we need not become extinct as wild creatures do when their resources run out. We can move our labour around the market as our skills and the demand for it requires, or we can retrain as an entirely different economic actor, like avatars in cyberspace. By changing our economic persona, we can take on different surroundings, strategies and priorities to engage with new competitors, in effect adopting a whole new array of survival parameters. It is just as if we slip out of one skin and into another: if the shipyard closes we may become instead a fireman, antiques dealer, gamekeeper, hairdresser or bank manager if we so desire, or if need drives us.

But the trouble is that the versatility of our avatar ecosystem badly compromises Nature's equations. It is a prime recipe for the eventual exhaustion of natural resources and environments because we can simply move to where we know there are more, or change our economic identity and start exploiting some other resource, until that too is exhausted. Where once we may have relied entirely on the healthy existence of a forest for our livelihood, for instance, we can now cut it all down, sell its timber and grow tobacco, acacia or palm oil instead. Yet forests support vital land-based ecosystems, benignly influence weather systems and store carbon, and by destroying forests those vital services are lost. And when through overfishing we cause a collapse in wild stocks we can then target some other species until that too fails, moving on again and again, leaving a trail of destruction that threatens entire marine ecosystems.

Thus, there is no hiding place any more from our extreme technological sophistication; no balance of power between us and the natural world as there once was; no equilibrium. The unreckoned costs of our hitherto anarchic economic development – pollution, climate change, environmental degradation, biodiversity loss – are sooner or later borne by all through the diminution of our planetary home. This is why the clock continues to tick towards inevitable environmental instability, social disruption and economic decline.

We therefore have to take decisive action now to return the cost-benefit equation into the realms of reality – the reality of the paramount importance of the long-term survival of mankind on a thriving, biodiverse planet. If we are to mitigate the economic anarchy that is destroying our planet we need to turn money, and its immense power over our behaviour, from being the environment's nemesis to its protector.

While we cannot change our innermost nature, which is gene controlled, we *can* train ourselves to behave better towards Nature. Money's position as the focus of our colonising instincts and the facilitator of hyper-economic activity is not all bad, because it gives us a potent lever for rebalancing economies with Nature. This is because ultimately all our economic drive and prosperity is predicated on one primary equation: we only exploit, or rather persist in exploiting, business opportunities so long as there is an anticipated benefit of gain over cost – a *profit*. This is likewise Nature's primal equation in that organisms expend energy acquiring resources only so long as there is an energy or survival gain to be had. At present in the economic world the cost-benefit equation is distorted because environmental costs are not factored in, so while there may be short-term gain for the individual or industry, a burden of cost is placed on the environment which is ultimately loss making for it and for society.

Pavan Sukhdev, CEO, GIST Advisory, and Goodwill Ambassador, UN Environment, and author of 'Corporation 2020', described some of the chief perpetrators to me thus: *"Today's corporation - the main vehicle of the private sector, accounting for almost two-thirds of global output and jobs, and a corresponding lion's share of our anthropogenic impacts on climate and nature - is the single most important institution of our times. Unfortunately, today's corporation is cast in a legal and ethical mould that belongs to the nineteenth century, the era of robber barons and horse-drawn carriages. It is designed as a machine to make money for shareholders, internalizing profits and externalizing costs, and not an institution to create value for all stakeholders. As the economy's main agent, it stands no chance of driving the vital transition society needs urgently towards tomorrow's green and equitable 'economy of permanence'."*

A new enviro-economic model

In its present form, the world's market system is consequently antiquated, anarchic and dysfunctional in relation to the natural environment. This relationship needs to be fundamentally reappraised in order to influence future market decision-making and avoid the worst market failures. We are fortunate in that we are capable of doing this; as conscious, intelligent beings we are in the unique position not only of being able to recognise the deep-seated problems inherent in our economic systems, but also to seek out and put into action sophisticated measures to correct them.

I believe that our failures are therefore not insurmountable, and that we can avert the coming market-driven environmental disaster. Once we accept that we are not nearly as free-willed and rational as we would like to think, that our present excessive behaviour in the world is entirely natural in the animal kingdom and extremely well precedented throughout the long history of Life (as will our demise be if we don't do something about it now) then we are at the starting line of finding solutions to our self-generated problems.

Yet if reforms are to work there is an overarching priority: they need to have science behind them. While it may be obvious that our demand for natural resources needs to be reined in sharply and that this requires a major reconfiguration of the old, failed economic paradigm, any new economic plan without science at its roots is unlikely to fare much better. The many inadequacies and failures of current enviro-economic policies therefore need to be examined as one would a disease or an engineering challenge, beginning with natural laws and principles.

The goal is to create a nature-based model that can divert the colossal energy of the marketplace away from its present course of environmental decline and destruction, and direct it instead to both our and the natural world's advantage. I believe this is perfectly possible, and that we have it in our power to leap towards a balanced economic system while avoiding the oceans of pain that will otherwise be inflicted on us and our fellow species if we continue with business as usual.

The central message of this book is therefore that, because we are still creatures of Nature, then to moderate our rapacious, fox-in-a-henhouse drives we need to study how Nature achieves the long-term synchrony between competing species that builds thriving, clean ecosystems and keeps them in balance, and then apply those same principles to the management of economies.

So it is time to turn our attention to *Junglenomics* itself and to look at why it is the logical and pragmatic way to go about protecting the natural world from the power of destructive markets.

Can we use our knowledge of ecosystems to manage economies better?

In its simplest form, the aim of *Junglenomics* is to harness the power of resource hunger, as represented by money and markets, to encourage not only individual species but entire ecosystems to live and thrive rather than degrade or die. The same principle could be applied to the poorest of the world; their economic welfare needs to be made profitable to others, much as making effective medicines is to pharmaceutical companies, or employing computer geeks is to creating best-selling video games. If it is profitable for companies to employ the poorest, that is exactly what will happen. This is the way ecosystems are constructed, each species gaining benefit from and providing benefit to others.

Unfortunately though, although ecological and economic systems are structurally close, the way they develop contrasts starkly. There is no significant pollution in natural ecosystems because organisms produce no malignant waste, only "profitable" waste on which other creatures thrive. Dung beetles are a classic example because they collect and break down the droppings of large herbivores, which would otherwise clog the ground. Another is the respiratory coalition between plants and animals that ensures each provides the other with oxygen on the one hand and nitrogen on the other. In contrast, we humans produce vast quantities of malignant waste such as plastics, gases and chemicals which nothing natural benefits from or consumes, and which therefore linger in the environment – in air, land and water alike, unwanted and sinister.

Technology has created innumerable new and complex niches in the economic ecosystem with interactions so complex that they almost rival those found in Nature. The Internet industry is a case in point. But technology develops too far and too fast to simultaneously devise the interactive checks and balances necessary to sustain the long-term stability that Nature enjoys. It leaves an unremitted trail of devastation, pollution and waste, with few economic actors clambering to clean it up because there hasn't been time to evolve the profitability necessary to make it attractive to do so. As a result, we accumulate gigantic rubbish dumps and pollute the land and seas with garbage and toxic waste.

To balance the economic ecosystem as quickly as possible, we therefore need to accelerate the development and evolution of those economic actors that profit from neutralising this waste, just as happens in ecosystems – by turning it into a profitable resource.

The principle here is the economic version of what is known in ecology as "symbiosis" – that is, beneficial mutual dependence. Symbiosis is one of Nature's most effective and efficient ways of keeping environments pristine. In the next chapter I will be exploring the potential for a whole raft of new symbiotic relationships between businesses to prevent or clear up pollution at source, while also providing lucrative opportunities for specialist anti-pollution services. As we'll see, a promising start has been made on industrial symbiosis in some countries, but its development is hesitant and far from attaining the necessary scale.

Accelerating economic evolution

As things stand the world has declared a war on terrorism, rightly so, but as yet there is no war on our terrorism of the environment, which is surely a far more important issue in the grand scheme of things. As a result, no really "big guns" have been brought to bear on our environmental impacts. Technology got the world into this fix and only technology can get the world out of it – new technology whose human wielders thrive by profitably utilising the pollutive output of others. Our leaders need to act as if our planet depends on it – because we know it does – by putting technological innovation and industrial symbiosis on fast burn, nurturing them as enthusiastically as one would instant cures for, say, cancer, or for violent radicalism. At present, most promising new technologies in this area have to struggle for existence in the marketplace because they have to start from scratch and there is little help for them. But if they are searched out, fostered and turned into financially rewarding resources, then inevitably economic actors will rush to colonise them and they will thrive, to both the planet's and our lasting benefit.

The same principle – accelerated evolution – applies to driving the development of new cleaner and less resource-consuming technologies – transport and energy are the obvious key areas. At present, much of this technological evolution is in the doldrums because it is so much cheaper to release waste into the environment. True, there are interesting innovations in progress – gas and battery-powered cars for example – but to become mainstream and have a real effect in the short time frame available for controlling carbon emissions and pollution, they need to be fast-tracked through more powerful economic incentives than the somewhat insipid ones used at present.

There are notable precedents for this: in wartime or during the arms and space races of the 1960s for instance. Today a standout example is the "XPRIZE", privately funded rewards offered for specific technological achievements, such as the two-million-Australian-dollar Wendy Schmidt Ocean Health XPRIZE competition to help heal the oceans by improving our understanding of how CO_2 emissions are affecting ocean acidification. Such examples demonstrate that given big enough incentives human ingenuity can achieve targeted technological breakthroughs in remarkably short order.

The broad stratagem of *Junglenomics* is to reconcile the interests of both markets and ecology by reassessing values and manipulating incentives and viability using Nature's ecosystemic example as a template. Being holistic it is applicable to all parts of an economy. Think of it as market potty-training, using strategies drawn from our knowledge of the way balanced ecosystems self-regulate. More ambitiously, it also looks to stimulate markets in an attempt to reinstate much of what has already been lost.

The benefits of predictability

If you think about it, applying natural principles to economics is a logical progression. The resource-colonising perspective underlines the continuity and direction of living systems through time and evolution. Isn't it illogical therefore to draw a line across time at the point when modern humans began economic activity and declare that from then on everything was fundamentally different from that which had come before? It wasn't; and it still isn't so different. The French have an aphorism for such continuity: *plus ça change, plus c'est la même chose* (what goes around, comes around).

However, although manipulating markets can be highly effective in mitigating unwanted outcomes, it isn't always easy to anticipate exactly how such interference will turn out. It can have unforeseen and unwanted secondary consequences that may confuse or disrupt intended aims. Not only may interference fail to cure problems, it may even exacerbate them and in the worst cases, it may even create new ones.

It is also well worth remembering that where there are winners from economic interference there may also be unintended and innocent losers. Take for example the financial incentives liberally doled out to oil palm growers. You could easily think this is a highly enlightened policy – certainly it was once thought so; after all, palm oil is a renewable biofuel that can replace more pollutive fossil fuels. So for a while it was greeted ecstatically as a potential planet saver.

Unfortunately, things didn't turn out as expected. There were devastating, unintended consequences on wilderness and wildlife that continue to this day. Oil palm growing has also resulted in serious pollution from fires, soil erosion, fertiliser, mill effluent and chemicals. Plantations have also caused the loss of much-needed, food-growing land and prevented access to common property for some of the poorest people, especially women. Ironically, when the entire life cycle of the product is considered the net environmental benefits are highly questionable [19].

However benign the original intentions, policymakers failed to predict and cater for these outcomes, a blunder of immense proportions that resulted solely from the absence of a reliable predictive model. If there had been such a model the cost-benefit of the development could have been evaluated differently from the outset. That isn't to suggest oil palm subsidy should never have taken place, but that, among other things, the subsidies could have been tailored to encourage the use of only the least ecologically valuable land and utilising a suitable model indigenous populations might also have been guaranteed economic inclusion. But if you create ideal conditions for a new, unregulated, land-guzzling, polluting economic species, then that is exactly what you can expect.

Predicting unwanted side effects from market interference is consequently a vital part of any conservation strategy. Predictability is the gold standard of economic crisis avoidance because knowing what is likely to come next makes for better plans and better outcomes. However, to predict accurately requires informed analyses and accurate modelling, and there's the challenge.

Lessons have been, and undoubtedly will continue to be, learned from errors in foresight and planning, but such trial and error is a clumsy and costly way to manage markets as new situations are often going to catch you out. It's like an endless game of blind man's buff, where you only know what you've got when you grasp it. A reliable, predictive model that takes off the blindfold is needed, and Nature can offer it. By viewing industries and businesses as economic "species" occupying market ecosystems it is possible to predict more reliably who the winners and losers will be. It also allows us to anticipate associated economic temptations that encourage environmentally and socially destructive exploitation of natural resources. The double profit gained by clear-felling rainforest timber to sell at the same time as planting biofuels is one such temptation that has, understandably, not been resisted because the financial rewards are so high, but it continues to produce devastating consequences for the environment, for species and for forest peoples.

Of course, manipulating incentives and viability to influence business and personal behaviour is not new, it's as old as the hills. So, what is new about *Junglenomics*? How does it differ from any other economic programme with similar aims?

The answer is that while well-understood methods that are used to manipulate market forces (taxes, fines, incentives and recently contrived instruments such as the carbon trading system) have immense potential, they tend to be used in an uncoordinated, scattergun way: there is no guiding blueprint like *Junglenomics* to follow, only conflicting and outdated economic dogma. They are also hampered by division, apathy, powerful financial interests, and politics.

The economists who devise environmental policy tend to regard almost everything, from environmental nirvana to human happiness, as potentially falling within the scope of their discipline. Classical economics is as a result almost a religion. Pollution, waste and over-exploitation are recognised, but only as failures; as glitches in the functioning of the ideal market paradigm (itself controversial) that only needs clever adjusting to put right. Like forest firefighters, economists rush to the scene of each new blaze with hoses gushing. The implication is that there is a "pure" maths-based economic tradition, a path of economic righteousness from which "unholy" deviations tempt the licentious and the weak, to coin appropriately Victorian vocabulary.

But for Nature and markets alike, the immense influence of resource hunger ensures that giving in to temptation is much more natural than self-restraint. The *Junglenomics* perspective is thus different: the market failures that cause pollution, environmental destruction and poverty are not glitches or deviations, they are entirely natural and predictable phenomena amply precedented throughout the history of life. In reality, economic life mirrors the goings-on of billions of years of natural history. It cannot be subjected to precise equations because it is dominated by the ebb and flow of innumerable competing actors, and complicated by the constant buffeting of the unpredictable winds of chance. Stability in Nature is achieved, but only by innumerable components finding niches, like pieces in a vast jigsaw. They create a whole that is mutually supporting – in effect a worldwide superorganism, a Gaia.

Indeed, I would go even further: in the *Junglenomics* world the economic "sinning" that causes market failure is a potential virtue. Why? Because it reveals both overt and hidden expressions of the resource-colonising imperative – resource hunger – the manipulation of which is key to the formation of an important part of the remedy – economic symbiosis. Instead of forever quenching market failures by firefighting them, markets need to be rebalanced to avoid failures happening in the first place. Resource hunger needs, not to be stifled, but to be harnessed to benign ends.

Although *Junglenomics* is a template against which environmental imbalances are held, with a view to correcting them, it is also much more than that: it represents an entire new mindset for the future – a paradigm shift in thinking. As a discipline, it generates an attitude towards business that, while it should never be hostile, cannot even conceive of new environmentally sensitive business activities arising without the mechanisms or symbiotic partners necessary to render it environmentally neutral. And, under a *Junglenomics* paradigm, no business would even bother to get out of bed for a business plan that was not environmentally neutral. Assesments of profitability would then always have to take potential environmental costs into account.

What *Junglenomics* is not

Given the widespread dissemination of pseudoscience, one is right to be wary of any new concept that seeks to reshape our future. However, *Junglenomics* carries no religious message, literal or subliminal, nor is it a political creed. It involves the grinding of no axes other than that of carbon emissions reduction, pollution control, environment and wildlife conservation, and the alleviation of extreme poverty. Any idea of a return to village economics as advocated in more verdant political quarters is nowhere on its menu either.

In fact, quite the contrary: *Junglenomics* stands four-square behind ongoing economic development and growth, albeit of a more beneficially structured kind (such as expanding symbiotic markets in the world economy) because that is Nature's three-billion-year-old way. It also espouses full recognition of, even an admiration for, the power and desirability of multinational economic activity so long as it is fully accountable for its behaviour towards people and the natural environment.

Junglenomics demands no great Damascene conversion from businesses either. It requires no one to *believe* in anything, or even to behave much differently concerning the pursuit of profit. In fact, it relies upon businesses remaining obedient to their existing, wholly natural drives, because that is what happens in ecosystems and ultimately what makes them predictable and manageable.

What it does require, however, is conviction, far-sightedness and determination among policymakers and world leaders, along with wide-ranging cooperation between participating governments.

It is strange to reflect that to the rest of the natural world humans are like Marvel Comic superheroes. We possess special powers – intelligence, imagination and a supreme dexterity far above those of any other creature. But in gaining these powers we have grown far too efficient as resource colonisers for our planet's, and ultimately for our own, good.

Under the *Junglenomics* paradigm the world would modernise the way it wields these formidable powers using natural ecosystems as a template. At present, we humans are too often led by our resource hungry instincts to do the wrong things, but with an ecosystemic approach our economic processes would become less anarchic, designed more (as ecosystems are through evolution) to give powerful incentives to do the right thing both for our benefit and for those other species with which we share the planet. By taking our cues from Nature we can begin to remove the chaos and confusion caused by our headlong dash for resources and replace it with balance and order, stabilising the climate and replenishing the natural world.

The alternative future is one of incessant crisis management, futilely patching and repairing a broken planet under a defunct economic model for hundreds of years hence.

1.   *Alex Evans: The Myth Gap, 2017*
2.   *E.g.: "Essential": Millburn & Nicodemus 2015*
3.   *Roland, The African Experience, p.37*
4.   *E.g.: "Competition, Evolution and Optimisation: Comparisons of Models in Economics and Ecology", Clem Tisdell 2001; Moore, James: "Predators and Prey: A new ecology of competition", Harvard Business Review, May/June 1993, etc.*
5.   *N Hanley*
6.   *Robert E Ricklefs: The Economy of Nature*
7.   *Geerat J. Vermeij: Nature: An Economic History*
8.   *Mackenzie: NS 2679 pp.8-9*
9.   *Paul Krugman, Princeton*
10.   *E.g.: S Levin, Princeton.*

11. Bar-Yam, New England Complex Systems Institute

12. A subject explored recently by Fritjof Capra and Pier Luigi in their book, "The Systems View of Life: a Unifying Vision" CUP 2014

13. Sanderson et al 2002

14. Halpern et al 2008

15. E.g.: Souza & Matsuzawa, "The Use of Tokens as Rewards and Tools by Chimpanzees". 2001

16. Barbara Briers et al of HEC business school, Paris. Psychological Science, vol. 17, p.939 (NS.2700 M Buchanan)

17. E.g.: D. Ariely, Massachusetts Institute of Technology, Stephen Lea & Paul Webley 2009 (NS 2700)

18. Vohs et al 2009 (NS 2700)

19. Shell/IUCN combined report 2008

Sources for hunter-gatherers: R Lowrie 1947; L White 1949; Duffy 1984; Turnbull 1976; Martin Gusinde 1961;. Wymer 1989; Zirzan 2005; e.g. Fowlett, Wynn, 1980s; Sahlins 2005; Lee 1963; Lee 1969; Truswell & Hanson 1976; Fisher 1982; Flood 1983; Turnbull 1976; e.g. Herskovits 1958; R Oliver, The African Experience.

Chapter 2
The Seeds of Destruction

"This ain't no upwardly mobile freeway –
This is the road to hell"
Chris Rea (1989)

A summary of the chief environmental challenges facing the world

Having begun by laying out the principles and justification for *Junglenomics*, the remainder of this book moves from theory to practice. I want to show how applying natural principles to economics is more than just a pretty notion, how it could help solve real time environmental problems long term. These problems have not only deepened considerably in recent decades, they also now cover a broader spectrum than ever before as destructive economic activity encroaches ever further into the natural world.

To set the scene, here is a list of the chief environmental challenges facing the world:

1. Pollution
Industrial by-products deposited directly into the environment via water, soil and air (e.g. CO_2, particulates, gases, liquids and poisons such as dioxins and sulphuric acid).
Non- or infrequently recyclable and single-use manufactured products (e.g. some plastics, including most polyolefins such as polystyrene and polyethylene, polyvinyl chloride, polycarbonate, most polypropylene and miscellaneous plastics such as bisphenol).
Transport emissions (e.g. CO_2, lead, benzene).
Power generation (e.g. CO_2, NO, SO_2).
Diffuse and point source agricultural emissions of environmentally persistent chemicals (e.g. farm effluent, pesticides, herbicides, methane, nitrates).
Radioactive emissions and outflows.

Spillages, leakages and illegal disposal of waste matter (e.g. crude oil, sludge).
Mining residues and used chemical run-off (e.g. arsenic, heavy metals).
Sewage (mixed with non-biodegradable products, e.g. syringes, condoms, sanitary towels, nappies/diapers, oestrogens, detergents).

2. Habitat Degradation and Loss
Deforestation.
Intensive agriculture.
Urbanisation.
Industrial development.
Reef destruction.
Sea floor dredging.
Ocean acidification (from excessive CO_2 absorption).
Water pollution (marine and fresh).
Climate change.
Excessive tourism development.

3. Decline and Extinction of Species
Habitat loss.
Pollution.
Pharmacopoeia (medicines and tonics).
Bushmeat hunting.
Poaching.
Overfishing.
Translocated disease.
Translocated species.
Climate change.

4. Human Poverty and Premature Death
Warfare.
Disease.
Drought and crop failure.
Lack of food-growing land.
Lack of clean water.
Lack of hygiene.
Overpopulation.
Environmental degradation.
Scarcity of medicine/medics.

Political and religious bigotry.
Corruption.
Resource competition.
Cultural disruption.
Cultural prejudice.
Lack of education.
Lack of economic opportunity.

It is beyond the capacity of any one book to explore all the potential applications for *Junglenomics* in this economically malfunctioning world, so I have limited myself to areas that seem to be of greatest environmental importance – pollution, greenhouse gas emissions, loss of natural environments and species, marine ecosystem degradation, land loss and agriculture. I'll begin with pollution in all its various guises.

The true cost of pollutive industrial waste

Of the various sources of pollution, the industrial kind is by far the worst because it represents a worldwide problem of immense scale and penetration. A litany of nasty, smelly, industrial and human by-products dogs the otherwise extraordinarily successful footsteps of the economic ecosystem. As if enacting some real-life Mordor [1], industrialisation has contaminated the world with toxic waste, poisonous fumes, pesticides, chlorofluorocarbons (CFCs), foul effluent, radioactivity and much else. In the unrelenting pursuit of economic expansion and wealth we have at the same time made a pretty thorough job of tainting our home planet; and it's getting worse by the year.

The cost of our failure to control industrial pollution doesn't just fall where you might expect – on natural systems and wildlife – it has a massive and growing impact on us in both economic and health terms. It manifests itself in numerous ways that we cannot help but be aware of it, yet its chemical and physical complexities are extremely difficult to understand, and some impacts are only just beginning to be recognised.

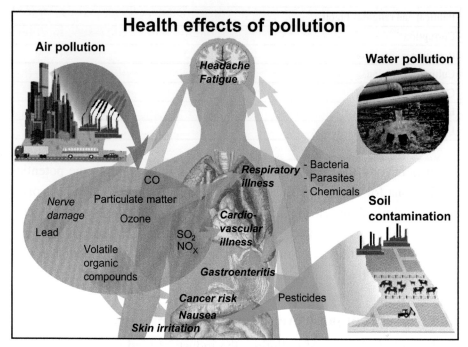

wikimedia.orgwikipediacommonsaaa Health effects of pollution

For example, the common occurrence of persistent organic pollutants (POPs), which include such sinister concoctions as dioxins, DDT and PCBs (polychlorinated biphenyls), are prevalent and inescapable. They are present not only in meat, fish and dairy products, but in the wild, for example in Mediterranean deep-sea fish. They enter the food chain from sources such as pesticides, chemical manufacturing and incinerated waste, and once in our bodies they take up residence in fat. Diabetes was previously blamed on our modern, indolent lifestyle, but now scientists have found damning evidence that POPs are to blame [2]. The current plague of diabetes already affects 180 million people worldwide, according to the World Health Organization (WHO), a number predicted to more than double by 2030 (the number of sufferers in the UK doubled in the 20 years to 2017. In the US 23.4m people – over 1 in 13 – were diagnosed with the disease in 2015). The personal cost for each diabetes sufferer can be high, but the financial cost is also great: in 2007 the diabetes epidemic cost $174 billion in the US alone [3].

However, we now know that pollutive industrial waste is causing other costs far greater than those involved in health issues like diabetes, the main one being climate change. Jonathan Loh of the Zoological Society of London has asserted that the overall financial consequences of a global ecological crisis are even graver than the economic meltdown of 2007-8 [4]. In 2006, economist Nicholas Stern shocked the world out of its complacency by putting a price tag on climate change. According to his report, the cost to the global economy of failing to reduce pollutive carbon emissions and to cater for the effects of climate change could be £2.3 trillion ($3.5 trillion). The environmental fallout has also been estimated in a report [5] by the OECD [6], where the economic costs of reduced productivity due to poor health from air and water pollution are rated as being high.

The Stern report also found other important economic costs associated with degraded ecosystems. While climate change is global, there is also an accumulated range of costs dependent on local circumstances. The following are just some of the pollution costs the report identified [7]:

i. Dealing with health and welfare effects of air pollution from 10,000 major sources in the US costs the nation up to 2.8% of GDP.

ii. Air pollution costs China about 3.8% of GDP in health impacts.

iii. Natural disasters cost the poorest countries more than 13% of their GDP.

iv. Not meeting international commitments for water and sanitation – governments have pledged, for instance, to halve the proportion of the global population who do not have access to safe water by 2015 – could cost $128.9 billion per year.

There is a great deal more – in the way of pollution and the environmental damage it causes – that could have been included here, but it is enough to remake the point that the world environment is getting into a parlous state and it is already costing us dearly both in health and our pockets, let alone in terms of lost species and environments, and in human suffering. If there was a silver lining to the 2007-8 world financial crisis, it is that it may have concentrated many influential, policy-forming minds on how vulnerable and brittle our world is both economically and environmentally. Toxic debts pollute the economic environment in exactly the same way as toxic pollutants and are doing in the natural one. Just as narrowly escaping from meeting one's maker can remind us of our mortality, so a combined financial and environmental crisis may help bring about a profound re-evaluation of our place on this planet and our entire relationship with it.

So how do we go about this re-evaluation?

Ecosystems on the edge

Looking at its beauty and glorious complexities, the wild world appears seamless, having a place for everything and everything in its place. What we see is not a construction though, it is the outcome of aeons of struggle, exploitation, competition and cooperation between colonising plants, fungi, animals and microorganisms. Nature has taken a very great deal of making, but like most things in a state of fine balance it can take very little to unmake.

While the equation underlying the viability of most organised entities, be they biological or economic, is based mainly upon the profitability of their particular operating strategy, it also relies on the relative stability of their environment. Disrupt that stability and the fossil record shows the consequences for species can be far-reaching. It is down to chance when major geophysical disruptions hit the world, but it has happened at least five times, and each time it has taken a great toll on species. The resulting destabilisation of environments leads to a reshuffling and, over the longer term, even a redesign of the fauna and flora they host. Of the big five, the best known is the massive asteroid that hit the Gulf of Mexico 65 million years ago, triggering the infamous K/T event that wiped out the dinosaurs, but there were very many more local traumas, including climate variations that resulted in ice ages. It still seems strange to me that crocodiles and hippos once frequented the river Thames in England, and that hyena, bear and rhinoceros were once fully at home in present-day Hertford, Hereford and Hampshire. It took an ice age to wipe them out, and in their place came the likes of reindeer, Arctic hares and foxes.

We humans are now inflicting a new such disruption on the world, one that threatens to be as catastrophic as those geophysical traumas of the past. And what we don't do directly, greenhouse gas-related climate change promises to do for us.

Stable as they may appear in the short timescale we experience, ecosystems don't stay the same over the long term. After disruptions, they gradually re-evolve, adapt or import a multitude of new flora and fauna to compensate and restore balance. Eventually ecosystems self-stabilise again, the potentially disruptive activities of each species being neutralised by the beneficial attentions of others.

All the same principles apply to our economic system. It is badly out of kilter with the natural environment and needs rebalancing. But left to its own devices rebalancing takes time, often a great deal of it; not the sort of time we would care to hang around for, but time counted in thousands or even hundreds of thousands of years. Not having that amount time to wait for our economic ecosystem to balance itself we have no choice but to take matters into our own hands and we have to understand how we go about this.

Why regulation alone is ineffective for solving environmental problems

A balanced economic ecosystem with stabilised, pollution-free environments is a goal any nation could achieve if it were enthusiastic enough. You might expect that achieving such a state would involve reams of new legislation; but that is not so – it doesn't have to be authoritarian. It needs to be more a matter of financial incentive and disincentive – carrot and stick – than rules and regulations. Nudging and nurturing economic actors of all shapes and sizes towards less pollutive behaviour and the recycling of raw materials can be achieved simply by incentivising economic symbiosis.

In the past, laws alone have been used to try to end environmentally damaging practices; indeed, the law has been used so widely to attempt to protect environments and wildlife that one could almost say that an 11th Commandment has been created: *thou shalt not damage the natural environment*. Certainly, a lot can be done through rules and regulations as a stopgap to help safeguard environments for the short term – the next 30 years or so. But the important question is, just how effective can laws alone be in preserving environments and species over the long term?

I have come to the view that legislation on its own is about as effective in preventing environmental insult as it has been at preventing murder, the coveting of wives and asses, thieving and all other biblically proscribed proclivities. This is particularly so where the financial incentives to "sin" against the environment are as strong as they are, such as the earlier palm oil example. But while there may be an unlimited supply of people to murder and wives and asses to covet, there is a limit on the amount of environment and wildlife we can obliterate before getting the planet into irreversible trouble. Time and again it has been shown that the force of law alone cannot hope to resist the power of the economic-colonising imperative for long. Sooner or later it will find ways to circumvent or undermine man-made rules. And while we play this unending game of cat and mouse the decline goes on.

Why should this be? Not "why" at the superficial level of money and self-interest that I discussed in the previous chapter, but why at the fundamental level? To answer this, we need to consider the role of the colonisation factor again. The effect of the drive to colonise on economies is no different to that in Nature. It is like the force of gravity on a river: just as gravity pushes river waters inexorably down to the sea, so the drive to colonise propels rivers of entrepreneurship and capital towards a sea of economic niches; and where these economic rivers are ruled to be counterproductive, we try to stop them largely through laws and regulation.

The narcotics trade is a classic example; alcohol prohibition in 1930s USA another, and environmental misdemeanour is no different. As with a river, legal dams alone cannot stop powerful market forces; they merely hold them back for a bit. Any stoppage is often only temporary. Eventually unrequited markets will find ways over and around such dams and rejoin their old course, just as sooner or later water inevitably overflows a dam.

So what is the answer? The challenge is to develop a permanent means to relieve the immense pressure we are placing on our fragile world. To do so we have to find ways to dry up the most destructive economic rivers of pollution and degradation, and to divert others along benign, pre-prepared channels. The best way to achieve this is to build a fully functional economic ecosystem, and there is nowhere better to learn how to do this than from Nature.

I am under no illusion that building balanced economic ecosystems that operate in sync with Nature will be easy. It will require a great deal of forethought, planning and determination. Flexibility is the key, for there can be no question of creating some economic straightjacket in which to stuff all and sundry willy-nilly. One size will not fit all, any more than it does in Nature. *Junglenomics*-compliant policies are almost by definition flexible and responsive, which means that those who carry out policy must not be enslaved to any one rule book. To achieve this, governments will first need make "environmental accounting" compulsory for almost all businesses. Yet another burden on business, I hear you say? No, because, like their financial counterparts, the job of environmental accountants is to save more money than they cost. Besides, it is essential to achieving the necessary revolution.

To compliment this and ensure rapid progress towards sustainability, governments then need to create "environmental liaison" departments. Here, specialist consultants receive environmental accounts, collate information, and advise governments about creating new market incentives and levies. They can then also act as information conduits in the reverse direction, advising accountants on impending legislation and levy changes to enable their clients to prepare, for example by modifying machinery or packaging.

Pavan Sukhdev likewise favours an evolutionary approach: *"Like any species, the corporation can and will evolve in response to its environment, which is policies, prices and institutions. The theory of change towards a new corporate model (he calls it 'Corporation 2020' because it needs to emerge so urgently) is about urgent reforms in four sub-domains of the environment through which today's corporation thrives: performance metrics that ignore externalities; taxation of the 'goods' more than the 'bads'; financial leverage without limits; advertising without ethics. The ball is in the courts of the respective regulators of these four domains to move the reforms we need. Accountancy bodies need to insist on standardization, disclosure and assurance of corporate externalities. Central bankers need to learn from the last four financial crises (Lat. America; US Savings & Loans; Asian Credit; Mortgage derivatives) that mismanaged credit was the common cause, and impose leverage limits; finance ministries need to redesign corporate taxation, by taxing the 'bads' more and the 'goods' less; and civil society as well as advertising associations should come down heavily on advertising that mis-informs and persuades, bombarding us 24/7 and converting our insecurities into wants, needs, demand and then even more "private profits, public costs"*

Importantly, liaison advisors would need to be as informed in business as in environmental matters and specialise in specific areas, from transport, to packaging, to cloth manufacture. Thus, to achieve the necessary rapid revolution in business practice with minimum pain, they would need to get inside the "world view" of individual businesses - to tap into their economic sensory prioritisations. The great German naturalist, Jakob von Uexküll, encapsulated the diversity of sensory prioritisation among animal species in the opening passage of his book, *A Stroll Through the Worlds of Animals and Men* (1934): *"...The best time to set out on such an adventure"* [the stroll], he wrote, *"is on a sunny day. The place, a flower-strewn meadow, humming with insects, fluttering with butterflies. Here we may glimpse the worlds of the lowly dwellers of the meadow. To do so, we must first blow, in fancy, a soap bubble around each creature to represent its own world, filled with perceptions of which it alone knows. When we ourselves step into one of these bubbles, the familiar world is transformed. Many of its colourful features disappear, others no longer appear together but appear in new relationships. A new world comes into being. Through the bubble, we see the world of the burrowing worm, of the butterfly, or of the field mouse; the world as it appears to the animals themselves, not as it appears to us. This we may call the phenomenal world, or the self-world of the animal."*

As with animal species, so with economic ones. After all, to perform efficiently, industries – just like species – must exist and function within certain parameters. They develop behaviours that aim to, and hence tend to, maximise their efficiency and profitability in that arena. The "self-world" they inhabit consequently becomes filled with a set of priorities that are specific to their niche (this is so even between individual participants in any one niche: take agriculture for example, where certain crops and conditions demand different growing methods and chemicals and so effect the environment in different ways).

Each economic actor participates in an economic ecosystem populated with a particular combination of fauna with which they interact – customers, suppliers, service providers, competitors and so forth. It is only with the benefit of that inside view of their niche that the best combination of plans can be devised to help a polluting business become environmentally neutral while remaining competitive and profitable – the essence of a well-functioning economic ecosystem.

The essential remit of such new advisory teams would be to facilitate the conditions that encourage the emergence of viable partnerships between polluters and pollution preventers and removers, and between waste producers and recyclers. Each instance would be approached as a problem to be solved in a limited time frame, yet for a long-term solution. Its "file" would therefore remain open until an acceptable (or zero) level of pollutive output was achieved; it would stay a work in progress. The present system of warnings and *ad hoc* fines would be replaced with assistance and compulsion in equal measures – carrot and stick discipline with no easy get-outs. This is after all how Nature goes about its business, how it develops ecosystems that flourish because the species that comprise them coexist so well with each other and with their environment.

There is plenty of room for competition in this paradigm, though not that which disadvantages lesser polluters by ignoring the external environmental costs of greater ones. Given the necessary incentives and conditions, inevitably technological innovators and entrepreneurs will rapidly emerge to seize the opportunities and fill the new niches. Just as their biological counterparts do in Nature, they will be drawn to the honeypot of profit to perform the services the present economic ecosystem so badly needs.

If in the end reform proves impossible – if a business cannot survive without destructive environmental consequences or bear its environmental costs despite transitional help, then there should be only one outcome: sooner or later it must head the way of the dinosaurs.

The next question is - what natural processes should governments be coaching business to emulate to minimise pollution and waste? In the last chapter I alluded to the foremost such process as a central theme of Nature, and hence of *Junglenomics*. By looking closer at why this should be and why the process is so successful in Nature, I can illustrate how *symbiosis* can be applied equally successfully to economies.

Symbiosis – the key to a balanced economic ecosystem

In Nature, symbiotic species evolve, not to do anyone any favours, but to benefit themselves in one way or another by making a profit colonising the resources other species offer. They do so not only by consuming them, or by living in or on them (benignly or otherwise), but also by extracting benefit from their by-products, their waste. This opportunistic, adaptive and ultimately mutually beneficial process is called *symbiosis*, and it gradually helps build the orchestral synchrony of species that epitomises a fully developed ecosystem. Building a similar, symbiotic system in the economic world needs to become a central medium-term objective for all economies.

Nature shows us that it is not the production of waste in itself that matters, but what happens to it afterwards; only then is it designated as either pollution or as a resource. Because Nature can only work in a reactive way, it tends not to favour less pollution-producing species; instead it evolves other species that clean up after each other, examples of which I will come to in a moment. We humans have the great advantage that we can, in principle, do both: we can not only find ways to clean up after ourselves, we can also alter our activities to reduce our pollutive output.

Alas, while for many decades we have recognised the need to act to reduce and clean up our pollutive output, it seems we have not yet recognised that our failure to do so sufficiently is a reflection, not of greedy and callous capitalist attitudes as many would have it, but of a lack of understanding of the forces at play and a predominance of disjointed and indeterminate policy. To rectify this, we need a blueprint to follow; and a supremely successful one has been there in front of us all the time – in natural ecosystems.

Symbiosis as Nature does it

The realigning of economic systems to emulate ecosystems begins with a simple question: how do ecosystems successfully manage to avoid polluting their environment and overexploiting resources while economic ones excel at it?

The answer to this, so far as pollution in concerned, is that while ecosystems produce plenty of potential pollution – vast quantities of it in fact in the form of waste products like gasses, excrement and dead organic material – Nature has evolved ways of dealing with it before it damages the environment. Not by dumping it in segregated disposal areas as we mostly do, but by recycling it via the activity of specialised organisms. Such organisms are of course entirely unwitting of the vital services they perform. They act entirely for their own benefit. Indeed, they have evolved simply in order to colonise the golden opportunities provided by the detritus of others. In so doing they build mutually beneficial relationships.

Such symbiosis is everywhere in Nature and materialises in some intriguing ways. In the forests of Borneo, for example, the giant rajah pitcher plant gets the nitrogen it needs by an unusual method. It is shaped much like a toilet, and its open "lid" secretes sweet nectar that is irresistible not only to insects but also to the mountain tree shrew (*Tupaia montana*). The tree shrew straddles the bowl of the pitcher plant to lick the nectar on the lid and simultaneously deposits a payment – its nitrogen-rich droppings – which fall into the bowl and are absorbed by the plant.

Giant pitcher plant with tree shrew - symbiosis as nature does it
©PaulWilliamsnaturepl.com

Though this relationship is essential to the pitcher plant, to the tree shrew the sugar may represent little more than a pleasant bonus. On the other hand, the symbiotic relationship between bees and flowering plants and trees is essential to both. Attracted by their nectar, the honeybees' staple diet, they accidentally transfer pollen from male flowers that gets caught on their fine hairs and distribute it to female flowers on their way around, thus pollinating the plant and helping continue the species.

Woodland trees and fungi similarly enjoy benefits that cut both ways. The trees gain advantage from the mycorrhizal fungi that grow around them, for while the tree feeds the fungus with sugar, it in turn receives nutrients, such as nitrogen and phosphorus, from the fungi. The fungi also take up poisonous heavy metals from the soil, thereby protecting the trees, as well as helping them resist frost and gain resistance against soil-borne pathogenic microorganisms. Similarly, young orchids depend entirely on fungi growing around their roots for their nutrients.

However, we don't have to look further than our own bodies to find an archetypal symbiotic ecosystem known as a "microbiome". In fact, we carry around more foreign cells in us than our own, and they perform a multitude of tasks that keep both us and them alive and well. Many of these "symbionts" live in the gut and help us digest our food, for example, and without them our digestive systems simply wouldn't work.

Symbiosis can extend beyond such immediate relationships too: organisms often regulate each other and provide a check on runaway populations. For example, grasses that are high nitrate consumers benefit from the presence of clovers that fix nitrogen in the soil. Any crowding out of clovers soon produces a reciprocal dieback of the grasses allowing in turn a recovery of the clovers. Without such a partner these grasses would rapidly exhaust the soil of nitrogen and go into decline.

One of the most remarkable and important examples of marine symbiosis is the relationship between tiny single-celled algae called zooxanthellae and corals. The algae, which give the otherwise colourless corals their many splendid colours, occupy coral polyps. The polyps are in effect little castles that not only protect the algae, but also provide compounds from their waste necessary for the algae to generate oxygen through photosynthesis. In return the algae provide essential oxygen and carbohydrates, helping corals both to grow and safely dispose of their waste. Zooxanthellae can be considered critical for coral reef building. This relationship is more than just a convenience – it can be a matter of life and death; for when the algae die or are forced out, corals lose their colour in so-called "bleaching" events, and many cannot survive for long.

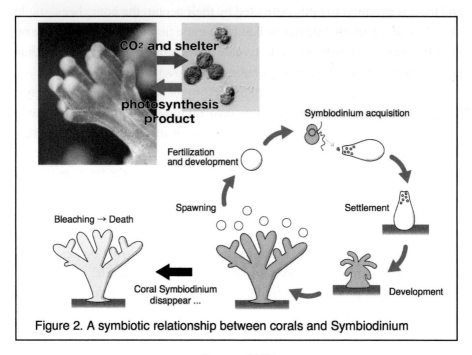

CO² and shelter

photosynthesis product

Symbiodinium acquisition

Fertilization and development

Spawning

Settlement

Bleaching → Death

Coral Symbiodinium disappear ...

Development

Figure 2. A symbiotic relationship between corals and Symbiodinium

Courtesy of OIST

To keep ecosystems in balance and thriving a great deal of symbiotic recycling is therefore essential. We humans create massive quantities of needless pollutive waste but have so far not understood its long-term significance enough to appreciate the vital importance of neutralising it. The consequences of unattended pollution, were it to take place in the natural world, could look very much like what is happening in our economic one. Imagine, for example, a great herd of wildebeest living on a vast, grassy African plain. But suppose that, in this case, it is a plain from which the organisms that usually attend to wildebeest droppings have been entirely wiped out; so instead of being broken down and mixed into the soil by the usual hordes of small and microscopic organisms, the wildebeest dung now steadily accumulates on the surface. Rains then turn this huge midden into a sloppy morass, sealing out light, air and smothering the grasses beneath (which cannot benefit because the microorganisms that convert the nutrients into an absorbable form are also absent). Eventually the once lush plain becomes a desolate wasteland with only a few isolated pockets of life surviving here and there. It is a situation that parallels the effect that certain economic wildebeests, such as the energy, cement and transport industries, are having on parts of our natural environment today.

As it is, numerous organisms (mostly worms, insects and bacteria) have evolved specifically to benefit from potential pollutants like wildebeest dung. It is to them not foul and pollutive but the very opposite – manna tumbling from heaven. Their instinct is to do no one a service but themselves, but by using the wildebeest waste profitably they unintentionally perform a priceless service for all. They not only act as Nature's pollution deactivators but fulfil a second vital role in the recycling of essential nutrients into the soil for further exploitation.

The scarcity of symbiosis in economies

If only economic systems could reach a similarly balanced state of their own accord, but alas the contrast couldn't be greater. The rapid rate of modern economic evolution far outpaces the potential evolution of accompanying clean-up industries vital for developing symbiosis and achieving systemic synchrony. New technologies can produce new pollutants and waste products, and in this high-speed ecosystem there often just isn't enough time for markets to develop profitable ways to do the mopping-up in time to stop them doing serious damage to the environment, unless strongly prompted to do so. These new ventures can also all too easily complete their developmental cycle and go out of business in a relatively short period of time – mere decades or less – long before a clean-up structure can form around them, and when they go they leave their waste behind them.

There are numerous instances of this. Take for example the Satilla River in Georgia, USA, where an industrial waste handler operated for just two years before being closed down for multiple environmental violations. Years later pollution still leaks from the site into surrounding groundwater.

So, one of the effects of this rapid metabolic rate in economies is that certain operating costs may never be met. These costs are of a type that rarely figures in the balance sheets of industry without compulsion. They are the degradation of land, air and water – external costs, or "externalities" as they are termed.

Externalities can be tolerated at modest levels, but when economic colonisation and market evolution begin to rapidly develop, as they have done since the technological revolution of the 20th century, then, as we know, pollution problems become greatly exacerbated. In such growing conditions, profitable opportunities burgeon and innumerable opportunist market species inevitably emerge to exploit them, multiplying the pace of economic development and spreading it to all corners of the globe. The result is that more and more external costs are not met and the problems compound.

Most worryingly, if the economic system continues to be left to its anarchic self, as it largely has been, the damage to the planet could become irreversible. It is therefore hard to understate the importance of symbiosis for maintaining environmental stability in both ecological and economic systems alike.

Getting symbiosis into the economic ecosystem

There is an old English adage traditionally associated with scrap merchants that goes, "where there's muck, there's brass". It could equally be the motto of the equivalent class of animal – scavengers and recyclers such as vultures, dung beetles, fly larvae and bacteria – the detritus eaters, or *detrivores,* of natural ecosystems. But this saying can obviously only come true where the biological or economic technology has been invented that is capable of turning that "muck" into a viable economic niche – one that earns enough "brass" to be worth doing.

The trouble is, it can take a great deal of time, research and investment to find ways to exploit many waste by-products profitably, even where it is possible at all. Uses first have to be found and product demand developed. In the case of the vast quantities of carbon dioxide in the atmosphere released mainly through burning fossil fuels, there hasn't yet been sufficient time for a market coloniser to develop the technology and create the market to profit from recapturing it and selling it on in sufficient quantities. Left to itself it could take another hundred years or more for such a naturally occurring symbiotic economic species to evolve. Yet it is clear that the sooner this happens the sooner this particular environmental problem will get an ecosystemic, market-based solution. But carbon-related global warming poses such a serious threat that we can't afford to wait for that to happen of its own accord – we have to make it happen.

In the meantime, if we wait for markets to find solutions without outside intervention we have to keep looking to Mother Nature to absorb or recycle most of our waste and emissions. Unfortunately, Nature is becoming saturated, its systems choked by the unprecedented volume of by-products from our ever-expanding economic activity.

In many ways, economic hyper-development resembles a planetwide algal bloom: it has given rise to a proliferation of gas emissions, toxic waste and environmental degradation that stifles the life out of living organisms. Industrial "species" have evolved far too quickly for anything like enough waste-recycling ones to evolve alongside them. In the end the triumph of long-term synchrony over short-term expediency in eco- and economic systems alike can only be provided by each economic or biological unit causing their environment only the degree of stress that it can tolerate without degradation. And because all organisms give rise to potentially toxic waste, be it only in death, that most depend on just who else they are sharing that system with – in particular those that can make a living out of clearing up after them. Of course, some economic species for which industrial waste is a profitable opportunity do exist, but our economic system is very short of such recyclers. As a result, the vast majority of waste around the world is still seen as a problem best buried – often literally.

The answer is clear enough though. Only by stimulating the rapid emergence of a whole new array of pollution and waste-guzzling economic species can we emulate Nature's tried and tested formula for ecosystems – symbiosis. Instead of always trying, and mostly failing, to patch up our battered planet, we can learn to fundamentally remodel economies to live more benignly alongside and within ecosystems for the long term.

To conserve the planetary environment in a fit state for our descendants, the world needs to become far more proactive in promoting viable symbiotic economic partnerships than it has been. This requires economic stimulation to encourage the accelerated development of symbiotic economic fauna.

We can do this by manipulating the colonising imperative underlying all our economic decision-making – by making neutralising, or preventing, pollution a profitable activity through economic incentives. Create the right conditions for symbiotic economic speciation and natural resource-colonising forces will flock to construct the ecologically neutral economic ecosystem we so desperately need. This is fundamental to the *Junglenomics* paradigm.

Symbiosis pioneers

It would be misleading to suggest that there has been no recognition of the value of symbiosis, nor efforts to engage it into economic life; on the contrary, I am glad to say that there are some shining examples emerging in Europe.

Take the UK's National Industrial Symbiosis Programme (NISP). Founded by Peter Laybourn in 1999 and rolled out as a national programme in 2004 – the first of its kind in the world – NISP has won the highest plaudits and has been accredited by the European Commission as an "Exemplar of Innovation". (I find it disappointing though that it was not until 2012, at the Rio+20 Summit, that NISP was invited to share its inspiring experiences with the rest of the world.)

NISP operates by bringing companies together to share synergies and information. The beauty of it is that it isn't about conforming to regulations – it's about profit. Indeed, some companies find that cooperation, especially in the more efficient use of raw materials, can be highly profitable. It has been estimated that if rolled out across Europe NISP could save 1.4 billion euros and generate additional profits of 1.6 billion euros in sales. It shows that being ecosystemically efficient can become profitable – something it needs to be if the economic ecosystem is to start functioning more like a natural one.

NISP's *Junglenomics* credentials are therefore gold standard, but it adds up to very little in isolation. Its model needs to be promoted at the highest levels through intergovernmental channels and rolled out right across the world without delay.

There is also the Waste and Resources Action Programme (WRAP), another enlightened UK-based organisation that enjoys prime *Junglenomics* credentials. WRAP not only innovates ways to recycle resources to obtain maximum use from them and is a leader in reducing food waste though its Food Waste Minimisation Programme, but it also works with business to help design and develop sustainable goods, particularly textiles and electronics. It presents a complementary model to that of NISP that makes it equally important. Similarly, it needs to be heavily promoted and nurtured worldwide.

The third organisation I want to mention is the Kalundborg Eco-Industrial Park located in Denmark. It stands out for praise here because it is the world's first successful example of a group of companies coming together unprompted, entirely for selfish ends, including one generator of power, to profit from the sharing and recycling of resources in industrial production. For just one of their numerous examples, the collaboration is estimated to have saved more than three million cubic metres of water. As such it is a model for worldwide industrial symbiosis of the future.

Making waste profitable

All this is of course highly commendable. These organisations are significantly widening the scope of what is recyclable and demonstrating, through example, that ecologically benign behaviour can be profitable. However, two questions arise here. Firstly, NISP, WRAP and Kalundborg may set the tone for the future, but how long is it going to take for such practices to be adopted all over the world, particularly in the US, East Indies and BRIC countries where they are most needed?

And secondly, what about waste that isn't currently profitable? In addition to CO_2 (and due to its importance, I'll be devoting a separate chapter to it) there is also a vast amount of other pollutive output that it doesn't currently pay to clean up. Organisations like NISP are not there to make unprofitable waste profitable, only to identify existing potential for profit through synergies and cost savings in waste and by-products. This is as it should be, but the really important challenge is make the next leap and render profitability to the vast quantities of presently unprofitable pollutive waste, or as a last resort price it out of the market altogether so that is ceases to be created.

In ecosystems there is only one category of waste – profitable stuff. It is all useful to other organisms. If this were the case in economies, we wouldn't have a problem because a business would always appear on the scene to exploit it. Unfortunately this is not the case. In modern economies there is a very great deal of non-organic waste by-product – at least three different categories of it – and there lies the root of the world's pollution problems.

The first of these categories is the one just mentioned – waste that is profitable for others to reclaim and sell on, such as metals and rare earths that readily create viable niches for recyclers. Producers of this kind of waste thus have no liability to clean up after themselves (though the processes through which they create it, such as mining and smelting, may well do). In effect they have their own armies of economic "dung beetles" scurrying around after them, and as such they conform well to Nature's symbiotic principle.

The second category is waste that is potentially recyclable but may not be so profitably, at prevailing market prices, without Kalundborg type set-ups and sophisticated civic waste separation processes – plastics for example, of which 95% of production is currently lost to the world economy. Cheap raw materials or expensive recycling costs result in this waste being more economic to keep manufacturing, a consequence of which has been what we call the "throwaway society", plastic bags being a typical example. This category of waste is potentially redeemable either via enhanced NISP activity or through economic action – imposing the appropriate economic incentives to make recapture and reuse more profitable than using fresh raw materials.

As it happens there is an exciting new business that claims there are almost no plastics it cannot recycle. Founded by Tom Szaky in 2005, "TerraCycle" says it is on a mission to eliminate waste. The company already operates in 24 countries and is expanding rapidly. It can recycle everything from chocolate bar wrappers to cigarette butts, turning them into plastic granules that are bought in bulk by manufacturers. These granules are then converted into a whole range of items, such as bottles (Ribena bottles are made from recycled plastic), carpets, clothing, lumber and containers, at considerable energy savings compared to manufacturing new plastic.

Companies like TerraCycle are part of a new arterial highway towards what is known as *the circular economy*" in which raw materials are continually made and remade into different products instead of generating waste and polluting the environment.

Despite TerraCycle's initial success however, still the vast majority of potentially recyclable waste goes to landfill sites because the separation and collection of plastics in household and business garbage is too costly. It is a model that, to work on a really big scale, needs a symbiotic partner to create its waste plastics supply chain. For that to happen the collection process needs to be profitable to another economic actor, which to be kick-started requires the manipulation of taxes to favour recycling over fresh manufacture. In the meantime, municipal authorities must fill that niche.

Here's another example of needlessly wasted plastic (and metal) that could so easily be recycled to make useful products: shotgun cartridges. Millions go needlessly into landfill every year when they are easily recycled. Agri.cycle in the UK is one company that welcomes them with open arms, yet very many game and clay shoots simply don't bother, perhaps because for economics' sake the company has to make a collection charge. If just a 1 or 2 penny or cent recycling levy were to be charged to the manufacturers (who would inevitably pass it on to the buyers), and the recycling companies could reclaim this, then it would pay the recyclers to collect them – and they would be out there pushing for business rather than waiting for green-minded volunteers as they do at the moment. Spent cartridges, like so many other plastics, are a useful resource. All that needs to be done to avoid a gross waste of all the energy and materials that went into manufacturing them is to endow them with economic value. Nothing is wasted in Nature because almost everything is a useful resource that organisms profit from. This proposal about cartridges, like all other recycling, is simply a matter of engineering circumstances to emulate Nature.

However, the recycling capabilities of individual authorities is so uneven that no manufacturer or company can be confident that the plastics it manufactures or uses will not go into landfill. In the whole of the UK, for example, polystyrene – widely used in packaging fragile items, can only be recycled in three places, each great distances apart. The result is that much of it still goes to landfill.

Now that China has ceased taking the vast quantities of European plastic waste it used to, and that the public have become so aware of plastic pollution, largely thanks to Sir David Attenborough's TV series *Blue Planet*, minds have at last been concentrated on finding solutions. Some offending plastics such as cotton buds and straws can easily be got rid of via bans. But the real answer lies not in driving out plastics use altogether because it is an extremely useful, versatile and hence widely used material, for example for extending food life in a world where food waste is endemic, and in making essential medical equipment. Instead it is to use levies on hard-to-recycle plastics both to drive businesses towards using only the most easily recyclable kind, and, by ring-fencing the financial proceeds for investment, to help finance a general move towards profitable recycling. This act alone would greatly hasten the world towards a circular economy in which resource-wasteful throw-away plastics would become a thing of the past and would help consign this primitive phase of our economic development to the landfill of history.

In this same category, discarded or lost fishing gear provides a classic example of a market failure that could be corrected relatively simply. The damage the astonishing 640,000 tonnes per year of discarded or lost "ghost" gear causes to marine animals and ecosystems is well-documented and severe; yet it is also relatively easy to recycle, and there are already a number of companies that specialise in this (the Los Angeles-based company, Bureo for example).

The basic infrastructure for a market-based solution is therefore already in place. All it needs is for the numbers to be tweaked to turn used nylon into gold, for example through a scheme in which fishermen could be repaid deposits when they returned old or damaged nets. Net manufacturers could then recoup their costs by selling the waste netting on to recyclers to make, for example, carpets, skateboards and sunglasses frames. Government incentives could also ensure that it is worth the manufacturers' while to receive *all* recyclable nets, regardless of origin, allowing used nylon to take its rightful place in the world economy as a valuable resource. This already happens naturally with metals like lead and copper, and it is purely a matter of good planetary housekeeping to make sure it happens by artificial means whenever and wherever it is environmentally desirable to do so.

To its great credit the EU is fast becoming a world leader in creating a circular economy. Its "Circular Economy Package" (launched in December 2015) consists of an ambitious programme of action not only to recycle more raw materials, but also to incentivise the manufacture of items like mobile phones and small commercial vehicles to be more easily repaired and reused. Measures to encourage symbiosis are also included, and targets of recycling 65% of waste and 75% of packaging waste by 2030 have been set.

The new era of near-universal plastic recycling that we seek is no distant dream. It could be with us within a decade if governments were to manipulate incentives in its favour. Some businesses, leaders amongst them being 'Plastic Energy' and 'Recycling Technologies', are now able to convert waste plastics back into valuable fuel - *profitably*; and that's the key to the whole problem. They have created a working unit the size of three truck containers that can be shipped anywhere in the world. There they can be bolted back together at garbage dumps, by rivers, or at depots next to where vast quantities of floating waste plastic caught in giant sea-booms is brought to land.

These exciting, enlightened projects need to be fast-tracked by governments' around the world, especially in the US and the rising new consumer societies of countries with huge populations like China and India. But there is no sign of that happening yet, probably because they have not woken up to the immense waste and hence loss to their economies that the single-use of resources represents. One can only hope that as the European lead starts to demonstrate the economic benefits that can accrue, they may quickly react and follow suit.

Yet still there's a long way to go. Currently the sorting of household waste is a complicated chore for all but the dedicated, and stories of waste mountains abroad do nothing to instill confidence in consumers that it's really worth doing at all. Fly tipping is endemic all over the world. But imagine how different it could be if we were *paid* for our waste.

Not long ago I saw a TV advert that promised a free robot toy for every new client. The toy was plastic, cheap and unexciting and would most likely soon be discarded by any sensible child (adults are less predictable). Tens of thousands of them would sooner or later end up in landfill. What a waste of raw materials, energy and carbon emissions – just for a cheap, sales promotion gimmick, when something cheaply manufactured and recyclable such as a money-off voucher would do just as well.

This is the world we live in today. The world of the future must, and I dare to believe will be, one in which synthetic materials are as transient as the organic matter that comprises our bodies. Instead of first use and disposal, the future world will be one where materials that comprise at one period in time a child's plastic toy, are in the next an aircraft part, then a computer casing, then perhaps a $5 bill, then green fuel and so on round and round - each a magnet for the attentions of resource-colonising imperative. Perhaps then the world's landfill sites from this era of waste will be prized for the treasures they contain. Bring on the circular economy.

Category 3 waste – the unacceptable face of consumerism

The third category of waste presents a mighty problem. This type may not be viably reusable in today's markets at any price. Think of stuff like non-recyclable plastics, not to mention all those other things that your local recycling centre (if indeed you have such a thing in your country) still asks you to dump in the skip marked "non-recyclable". Worse still, this category of waste may also be highly toxic, for example radioactive material, heavy metals, pesticides and benzene – what we might call "black" waste.

In my opinion there are four potential ways to stop this X-rated type of pollutant waste getting into the environment. It must either be contained at source, filtered at the point of emission ("end of pipe"), or the process that produces it replaced by one that is non-toxic and recyclable. That's three, the fourth option is for the producer to be closed down.

There's currently no practical prospect of creating symbiotic partnerships to recycle black waste because either there is no foreseeable likelihood of a profitable end use for it, or there is no cost-effective method of recapturing and recycling it. Until and unless this situation changes then all black waste should be priced out of the market. It has no place in any self-respecting economic ecosystem.

Black waste has no parallels in Nature because there nothing is synthetic and almost everything is recycled. Imagine if the wildebeest herd I alluded to earlier emitted engine oil and polystyrene pellets instead of urine and dung. They would inevitably end up paying for their own waste – by having their environment degraded to the point of destruction, just as we are.

Waste In Nature

Recyclable and Profitable

Current Waste In Economies

Category 1	Category 2	Category 3
Recyclable & profitable	Recyclable & potentially profitable	Non-recyclable & potentially hazardous
E.g.: metals; rare earths; furnishings; paper; glass	E.g.: many plastics; polystyrene; polypropylene; CO2; methane	E.g.: radioactive material; some plastics; heavy metals

Potential Future Waste In Economies

Category 1	Category 3

So the bottom line is that to get closer to Nature's zero pollution, a 99.99% circular ecosystemic model, we have to fill the gaps in the economic ecosystem through which pollution slips untended, by creating all the missing economic species/actors ourselves.

That's all very well, you might say, but how the heck are you going to get tens of thousands of businesses around the world to conform? How do you manipulate the market to make it cheaper to deal with recyclers rather than the dump or the drain? How also can you get cheap-to-make used items from the rubbish bin back to the factory line – that is make them into desirable raw materials again when it's so much cheaper to make them anew?

The answer lies in reinvigorating an old, severely misunderstood and underemployed concept with a title that, rather unusually, speaks for itself – the *Polluter Pays Principle*.

New life for the Polluter Pays Principle

Making polluting businesses pay for their clean-up costs in some form or another has been mainstream policy in developed nations since at least the 1970s. This internalisation of environmental costs by business is the essence of the *Polluter Pays Principle* (PPP) [8], and it still lies at the heart of most contemporary anti-pollution policy in Europe, Australasia, North America and elsewhere.

Under a PPP regime, instead of being legislated against, a polluting agent has a price imposed upon its release into the environment. Ideally that price should reflect the cost of three things: cleaning it up, disposing of it safely, and restoring any environmental damage. Pollution is thereby not so much forbidden as made into a reckonable business overhead. The PPP thus puts a financial cost on damaging the environment, a sound *Junglenomics* principle because a damaged environment is by inference a less habitable one. If properly priced and enforced it should quickly become apparent to polluters that prevention is a whole lot cheaper than cure, and it should encourage them to adopt pollution control methods.

There are other good potential consequences of the PPP too. For example, it can stimulate healthy new markets to provide services for pollution avoidance, mitigation and removal, all major *Junglenomics* priorities. It can even encourage the restoration of already degraded environments if suitable incentives are incorporated. As a result, the PPP became widely adopted internationally, and by June 1992 more than 178 governments at the United Nations Conference on Environment and Development (UNCED) had adopted it as part of the Rio Declaration on Environment and Development.

Making polluters pay is clearly an important element in building balanced economic ecosystems because it incentivises them to create the kind of symbiotic partners I have been advocating. After all, polluters that pay to ensure clean-up are then no longer polluters. They become members of a pollution-neutral fraternity, gold standard players for any balanced economic ecosystem.

So why has the PPP failed so badly at solving the world's waste problems? After all, you may be thinking that PPP sounds like a classic *Junglenomics* regime because it creates a symbiotic market for cleaning up pollution; of course you'd be right. In principle internalising environmental costs is an effective method to help protect the natural environment, one that I recommended above to give recyclable materials an advantage over non-recyclable.

But there is a strong proviso: because PPP directly interferes in markets it is essential that it is fully understood, well set up and managed, as well as appropriately applied. In the event, all too often this hasn't been the case. As a result, the PPP's effectiveness has been disappointing and it has not achieved anything like its potential, as today's severe plastics problem illustrates.

The easiest way to see for yourself how incomplete the application of the PPP has been is to consider your local municipal garbage tip. Ask yourself, who is *paying* for the disposal of all the items that go into the "non-recyclable" dumpster? Yes, stuff goes into other skips for profitable recycling at no cost to you and me – aluminium cans for example – and that's great. But the disposal of a substantial proportion of the rest gets underwritten by us through our local taxes. In other words, it is heavily subsidised, not paid for by the business that manufactured it as the PPP says it ought to be. The figures are staggering: in the US the average cost of waste disposal in landfill rose to $49 per tonne in 2016. Multiply this by the 230 million tonness of trash that municipal authorities have to deal with each year, and you get a staggering nationwide annual cost of $11.27 billion - all of it paid for by you and me through local taxes. This is a criminal waste - not only of your and my money - but of potentially valuable resources leached from the world economy.

Meanwhile, at the worst end of the scale, the matter that cannot be recycled at any price is sent to expensive landfill sites or to be incinerated, with pollutive consequences, again paid for by us. This begs the question:

why should *we* pay to clean up and dispose of the waste of profitable, free-market businesses when part of that profit is made because they do not have to be responsible for post-use disposal of their products or product wrappers?

Additionally, ask yourself this: would goods and food packaging, for example, be as over the top as they so often are if those that produced them had to pay for their safe disposal, or better still, for their recycling? It doesn't happen; but it should. Most of the ludicrous over-packaging we see on Walmart's, Tesco's and others' shelves would soon disappear.

Ring-fencing PPP proceeds

This last passage criticises the failure of the PPP to be applied as broadly, effectively and fairly as it should. But an even bigger failure in the application of the PPP represents a radical divergence from the Nature-based model advocated in *Junglenomics*. Here's why.

PPP works well so far as levying fines and costs force manufacturers to produce less polluting goods by using non- or less polluting processes; but the resulting revenues are mostly expropriated for other uses. This is a fundamental mistake. All "polluter pays" receipts should be retained and fed back either into research and development into anti-pollution technology, or to subsidise recyclers like TerraCycle, as appropriate.

The reason for this is simple but important. As I have emphasised, to create the balanced economic ecosystem the world so desperately needs we need to fast-track the evolution of symbiotic clean-up niches, attracting economic actors to colonise those niches and thereby prevent or mop up pollution.

To give an example of this misappropriation of PPP receipts, when in the 1990s the British government introduced its first PPP legislation in the form of an "eco-tax" (ecologically based taxation) on the disposal of non-recyclable waste in open landfill sites, it made a critical error. Instead of feeding the revenue from this "Landfill Tax" back into research, development and investment in waste avoidance and recycling techniques and technology, the government siphoned the money off to reduce employment tax, a completely unrelated issue with no direct environmental connection.

Used in this way PPP might be more accurately named PPRFGB, which stands for "Polluters Pay to Rescue Failing Government Budgets", the "Principle" part of the equation being lost to budget expediency. Moreover, because polluters' fines are ultimately paid for by increasing the prices of the offending goods they produce, it is we, the consumers, who in the end pick up the tab. While we may not mind paying extra so that the environment and wildlife are protected, we should resent our contributions being quietly diverted to non-environmental matters.

So the *Junglenomics* bottom line is that, for any economics-based, pollution solution like PPP to succeed, the regulatory stick needs to be combined with a good deal of economic carrot. To achieve this, it is essential that all pollution tax revenues be ring-fenced. All too often governments impose disincentive taxes to try to influence economic behaviour without completing the equation with correlating incentives. Pollution penalties too easily become cash cows for revenue-strapped governments – a perverse incentive to keep polluters alive and well and still polluting.

The UK government *"considers that hypothecation, or 'earmarking' revenues for a particular spending purpose, is an inefficient way to manage the public finances. Like all Government receipts, revenues are remitted to the consolidated fund to support general expenditure. This allows the Government to allocate resources most efficiently across the economy"* [9]. Because it has no dedicated environmental programme attached to PPP, this misnamed "levy" represents merely another tax burden on business and the public rather than helping provide long-term cures for its environmental ills.

The European Commission isn't much better. Even the much heralded "climate levy tax", raised by European Community governments on energy users, ostensibly to help reduce energy consumption and efficiency, is in effect just another revenue source for their treasuries. Thankfully though, some of this cash does go to fund the Carbon Trust, which is actively engaged in new energy research and venture capital funds. The Carbon Trust also finances a number of loan funds to help small and medium-sized businesses buy energy-efficient equipment, which is likewise commendable. But though this is some consolation, it is not nearly enough.

Failure of the climate levy tax

Unfortunately, there is yet another fly in the ointment. At the time of writing this climate levy tax is charged across the board – including on nuclear and large-scale hydroelectricity energy, even though they are carbon-free technologies. It fails miserably on two fronts therefore. It not only misses the golden opportunity to further incentivise the development of clean energy through dedicated R & D, but it unfairly raises the unit price of cleaner energy. Replacement with a carbon tax could solve this (Australia introduced one in 2011, though the government has controversially rescinded it since).

Interestingly, the European Union strengthened its anti-pollution regime in 2009 with measures that impose a new onus on potential as well as existing polluters. In addition to the duty to prevent pollution, or failing that, to clean it up, polluters now have to warn their national Environment Agency of impending pollution incidents. This is an improvement, but it is still a hand-to-mouth system, because firstly only Sites of Special Scientific Interest and protected species and environments are covered, and secondly there is no insistence that potential polluters have adequate technology or symbiotic partners to ensure such incidents need never happen in the first place, as *Junglenomics* requires.

Furthermore, when used only as deterrent, environmental penalties alone are intrinsically anti-business. Driving up costs and sending business and jobs abroad to less scrupulous economic regimes will not help. They will only engender the kind of business-inspired political insurgency that pressurised President Bush to renege on the Kyoto Protocol so soon after assuming office.

The future lies more in evolving clean businesses than in strangling dirty ones – at least, unless there is no foreseeable technological solution to them. Frontal attacks on powerful industries via legislation and punitive taxation without powerful accompanying incentive, and without help to evolve improved sustainability, only encourage them to divert resources towards public relations and political influence rather than remedies.

In contrast, if large polluting industries are themselves given the financial incentive not only to purchase services from a third party, but to themselves participate in the potential profitability of a new generation of sophisticated pollution control businesses subsidised by their own money raised in levies or fines, then a much more cooperative atmosphere ought to be possible.

POLLUTIVE INDUSTRY

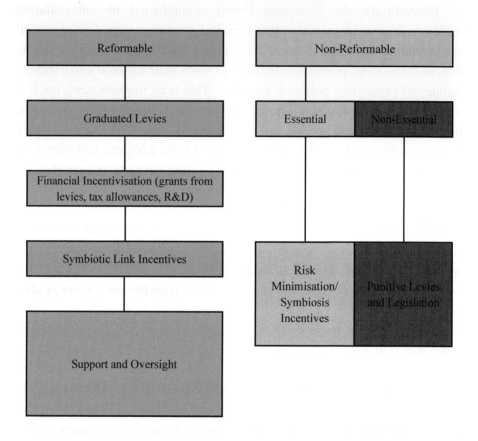

Recognising the writing on the wall (the stick) and being offered a soft landing to change (the carrot) is the logical and more gentle way to balance the economic ecosystem.

Cutting "the crap"

In 2013 the British prime minister, David Cameron, exasperated by mounting "green" costs on industry at a time when his government was trying to reinvigorate the UK economy after a deep recession, spoke of "*cutting the green crap*". It was a ham-fisted phrase to use and unfortunately sent out entirely the wrong message, but one can see what he meant. Too much penalising green baggage had been allowed to accumulate without clear objectives. Used this way the PPP is a blunt instrument. In contrast, this book aims to clarify what those objectives should be and how to go about them in an ordered manner. While it may be widely agreed that the economic world cannot be allowed to follow its naturally anarchical, externality-accumulating course, the overwhelming need is to cure the disease without killing the patient with any kind of "crap" – green, yellow or pink.

Damaging or even collapsing established economic equilibria and precipitating avalanches of economic decline and instability is, to put it mildly, counterproductive. Many of the chief perpetrators, car manufacturers, oil producers, power generators and food growers for example, are vertebrae industries in the world's major economies. Their demise could cause destabilising repercussions that could do far more harm than good – recession is not conducive to good conservation practice. Experience also tells us that the more marginal businesses become the less they can afford to spend on environmental considerations.

Don't get me wrong, this book is not a crusade for impossibly pristine environments everywhere. Merely to stop decline in its tracks would be a triumph. The spiking of clean-up costs as they progress anyway means that a 100% clean environment would be impossibly expensive; besides, the environment is known to be capable of absorbing a degree of non-persistent pollution without harm.

However, the "precautionary principle" [10] throws the gauntlet down so far as suspected harmful substances are concerned, and it is surely right that tolerance of such substances should be very low. Some prioritising is therefore unavoidable, and the focus so far as pollution is concerned needs to be where it counts most – on the air we breathe, the water we drink and the food we eat.

But the past clearly shows that none of this is going to happen at anything like the rate it needs to unless governments worldwide prioritize it - which means creating fully empowered senior ministerial departments specifically dedicated to achieving economic symbiosis.

In the US, the President has purposefully set the Environment Agency back decades because he wrongly regards environmentalism as the enemy of jobs and business. He claims to have a fine business brain, but if he truly does, he will surely come to realise that a major source of new business and jobs can be unleashed through the creation of a symbiotic economy. If he wasn't so busy tweeting and watching Fox news he might for example have read the 2018 Report of the Global Commission on the Economy and Climate, which found that bold action could yield a direct economic gain of at least 26 trillion dollars through to 2030, compared with business-as-usual.

1. *J R R Tolkien's wasted lands in "The Lord of the Rings"*
2. *Diabetalogia, vol.51, p402*
3. *American Diabetes Association*
4. *WWF Living Planet Report, 2008*
5. *The Costs of Inaction on Key Environmental Challenges, 2008*
6. *Organisation for Economic Co-operation and Development*
7. *As selected by New Scientist: 6th November 2008: Catherine Brahic*
8. *Principle 16 of the Declaration of the United Nations Conference on the Human Environment, adopted at Stockholm on 16 June 1972 stated that: "National authorities should endeavour to promote the internalization of environmental costs and the use of economic instruments, taking into account the approach that the polluter should, in principle, bear the cost of pollution, with due regard to the public interest and without distorting international trade and investment."*
9. *Priti Patel MP: 18 November 2014*
10. *Out of the 1992 Rio Conference (the Earth Summit) came Principle #15: "In order to protect the environment, the precautionary approach shall be widely applied by States according to their capabilities. Where there are threats of serious or irreversible damage, lack of full scientific certainty shall not be used as a reason for postponing cost-effective measures to prevent environmental degradation."*
11. *Also see: 'Polluter Pays, Myths and Legends' (The Australian Journal of Ecotoxicology Vol. 8, pp.51-56, 2002) which proposes the Precautionary Principle as the only effective way forward for controlling chemical pollution*

Chapter 3
People Pollution

Why "small and easy" doesn't work

Up to this point I have focused on business and industry as the perpetrators of pollution, but we should not lay all the blame at their door. As individuals, we too contribute to pollution; and as consumers we create the primary demand that entices businesses to do so. We each therefore share some of the responsibility for the world's environmental problems, and as such we too need to sharpen up our act.

Like business though, we mostly cannot help ourselves. We buy goods from environmentally detrimental sources simply because they are accessible, affordable and desirable. Even the most environmentally conscious of us can only make "green" choices to the degree that the available information allows us, such as on packaging for example. Even then its accuracy can be hard to corroborate. Though some people are extremely conscientious about their consumer habits and urge others to follow their lead, in the end market forces – especially driven by obtainability, price and convenience – dominate mainstream consumer behaviour.

Whatever one feels about this state of affairs, it is a fact of life as much for individuals as it is for businesses. It is also a fact of Nature. A change in community culture towards greenness is welcome, but only to help pave the way for more deep-rooted change. A green culture that is not underpinned by classical economic incentive is never going to have more than a peripheral effect on consumer habits. It will restrict itself to those who feel most strongly about it and can afford the inevitable price premium that comes with it to make it profitable. While they have grown strongly year by year, organic food purchases still represent less than 5% of all sales in the US. In China, despite food scandals and equally strong growth, organically grown food still represents merely just over 1% of food sales. We therefore have to find ways to influence whole populations and large corporations alike, not just a dedicated minority; the rest just don't really care enough.

In 2008, worldwide recession hit the organic food movement as people tried to cut living costs, demonstrating that even the limited progress made during more prosperous times is soon eroded when belts are tightened. The paltry £28.60 that British shoppers spend on average each year on organic products highlights the futility of relying on social pressure to change consumer habits. While the cost to the environment of organically grown food may be less, it costs more money to produce, and so it is stuck with the reputation of being an expensive luxury.

So far as consumer habits are concerned, the green movement strives to turn around our environmental fortunes by trying to educate the wider public on responsible consumerism especially including recycling. They hope that suitably informed, conscientious individuals can lead markets towards better behaviour. But one has to seriously doubt that this can ever be achieved by what is in effect micro participation by minority middle classes behaving conscientiously within developed economies. This is not only supremely optimistic but it also breeds complacency ("It's OK; I took my bottles to the dump today – I've done my bit for the planet"), apathy ("I don't really care because enough people are doing it, aren't they?") and some scorn ("Oh God, not *another* eco-warrior").

People become complacent about the environment because they believe something really ecologically useful is being achieved by this kind of overhyped "greenness" in Western societies, when in fact its beneficial effect is minimal. Even worse, the "small and easy" approach so beloved of green activists is actually worse than doing nothing at all – it is a recipe for failure. This firstly is because it addresses such a tiny part of the world's ecological problems, and secondly because most people don't adhere to it anyway [1]. Public awareness of the plight of our planet is certainly no bad thing, but I'm sorry, your expensive "eco-home" is not going to save the planet, nor is the few dollars of carbon offset that made you feel less guilty about your flight to the Bahamas. Nor is it saved even if a million of us do the same, not while seven billion others do not, and while giant industries are raping the forests, plains and seas, and filling the skies with excess carbon and pollution.

The upshot is that a bland flood of "sustainababble" has pervaded our lives and dulled enthusiasm and belief in real change. It is full of politicised green agendas whose self-evident impracticality destines them to drift into the ether unheeded.

Don't get me wrong, I support micro-economic environmental schemes, mainly because they can sometimes eventually influence culture higher up at the all-important political level. But that culture will only achieve real results when it goes universal, and that requires joined-up thinking and significant policy change at a national level, in addition to grassroots efforts by you and me.

The greatest problem for the ecological movement is that it is economically hobbled: it nearly always costs you *more* to be green, and this is plain wrong. It is nonsense economics. At present, ecologically sound individual behaviour relies mostly on appealing to conscience and health concerns, a policy that is never going to generate widespread reformation on the macroeconomic scale for one good reason: it is not price oriented. If external environmental costs were more fully charged on environmentally expensive food production, people would be rushing to buy organic because it would be cheaper, or at least no more. More farmers would then engage in it, and prices would fall. Persuasion, peer pressure and tiresome green sermons on New Age living would thankfully become irrelevant.

The same principle applies to animal welfare standards. A certain British television chef got engaged in a long-running battle with the supermarket giant Tesco over its allegedly substandard chicken-rearing conditions. Tesco made it clear they would not alter their practices to comply with accepted animal welfare standards unless the market demanded it, and while demand remained for the cheapest possible chicken, profitability not conscientiousness rules the marketplace. The sooner this plain fact of economic life is turned to environmental advantage, the sooner lasting progress in conservation can be made.

Profound and long-lasting reform cannot come from grass-roots efforts, therefore. It has to come through market manipulation at the top of the chain – via government, business and industry. If the cheapest and most available choice is the more environmentally expensive one, then something is badly out of kilter in the way we run market economies; yet this is indeed how things stand today all over the world. There should be no need to rely on conscience-based choices. It doesn't take a genius to recognise that for the market to favour them, environmentally friendly goods need to be cheaper or more cost-effective. The enforced "pricing-in" of external costs is thus the only effective way to squeeze cheaper, but environmentally more expensive alternatives off the shelves.

Won't that put up prices? In the short term, possibly, though it can be cushioned and spread out if new externality levies are ring-fenced and used to close the price gap. But the "green" label presently carries a significant premium largely because it is marketed mostly to the more affluent and is not produced in high bulk (for example, in 2009 just 4.3% of agricultural land in Britain was in organic production [2], while only about 0.8 percent of all U.S. cropland and 0.5 percent of all U.S. pasture was certified organic in 2011, according to government figures. Despite some rebound in organic food sales since the financial crash of 2008-9, the amount of land in the UK both devoted to and in the process of being converted to organic farming continues to shrink. By 2017 the number of organic producers was down 34% since the 2007 peak. The vast majority of organic land is anyway pasture and thus dedicated to growing meat rather than vegetables - a practice which is now widely recognized as detrimental both to personal health and the environment.) Ensuring green goods are cheaper through full Polluter Pays implementation should rapidly increase the size of that market to unprecedented proportions. It would become very big business indeed.

Mass markets allow competition and innovation to force prices back down ensuring that the *Junglenomics* agricultural future would be green, cheap, and here to stay.

Bags and bottles

Relatively simple economic measures could also reduce the litter problems that plague most countries, putting money in peoples' pockets at the same time. Take plastic bags and bottles for example: manufacturers may produce the bags and bottles but it is not they that litter the streets with them. The only reason people discard them is because they have no value and are easily replaced.

Yet plastics that reach the seas – which every year vast quantities do – gradually break down to a fine powder of granules that never disappear. They are then ingested by marine creatures – even the smallest such as krill – and thereby enter the food chain, returning to enter our stomachs via creatures that eat them with as yet unknown health consequences.

Some years back during a visit to Essaouira, an attractive walled city on Morocco's Atlantic coast, I was disappointed by the hundreds of plastic bottles littering the beaches and dunes for miles. Of course, municipal authorities could have sent out teams regularly to clear them up at public expense, but the *Junglenomics* remedy makes such refuse into a resource by giving reusable or recyclable items like bags and bottles a value – in effect giving them nutrient status – so that people could profit from retrieving them; better still they would be less inclined to discard them.

This basic principle explains why in the Middle Ages the streets of London were scoured clean of dog excrement, a practice known as "pure finding". The excrement had become a valuable commodity to leather tanners, who used it for purifying skins. More recently in Australia, refillable glass and plastic bottles have been recorded as achieving a 97% return rate. There seems no reason to doubt that the same principle could be applied everywhere if only governments would stop hesitating and set the necessary incentives.

In 2015, after years of procrastination, the British government finally introduced a 5 pence tax on plastic bags – another classic *Junglenomics* solution. The results startled most people – disposable bag purchase dropped by 85% in the following 12 months, reducing them by about 6 billion, a triumph of pollution management. Speculation began as to how this simple expedient could be introduced to other items such as disposable coffee cups, another significant source of pollution. What, one may ask, are they and other governments waiting for?

Sewage and chemical pollution

Sewage is another major pollution hazard; and as the public is the polluter, under the PPP it is right that they should pay for its safe disposal. And we do so: the vast majority of sewage treatment is delegated to specialists by local authorities and paid for with our taxes. We rely on these specialists to do a good job for us.

However, frequently they fail. Of the beaches tested for water quality in the UK in 2009 [3], nearly half presented a one in twenty chance or more of giving gastroenteritis to swimmers, according to a calculation by the Marine Conservation Society (MCS). The Environment Agency blames high rainfall, which trips emergency overflow systems into action – so-called Combined Sewer Overflows (CSOs). With floods becoming increasingly common in Britain, raw sewage overflows from CSOs have become frequent despite some £8bn ($12bn) having been spent by water companies over the last 20 years.

The MCS view is that CSOs are no longer for emergencies, and that overflowing raw sewage into the sea has become mainstream practice. In Llanelli, South Wales, where the pollution was measured in 2009 at ten times over the limit, CSO sewage dumping was reported to have ruined the local cockle beds. So much for the Polluter Pays Principle then.

It is little different in the US: the Environmental Protection Agency (EPA) estimates that every year in each of the 3,031 counties across the nation the amount of untreated sewage that enters the environment is enough to fill both the Empire State Building and Madison Square Garden. In 2004 a report by NRDC [4] and the Environmental Integrity Project (appropriately named, *Swimming in Sewage*) showed that sewage overflows – some legal, some not – are creating an environmental and public health crisis. And that is not reckoning with what it is doing to wildlife.

The same applies for the EPA in respect of chemical seepage into water supplies, for example from common garden weedkillers like atrazine, which is also causing concern in the US. The EPA came under stinging criticism from Erik D Olson, one of its own former lawyers, and a lawyer for the Senate Committee on the Environment and Public Works. *"The public believes that the EPA has carefully reviewed all the chemicals that are used and has the authority it needs to deal with risks, but that's often not the case,"* said Olson. *"The EPA is working with weak laws, basic research at the agency is often seriously under-funded, and in some cases there's institutional inertia against change,"* he added. *"That's contributed to a sense that the agency is often slow to react to new science showing risks."* [5] How much worse is this since President Trump's administration has virtually emasculated the EA?

In contrast to this and to its credit, the European Union has banned atrazine, among other dubious chemicals, in line with the precautionary principle. In 2009 the European Commission (EC) announced its intention to take the United Kingdom to the European Court of Justice over non-compliance with European Union environment legislation. The EC declared that *"the urban waste water collecting systems and treatment facilities in London and Whitburn in North East England are inadequate and a threat to human health."*

Meanwhile at the other side of the world the situation is as bad if not worse. Violent clashes between more than 10,000 villagers and armed police in Quanzhou city, Southwest China, were reported in September 2009. The protest was against a local waste water treatment plant reportedly polluting local water and air. Mass riots sparked by environmental problems have been increasing by one third per annum, according to China's then environmental protection minister, Zhou Shengxian.

Just a few minutes Internet browsing is enough to confirm that sewage pollution is a growing international problem. It is a threat to the health of both humans and ecosystems and it demands comprehensive, long-term solutions. Pollution of all kinds often crosses national boundaries, making prosecution and prevention more complex and demanding extensive international cooperation. The new-found cooperation between nations over the problem of global warming needs to become much broader. It needs to encompass not only global warming, but *all* the areas that threaten the future ability of the Earth to support our species.

I don't claim that this will be easy. Reforming stable and supposedly corruption-free democracies is one thing, but much environmental damage is taking place either in less easily reformed or less enlightened countries, or in the great extra-national arenas of the world's oceans and atmosphere. This often coincides with where there is most to lose in terms of species and environments.

Yet when the infamous "Great Stink" from London's river Thames grew too awful to bear in the noses of the 19th-century British parliamentarians, it became a catalyst for extraordinary energy and innovation. The result was the greatest sewage system ever seen – a vast underground architectural wonder of the world that few people know about today, even Londoners.

The 21st-century Great Stink is now upon us, and it demands an equally ambitious level of response. For as the world's population grows and freshwater supplies diminish the problems can only get worse. We surely cannot legitimately complain about polluting manufacturers, miners and farmers while we fail to deal with our own pollution. It will take public service reform, innovative technology and, at least in the short term, money, but it is an essential and unavoidable investment in our own future.

Nature's way – the *Junglenomics* way – is to render even this inglorious waste *profitable*, as was so well demonstrated by the tanners and pure finders of medieval England.

1.   E.g. Michael Maniates: Is Sustainability Still Possible?: The Worldwatch Institute 2013

2.   Soil Association Report 2010

3.   Odds derived from World Health Organization figures

4.   National Resources Defence Council: http://www.nytimes.com/2009/08/23/us/23water.html

5.   New York Times – August 23, 2009

Chapter 4
Cars 'n' Trucks 'n' Planes

Valleys of smoke

Los Angeles was once known by Native Americans as the "Valley of Smoke" because smoke from their campfires lingered in the air. Today we know the reason to be its geography, which acts as a trap, preventing currents of fresh air from sweeping in from the surrounding mountains. Today's trapped "smoke" is altogether different however. It is generated by the accumulation of huge volumes of noxious and toxic traffic fumes, and is a major problem for the city's population.

Such air pollution is another headline symptom of an overextended economic ecosystem in need of profound reform. Previous attempts to curb it have only been partially successful. In the US, for example, a Clean Air Act was passed in 1963, reducing sulphur dioxide (SO_2) and nitrous oxides (NOx) from industry by more than a third, eventually reducing acid rain by some two thirds. Yet despite such measures the steep rise in traffic volumes means that almost all major cities and their surrounding areas have continued to be plagued by severe air pollution.

Industrialised nations cannot help but be aware of the poor and declining air quality in their cities and the heavy economic and social costs associated with it. Even China has purportedly woken up to the fact. Beijing notoriously had to restrict traffic and bring steelworks and power stations to a halt so that the persistent smog (a mixture of natural fog, smoke and fumes) could be reduced enough just to allow the 2008 Olympic athletes to breathe properly, let alone compete.

Yet still not much seems to have changed in China. In late December 2015, the Beijing authorities felt compelled to issue two pollution red alerts, the first of their kind, just a week apart. The second was announced due to four days of hazardous smog affecting a massive area from Xi'an in central China to Harbin in the north-east, encompassing twelve major cities.

It is estimated that pollution overall contributes to the deaths of between one and one and a half million people a year in China. That's a shocking toll, one that will not be greatly ameliorated by its decision in late 2015 not to open any more coal-fired power stations for three years. China's National Air Pollution Action Plan is making some difference in major cities, and substantial investment in wind and solar energy is under way, but in the semi-independent provinces the recent economic slowdown has bred a reluctance to risk jobs with major infrastructure changes. Yet while in 2014 and 2015 levels of fine particulate pollution in the Beijing area dropped by over 25% as emergency measures bore fruit, the improvement was short-lived, and in late 2016 and early 2017 levels spiked again.

India is no better: it has thirteen of the world's top twenty most polluted cities for particulates [1].

Meanwhile in the West the air is still far from clean. Even Britain, despite its relatively enlightened attitude towards environmental issues, is the third highest contributor to levels of air pollution in Europe, a failing that costs it up to £149bn a year [2]. London is only one of several British cities that are comfortably failing EU safety limits, prompting calls for private legal action against the government, since successfully being prosecuted for the third time in February 2018 by ClientEarth, an activist organisation. Meanwhile in the US things are still so bad that nearly half the population lives in areas where air pollution is often dangerously high [3].

Pollution in general is a worldwide problem of immense proportions. According to a 2017 report published in the medical journal *The Lancet* by more than 40 international health and environmental experts, nine million people – representing some 16% of all deaths, died premature, pollution-related deaths in 2015 alone. Another report, this time from the National Health Effects Institute (2018), records that over 95% of the world's population is exposed to air pollution.

Air pollution is not a new problem. London was famous in the 19th and 20th centuries for its smog. I had first-hand experience of one of the last of them in the 1950s – swirling, choking mists so dense you couldn't see further than a yard or two in front of you. With streets all but emptied of traffic and people, an eerie quiet descended, occasionally broken by solitary, echoing footfalls or the lowing of foghorns from freight barges feeling their way tentatively along the river Thames.

However, although these "London Particulars", as they were known in the 19th century, usually brought the city to a virtual standstill, they were not unloved by everyone. Perhaps their most famous fan was the impressionist painter, Claude Monet, who remarked that more than anything about London he loved the fog. Fog famously insinuated its way into Charles Dickens' opening of his novel *Bleak House*, while in real life the serial murderer Jack the Ripper used its cover to carry out his macabre deeds. And while in the 1935 film *A Damsel in Distress*, Fred Astaire sang about how "*a foggy day in London got him down*", he soon changed his tune after he met heiress Joan Fontaine.

The reality of London smog was rather less romantic than this though, for the cumulative cost in health and the disruption of commerce was high. As many as twelve thousand people may have died due to the notorious four-day smog of December 1952, while tens of thousands more became ill. A Covent Garden performance of *La Traviata* even had to be cancelled, a shocking headline at the time. The smog was caused mainly by coal smoke from domestic fireplaces and power stations and is still considered the worst pollution incident in British history. Driven by public alarm at this event, four years later in 1956 the British government cut its anti-pollution teeth with their first Clean Air Act, though like its American equivalent, it should perhaps have been called the "Less Polluted Air Act".

Nevertheless, the considerable success of the range of new regulations contained in this Act in ridding London of its "pea-soupers" could be viewed as a powerful endorsement for the use of the law to counter pollution. Yet despite this initial success, 60 years on London's air is still filthy.

Why is this? Today the culprit is no longer coal fires and factories, it is the combustion engine.

The oil fuel party

Little more than a mere 100 years ago there were none; but now it seems that, like some recently evolved, rampantly colonising new species, cars, motorbikes, trucks, powered boats and ships, and aeroplanes have invaded the world. They have manoeuvred their way into our lives, not just by getting us from A to B much more quickly, but also, in the case of cars, boats and motorbikes, because they are so much fun to drive. Indeed, they are such fun that there is something appealingly decadent about getting behind the wheel of a car or motorbike and burning up the miles. It doesn't have to be a

Ferrari, Porsche, Harley-Davidson or a Suzuki Hayabusa (though it helps), but few would deny it is an extension of their very being.

Most of us take quite a bit of trouble choosing our vehicles; they have to fit our requirements and aspirations alike. Because of this they often reflect our lives, our priorities and even our personalities. They can be sporty, elegant, antique, muscle-bound, extreme, pretentious, run-down, or just utilitarian. When we can afford to, many of us choose them with as much care as our clothes. What's more we forgive ourselves a multitude of environmental sins in this delicious indulgence. They may be smelly, noisy and kill or maim tens of thousands of people every year, but still we don't tolerate anyone interfering in the freedom of the open road. It is a brave government that tries to curb that liberty.

Burning oil fuel to power our engines has as a result become our most polluting self-indulgence. Only relatively recently have we been brought down to Earth in the certain scientific knowledge that this immoderation is poisoning the atmosphere and may well be the single greatest man-made contributor to climate change. We must rein ourselves in or ruin the planet, we are told. The party is over.

But is it? This attachment to cars has been no enforced union – governments have shamelessly encouraged us. From the Ford Model T to the Rolls-Royce, in the developed world car manufacturers have been major contributors to both economic prosperity and quality of life, and, in the past, this has earned them an official seal of approval along with a free pass on pollution. But things have changed. A new awareness of its dark side means that the shine has gone off the combustion engine. Because their "carbon footprint" is too great we no longer get a pat on the back for buying the latest gas guzzler. In some quarters we are even considered antisocial for indulging our motoring fantasies. Drivers are steadily becoming environmental pariahs and "Aston Martin Ventura" may become words that can only be safely spoken in a whisper.

So, you may well ask, what did we, the motoring public, do wrong? Surely we only did what governments and economists wanted us to – *encouraged* us to? And now suddenly they want us to change overnight. They want to take the fun out of driving, to make us feel guilty enough to "offset" our shameful indulgences by paying for someone somewhere else to absorb the carbon we have been so recklessly emitting from our exhausts, or by driving something that makes us feel like an idiot.

How did we end up here? It isn't that we didn't have plenty of warning – governments have known for decades the oil fuel party couldn't last. The first Middle East oil crisis in 1973 emphatically brought that into view. Following that, oil fuel burning steadily grew into a major pollution issue. So why, over 40 years on from that crisis, do we still drive so many cars that burn a gallon every 15-20 miles and earn such disapproval? Did no one see it coming? Why have government efforts to reduce pollutive emissions been so weak and failed so miserably? Change is only now very slowly grinding into gear, and fuel efficiency is at last high on the agenda. But can we expect fuel consumption to reduce quickly enough, or even much at all, given governments' past records?

I for one have little confidence that it will. It seems the market still wants more power, more macho, more status, and more fun; and what the market wants is what it gets. Somehow these markets need to be reconciled with the environmental realities of the 21st century without turning car driving into a guilt-ridden indulgence.

The curious thing is that, until recently, engine fuel efficiency barely changed in decades. My 1954, 2-litre Triumph sports car does around thirty-five miles to the gallon, yet nearly 60 years on it mostly takes a smaller-engined modern car just to match this, and it is less pollutive than a modern diesel engine. This anecdotal evidence is backed up by statistics from a survey published in 2009 [4]: US fuel efficiency in cars, motorcycles, trucks and buses up to 2006 had hardly improved since the days of the Ford Model T. Nett improvement rose from around 14 mpg in the 1920s to just 17.2 in 2006, after reaching a nadir of 11.3 mpg in 1973. Over the same period, we have sent men and machines to the Moon, Mars and Saturn, unlocked the secrets of DNA, explored quantum physics and developed digital and computer technology to extraordinary heights. Yet in all this time vehicle fuel consumption has been in near limbo. Global fuel consumption and associated CO_2 emissions from heavy-duty vehicles (HDVs) are increasing rapidly, particularly in emerging markets such as India, China, and Latin America. The International Energy Agency's (IEA) analysis suggests that trucks are the fastest-growing source of global oil demand. At 17 million barrels per day, the road freight sector constitutes one fifth of the global oil demand and could account for 40% of oil demand growth to 2050. This translates into 15% of the increase in global CO_2 emissions from energy production and use. Without action, worldwide fuel consumption by HDVs is on track to overtake passenger vehicles within 20 years, the Global Fuel Economy Initiative (GFEI) claims. Yet according to Fatih Birol, executive director of the IEA: *"there has been little public attention paid and there are not enough policy measures"*.

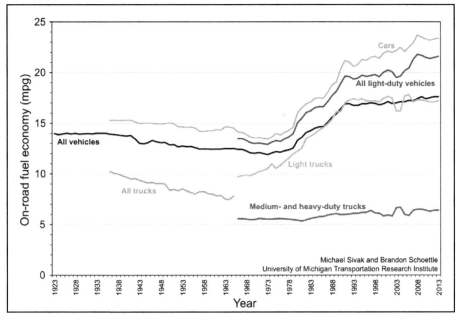

On-road fuel economy of vehicles in the United States: 1923-2015. Courtesy of Michael Sivak

That is not to suggest there have not been plenty of smart, new fuel-saving ideas over recent years, only that they have not been fully developed and deployed in mainstream markets. There can be just one reason behind such inertia, and that is a lack of commercial incentive. As we know, very little happens in markets if it isn't either profitable or legally necessary; so because for decades markets haven't demanded it nor governments insisted on it, inevitably improved fuel economy has been slow.

So is it any wonder that, with the vast increase in traffic volumes, vehicle emissions have risen so steeply? If strong enough incentives had been in place over the past 50 years could we not have expected average fuel consumption to be a hundred miles per gallon or better by now? Indeed, would we still even use gasoline very much at all? It is true that some emissions improvements have been made, though only under pressure – by lowering sulphur and removing lead from petrol for example; but not much else.

Legislators might want to point out here that the development of the catalytic converter (CAT) proves they have not been entirely idle. However, while the introduction of the CAT seemed at first to provide some answer to the growing vehicle emissions problem, most of the exhaust gas leaving the engine through a CAT is carbon dioxide. In addition, the US EPA has stated that CATs themselves are a growing cause of global warming due to their release of nitrous oxide, a greenhouse gas over 300 times more potent than CO_2. Not much there to cheer about then.

Legislators may then highlight the major efforts now being made to encourage the development of fuel-saving engines, tyres and bodywork, as well as alternative fuel sources, especially electricity. That may be so, but there are problems yet to be overcome with all the alternatives, so improved models are still not being adopted by the market at anything like the rate they need to be. The popularity of electric vehicles has been growing quickly due to their increased range and reduced battery costs, backed up by government subsidies and environmental benefits. However, at the end of 2016, the overall number of plug-in electric cars represented merely a tiny fraction (0.15%) of the 1.4 billion motor vehicles on the world's roads. Considering the urgency, this is slow progress. Global annual sales of plug-ins have passed the 1 million mark, but this still represents just one in a hundred vehicles sold. There is still little apparent urgency. As a result, the continuing very high level of externalities from the combustion engine means that the motor industry still has all the classic symptoms of environmental market failure stamped all over it.

That said, there are some promising signs: in the first quarter of 2018, 142,445 electric vehicles – private cars, lorries, trucks and buses – were sold in China, a 154% increase on 2017. You could say it's start, but is it too little too late? In developing countries, the problem is getting worse, with old, highly inefficient and polluting vehicles a major and growing cause of air pollution and CO2 emissions.

It would be unfair to blame motor manufacturers for their failure to adapt vehicle technology to the demands of the modern age. Their job is to maximise company profits, to do which they need to please buyers, not environmentalists. What the lack of progress over the past half century does show however, is how poor they have been at anticipating markets trends. It also underscores immense complacency among governments in whose jurisdictions they operate because they have singularly failed to create the necessary market conditions to make these much-needed improvements happen. Public indifference to fuel efficiency in less enlightened times must have contributed to this, but we should surely have expected better of our leaders in recent times, especially as scientists have been issuing warnings for decades.

And when governments finally woke up to the scourge of traffic emissions, instead of backing lower fuel consumption and cleaner engines, which seemed to be the obvious way to reduce all emissions, the focus has been on CO_2 reduction almost at any cost. Somehow health and environment-damaging pollution has been left out of the equation, as the following sorry tale so clearly illustrates.

The diesel fiasco

The story of the rise of diesel as the new heir to the automotive energy market in Europe begins in the 1990s when carbon-generated climate change first became a major priority. With the central message of the 1992 Earth Summit still ringing in their ears, governments were looking for quick and easy ways to reduce carbon emissions; for Europe, diesel engines fitted the bill nicely because they did exactly that, cutting CO_2 simply by being more fuel-efficient. By the end of the decade diesel car sales in Europe had risen from 15% to 25%. The subsequent development of a new fuel injection system [5] that made diesel engines quieter and more powerful meant that by 2008 half of all new cars in Europe were diesels.

In contrast, across the pond in the USA, diesel cars had been slow to catch on due to their early reputation as nosy, smelly and slow. But intense marketing by European manufacturers was having results, and by 2015 diesel numbers had risen from 1% to 3% of all cars, and were growing at around 40% a year.

But it turns out that in their zeal for a quick carbon fix something had been overlooked by European legislators; it was something very obvious, yet so important that the entire issue was to blow up spectacularly their faces. They forgot about particulate pollution.

Actually, it's somewhat charitable to suggest they "forgot" about diesel pollution, because the truth is that European governments knew all about it but in the spirit of the times chose to make carbon the priority. This CO_2 tunnel vision encouraged them to swallow hook, line and sinker the industry's claims to have produced a new generation of "clean diesel" cars. And so it was that the momentum for diesel became established, with variations such as diesel-electric hybrids making even better carbon improvements – around two thirds better than petrol engines.

But by 2015 suspicions were growing that this hyped "clean diesel" technology was not really doing what it claimed. Measured air quality simply did not match anticipated numbers based on manufactures' NOx and particulates emissions data.

Then the lid blew off. In September 2015, the giant German car manufacturer, Volkswagen (VW), became mired in a scandal that brought it nearly to its knees and rocked the world's faith in diesel as the carbon-friendly alternative of the future. They faced an accusation from the US Environmental Protection Agency that they had been covering up unacceptably high emissions of poisonous nitrogen oxides and particulates – tiny particles that penetrate the lungs, heart and brain – exacerbating asthmas and causing strokes, heart attacks and cancers. Astonishingly, it turned out that while VW were claiming their diesel cars were planet friendly, unknown to them some of their engineers had surreptitiously installed "defeat devices" designed to register when the emissions were being tested and give false readings.

Unfortunately, at the time of this discovery a lot of diesel pollution damage had already been done: VW had sold some 11 million of these cars around the world both in its own name and under other marques such as Audi and Skoda.

Anyone shrugging their shoulders at this scandal should consider this: imagine if each month a jumbo jet full of Londoners went down, killing everyone on board. That's every single month, year after year. That is the effect of diesel fuel-generated pollution in London, where a major report [6] showed that annually some 6,400 Londoners were dying prematurely from prolonged exposure to NOx and particulates. That these people die quietly in hospital beds rather than in the public glare with dramatic headlines, creates a tendency to do little more than tut and sigh, when really we should be as shocked as we would by any major plane crash. The human suffering is no less, nor is the grief of families and friends, after all.

Now also imagine the same monthly fatal plane crashes also happening in all major cities in Europe and most others around the world – from New York, to Tokyo, to Mumbai, to Beijing – every week, year in, year out. Merely calling this cynical and callous affair a scandal seems grossly inadequate. It is surely a criminal act.

The upshot of this contemptible deception is that, despite claims by other manufacturers that they had not likewise been cheating, and despite its many good points, without a rapid, confidence-restoring technological solution to its noxious emissions the diesel engine's days may be numbered. Europe has its work cut out to reverse years of high pollution and justify hundreds of millions of euros of investment in diesel engine development. Yet despite compelling evidence of the health damage fuel emissions cause by releasing carbon and pollutants into the atmosphere, policy remains lacklustre, a fact frequently underlined by high pollution alerts in and around major cities.

So, why have vehicle emissions not been regulated by a similar legislation to the Clean Air Acts? Indeed, why are dangerous vehicle emissions still tolerated at such high levels in cities all around the world?

One likely answer is that properly tackling the source of the problem has been simply too big a task in democratic countries. Taking on the voting public's perceived inalienable right to drive their cars anywhere, anytime is politically extremely challenging, as much as getting America to change the rules on gun ownership. Our 100-year affinity with the motor car is not going away anytime soon, so the combustion engine remains both a blessing and a curse on the modern world. It provides a freedom undreamed of by earlier generations, but it is also a leading source of contamination, environmental decline, and indirectly, of species extinction.

The folly of overpricing oil fuel

Overall there is little doubt that, if results are anything to go by, Western governments' policies on reducing oil fuel use for the most part have been and remain pretty uninspiring. In Europe, fuel taxes have long been believed to be the most effective way to deal with the problem. This is based on classic economics assumption that if a thing gets more expensive the demand for it reduces. Yet despite huge rises in European gasoline tax in recent decades, on the pretext of reducing fuel consumption, there are ever more cars burning ever more fuel with each passing year.

It is not only governments that deceive themselves this way. When, under immense pressure from striking farmers and truckers in September 2000 the British government was harried into reducing petrol tax a little, the environmental lobby were aghast [7]. They claimed this was a disastrous climb down that would only lead to more environmental pollution.

Climb down it was; but the greens could not have been more wrong about it being disastrous. Records show that price actually makes little difference to consumption; which means raising or lowering fuel prices has negligible effect on pollution. Research shows that it can take up to ten years before people respond to changes in petrol prices [8]. In 2014, when the oil price was hovering not far from its all-time high at around $100 a barrel, road miles travelled in Britain increased to 311 billion, the highest since 1988, resulting in fuel usage rising by 2.4% [9]. The reason was a recovering economy. Indeed, the record shows that fuel consumption is related much more to the state of the economy than price. In the US passenger miles travelled reached peaks in 2007-8 despite an oil price spike, and fell away rapidly due to the economic crisis without regard to the coinciding plunge in oil price [10].

In Britain, until the recent oil price slump, motor costs represented the largest single item in the average household budget, even ahead of mortgages and food, yet still oil fuel consumption has been continuing its upward trend. They are also paying further fuel costs built into the price of goods they buy in the shops.

The bottom line is, for as long as there remains no viable alternative (electric cars may be developing but are still no real competition), most people and businesses will have to continue to use oil-fuel-powered vehicles for as long as there remains no practical, cost-efficient and consumer-friendly alternative to oil fuel. Efficient, cheap transport is central to the maintenance of modern high-tech, high-speed economies, and having built these economies on the back of the combustion engine we need to think very hard before we abruptly withdraw support by making extortionate tax rises without viable alternatives first in place.

Yet in the face of its obvious failure to reduce fuel consumption, high tax fuel policy remains a central tenet of European anti-pollution strategy. It is hard not to come to the conclusion that the whole fuel price versus fuel use issue is a dangerous distraction from genuine pollution and CO_2 control, which demands a much less confrontational and less economically destructive approach.

Who is the real polluter?

So how should the fuel emissions problem be addressed if not through fuel pricing? You might think of the earlier phrase "the polluter should pay". That is true, but you first need to ask, *just who is* the true polluter –

the vehicle user or its manufacturer? Drivers would argue justifiably that on the whole they have little option but to use oil fuel because alternatives remain expensive and impractical, and how oil fuel cars and trucks perform in respect of pollutive emissions is not within their control. They would say that it is manufacturers who design the fossil-fuel-dependent technologies that give rise to the pollution; ergo manufacturers are the polluters by dint of the emissions their vehicles produce.

On the other hand, manufacturers would argue that they are market-led: they simply make what people want; consequently, if they do not want cleaner and more fuel-efficient vehicles, users are to blame.

So which donkey do we pin the polluter tail on? The answer has to be on the one who *can* make the necessary improvements to engine performance. That points the finger firmly at manufacturers. Who pays for increased fuel efficiency initially is irrelevant; in the end the consumer always ends up footing the bill because manufacturers necessarily pass on their costs to them. This means the market needs to be manipulated, not to make people pay to clean up already released emissions, because we know that isn't possible, or to stop them driving because that is economic suicide, but to drive the rapid development of much less pollutive and more fuel-efficient engines.

A glance into Nature confirms this. In the wildebeest scenario, for example, Nature can solve a dung problem one of two ways: via evolutionary metabolic adaptations – ones that modify waste internally before it enters the environment – or via symbiotic speciation that profits from detoxifying it after it emerges: stopping it or mopping it. In other words, creatures can either adapt so as to pollute their environment less and keep it habitable, or other creatures can adapt to take symbiotic advantage of the dung emissions, clearing it up by recycling it at a nutritional profit.

The answer in respect of fuel emissions is therefore clear: symbiosis is not an option because there is as yet no secondary use for vehicle exhaust emissions and thus no market in them. The only other option is to focus the spotlight on metabolic change by evolving engine technology to use less fuel more cleanly in the short term, while developing cleaner alternative fuels for the medium term.

After decades of inaction this is exactly what is under way in vehicle manufacturing markets – better late than never. But how far have we got with it, and are we doing all we could to accelerate it?

The new engine regime – targets, rules and incentives

When an absurdly optimistic, voluntary arrangement with car manufacturers to reduce their new models' emissions and increase engine efficiency failed in Europe, wasting valuable time that could have been spent improving engine technology, compulsory targets were finally phased in from as recently as 2012, a frankly scandalous delay. The same happened in the US under President Obama in 2009, when he announced regulations that would require the fuel economy of new cars and light trucks to be raised by nearly a third by 2016, further increasing them in 2012 with a target date of 2025. He likewise introduced targets for heavy trucks.

The general effect has been to at last force manufacturers to put all their efforts into year-on-year improvements in fuel efficiency. These regulations were justifiably hailed as a win-win for the environment (due to reduced pollution), for the state (due to reduced dependence on oil imports), and for consumers, who would make significant annual savings from having to buy less fuel.

The emphasis is now rightly on a dual strategy – one for the short term and one for the long. An emphasis has also been placed on developing alternative fuels, and leading contenders include electricity, ethanol, propane, hydrogen, biodiesel and natural gas. Each has its supporters and detractors, and each its own set of technological hurdles, some of which with time, effort and investment should be overcome. Electricity and some biofuels, which when combined with oil are known as "hybrids", are leading the way in this welcome revolution. These, together with a new generation of much cleaner, oil-based, more fuel-efficient engines, must be the short-term favourites to capture the market, with some of the others set to take over from them in the medium term, depending on who can capture the market most effectively.

A word of caution needs to be spoken about two of these fuels, ethanol and biodiesel. Not only are the processes that produce them highly pollutive, but they are also land-hungry products that carry ominous reminders of the palm oil and soya debacle that has devastated huge tracts of natural wilderness and used up much-needed food-growing land, increasing food prices. Blending ordinary ethanol with petrol is common practice in several countries, including Sweden and the USA, but especially in Brazil where there is a history of its use going back to the 1980s. Unfortunately, while sales of electric and gas cars are stagnating, the use of ethanol is climbing rapidly. If sense prevails, biodiesel and ethanol will cease to catch the selectors' eye as fuels of the future. If not, instead of being its saviour, ethanol may well turn out to be yet another major burden for the natural environment to bear.

That need not spell the end of the road for ethanol, however. A form of it known as *bio*ethanol can be made, without competing for land, by fermenting the inedible waste from the sugar and starch components of food crops like sugar cane and wheat. In April 2004 Iogen, a Canadian industrial enzyme manufacturer, opened the first bioethanol plant using enzymes to break down woodchips and straw into ethanol on a commercial scale. Iogen is also busy commercialising its new patented process to make renewable fuel from landfills, waste water treatment plants, waste digestion facilities, and farm digesters using proven existing refining operations.

Recycling waste products in this way to make fuel is surely almost guaranteed to put a smile on Nature's face.

Evolutionising markets

One of the essential elements of natural selection is competition. Although chance occasionally plays a part, more often in natural systems an invading organism gains advantage over another and takes over its resources simply because it is more powerful. We humans are perhaps the supreme exponents of such invasive behaviour, having outcompeted and displaced innumerable other organisms because technology has made us more powerful than them.

The same competitive principle goes within economies, in this case for emerging fuels and engine types. To gain traction in the niche that is the vehicle marketplace, cleaner colonisers like hybrids need to become more powerful than existing incumbents by outcompeting them for its resources – its money in other words, as provided by the buying public. Money is guarded jealously and is mostly provided voluntarily to markets rather than on demand, so to claim a significant share of the vehicle market, the first thing a new technological "variant" vehicle needs to do is to be more cost-efficient to their buyers – to do the same things at less cost. In this way natural selection can be set in motion for them to outcompete their "dirty" predecessors, just as invasive plant species often crowd out native species by outcompeting them for resources.

Now one might think this simple cost-benefit equation is so obvious that a comparison with natural processes isn't really needed to make this point. Yet strangely, policies that make market-ready, more fuel-efficient cars cheaper, both to buy and to run, than their predecessors have so far been markedly absent. The issue is that for the most part cleaner vehicles operate at a significant price disadvantage. That's not a good way to get them to take over the market.

True, in the US federal tax rebates are widely used to bias markets, but largely to encourage alternative fuel cars that are not yet fully market ready, rather than more efficient and readily available gasoline-oriented ones like hybrids. The result has been a widespread disillusionment by purchasers of alternative vehicles, not only because they still suffer from all sorts of ongoing developmental problems, but also because of the lack of a nationwide infrastructure for refuelling and recharging. This is clearly reflected in the fact that in 2015 trade-ins for other alternative fuel cars in the US had dropped to just 45% [11].

So while targeting subsidies at the further development of future technologies is undoubtedly important for the medium term; the immediate priority is surely to clean up the existing transport infrastructure – the gasoline-based one, for which competitive pricing needs to be a main weapon.

US Republicans hit this nail on the head over President Obama's compulsory transport efficiency and emissions targets. They railed against them, citing as their main objection the substantial increased purchase and maintenance costs that wiped out any fuel cost savings and more.

They had a point. What is the purpose of forcing motor manufacturers to produce cleaner, leaner cars of any type, whether modified or alternatively fuelled ones, if they are much more expensive to buy and run and fewer people can afford them? It not only flies in the face of the Polluter Pays Principle, but also guarantees increased longevity for second-hand polluting vehicles around the rest of the world in the many countries - like Poland for example, where there is already a large market for them. So long as the favourable cost disparity remains, pure gasoline is likely to remain the preferred option for buyers in most countries for decades to come.

Circumstances are exacerbating this: the oil price's 75% plummet from its highs entrenched it even more as the first-choice fuel for the world. Despite some recovery in the price this has not changed - too much transport and manufacturing, including that of plastics, is heavily dependent upon it.

We need to get real here. I know that a lot of people repeat the mantra that it's time to abandon oil fuel and focus on getting straight to alternative cleaner fuels. Of course that must be the long-term aim, but it's far too simplistic (an argument I will also make for the control of carbon emissions). There has to be a transition not a revolution. Despite all the hype about alternative fuels there's still a long way to go to get them fully on stream, and while everything possible must be done to speed that journey up, in the meantime we have to work with what we've got. What is being done now with fuel efficiency legislation is certainly not bad, but it is too little too late. Forty years too late. Furthermore, the rise in vehicle numbers worldwide, as economic recovery has gained pace and emerging markets have flourished, has more than offset any modest gains in emissions control.

As was argued earlier in this book, Nature shows us that the way to change markets is by market means, but that isn't happening nearly enough. The unavoidable fact is that over 99% of new vehicles sold around the world still use engines powered by refined oil, and according to the Energy Information Administration's 2015 Annual Energy Outlook, only around 7% of US vehicles will run on electricity by 2040. Extrapolate that around the world and it's a good outlook for oil producers for a long time to come yet.

Like it or not therefore, on their current trajectory alternative vehicles aren't going to take over soon enough to make the impact that is so urgently needed to help tackle this major problem, and we desperately need to overhaul our approach. It is clear there needs to be a dynamic short-term policy that involves the ongoing use of oil alongside a plan that aims to phase it out at some future time. Oil is still the cheapest, most energy-efficient, readily available and easily accessible fuel, and it isn't going to run out any time soon.

All of which makes it a prime candidate for the attentions of *Junglenomics*.

The *Junglenomics* approach to emissions reduction

So how can the evolution of the vehicle market be accelerated? The ideal result – zero pollutive emissions – is technically and logistically unachievable in the near future, so it is unrealistic to target it. The aim for now needs to be maximum achievement in the minimum amount of time.

To do this successfully requires a concentration of effort and specialist expertise. Just as expert nurserymen, at the world-renowned plant nurseries at the Royal Botanic Gardens, Kew in London, nurture rare species from seed, to leaf, to flower, to seed again to increase their numbers using a whole array of finely tuned techniques and expertise derived from their extensive knowledge of plant science, so we need to emulate them. We need to analyse, understand and modify the market mechanisms responsible for vehicle emissions in a scientific manner, while at the same time carefully nurture and develop promising new species in economic glasshouses to take over in the medium term.

In *Junglenomics* parlance, the current situation in the automobile ecosystem is that there exists only a small number of different species of the genus *Automobilius*, most of which are not nearly as fuel-efficient as we need them to be, and they damage the environment to an unsustainable degree. I'll call these gas guzzlers, *Automobilius guzillius*.

We, the economics gods, now want to intervene in the automobile ecosystem to speed up the rate of evolution among the vast herds of *A. guzillius*, but without creating ecosystemic mayhem. We cannot be draconian because that could cause their manufacturers to decline, and they are essential elements of our economic ecosystem employing many people. But we do want them to evolve as quickly and painlessly as possible to be less environmentally harmful, using the principles of natural selection. Time being of the essence, we would set out to encourage maximum adaptive improvement of existing vehicle species, while at the same time diverting substantial funds for extensive research and development (R & D) into the evolution of new, non-oil-consuming species for the longer term, for example *A. electricus*.

Past experience has taught us that raising fuel prices is ineffective in getting *A. guzillius* species to reduce emissions, and has undesirable consequences in the broader economy. Improving its metabolism through accelerated evolution, which is within our godlike power, is the obvious way forward.

To get the fastest results, this solution cannot be imposed by regulation alone; we need to harness the immense power of the economic-colonising imperative – market forces (which got us to this difficult juncture in the first place) – using a multilayered approach. Firstly, substantial improvement can be achieved by manipulating markets strongly in favour of the best of the current oil fuel users. Not long ago *A. dieselius* variants looked like good candidates for this with their better fuel efficiency, but as we saw, their newly revealed pollutive emissions have left much to be desired. That does not mean that they are out of the picture, only that the focus must be on making them genuinely cleaner to complement their undoubted CO_2 qualities through better fuel efficiency.

A. hybridius (engines that combine oil fuel with electricity or biofuels) is the other promising species currently grazing on the fringes of the ecosystem and looks as if it could one day soon be a big player in the landscape; but to do so it needs to complete its evolution and get established as a major competitor much more rapidly than it would if left to its own devices.

So how can we fast-track *A. dieselius* and *A. hybridius* towards much greater cleanliness and efficiency in the short term, and at the same time give it the competitive advantage of being cheaper both to buy and to run than *A. guzillius*?

The answer lies in a combination of the Polluter Pays Principle and classic carrot and stick. To kick-start the evolutionary process requires combined emissions and fuel efficiency targets, with rising annual thresholds. That much has already been set in motion in Europe and the US, however it is just the first stage of the evolutionary process. The second is to apply the Polluter Pays Principle.

As they come off the production line, each new vehicle model should have to carry a verified efficiency and emissions performance certificate, much as houses do in Europe, in order to assess its pollution values, and to determine to what degree it will be "rewarded" in the market with price subsidies.

To manipulate price competitiveness, new vehicles whose performance falls outside the official emissions thresholds should be levied on a sliding scale for each kilometre per litre (kpl) or mile per gallon (mpg) "in the red". To emphasise disparities to buyers so that they can see exactly how much they are being made to pay for this, the levy would be charged at point of purchase and would be a non-tax-deductible expense.

Likewise, subsidies for improved efficiency would be received directly by the buyer as a separate sum and would not be taxable. So, for example, suppose a vehicle environmental levy (VEL) on its purchase price were to be set at say, $300 (£200) per average mpg, and the year-one threshold set at 40mpg (not unrealistic as plenty of cars already exceed this) with an upper threshold of 55mpg. The buyer of a vehicle certified at an average 60mpg would receive $1,500 on a new car purchase, while another at 35mpg would pay an extra $1,500, a differential of $3,000 (£2,000). The greater polluter pays, while the lesser polluter receives, creating a double whammy in favour of rapid selection by buyers and equally rapid adaptation by manufacturers. Thus less polluting new car species would be given a significant immediate hand-up in price competitiveness.

To satisfy buyers in the performance car market, this arrangement needs to be backed up with a separate levy regime that rewards the maintenance of mpg-acceleration ratios, rewarding or penalising them in the same way. Hence high-performance, high-efficiency models could also gain a significant price advantage.

Because some buyers will either look beyond the initial pain of the VEL or are simply too wealthy to care, a further measure should involve annual road levies. These could also be penalised or rewarded on the same basis, though perhaps frozen at year-of-purchase thresholds. In fact, many countries already do charge road levies in a discriminatory manner, but for the most part they are not nearly draconian enough. Worse still, their proceeds are not ring-fenced into the system – the money is siphoned off for other uses, which brings us to the next stage in the evolution acceleration process.

The importance of ring-fencing

One of the critical elements missing from fuel emissions policy is the same as I wrote about earlier in respect of industrial pollution. It is the lack of ring-fencing of levies and taxes. Recycling nutrients is an important process in Nature because it prevents the depletion of resources. It is equally so in economics especially where technological evolution needs to be fast-tracked, as it does here.

Unfortunately, this is not the case and hence a major trick is being missed. In fact, it's even worse because, astonishingly, even advanced electric models of cars such as the Tesla range and Nissan's utilitarian "Leaf" have value added tax (VAT is the European purchase tax) levied on them the same as any gas guzzler, when to give them market advantage they desperately need to be tax exempt. Sucking tax from clean engine markets, and worse still, vanishing it into the vast coffers of government rather than using it to accelerate vehicle evolution, is pure folly. In any case, alternative fuel vehicles are outnumbered by traditional gasoline vehicles, on which levies are legitimately raised, by at least 20 to 1, so there should be no shortage of tax receipts. Tax can be gradually reintroduced as clean vehicles come to take over the market, but it is a heavy burden for them to bear at this embryonic stage of their development.

The importance of the ring-fencing of levies within the targeted industry cannot be overemphasised. If we want to successfully establish a new rose in our garden we have to choose the spot carefully, prepare the ground, add necessary nutrients, keep it watered and protect it against competing weeds. Measures that suck billions out of motorists' and manufacturers' pockets without reinvesting the proceeds to nurture greener vehicles show a lack of real concern. They are like sticking the rose in a dry, mossy, frost pocket full of weeds and hoping for the best.

It is therefore essential that all surplus funds raised from VELs (above those used to subsidise the price of clean vehicles), together with a contribution from fuel tax, go into subsidising clean engine R & D.

This is not only perfectly feasible but also precedented. In March 2009, the European Union parliament approved an emissions tax for heavy trucks that was "earmarked" for greener technology development and expanding alternative transport systems [12]. There are many emergent vehicle technologies lurking in the wings in need of a helping hand to get established and also many specialist symbiotic part makers.

Take infinitely variable transmission (IVT) technology for example, an innovative gearing technology that optimises engine efficiency [13]. Such technologies could have helped to colonise the marketplace much more quickly had they received significant investment from levied funds, combined with a favoured tax status. But low oil prices and a drive towards hybrids has left its mechanical efficiency technology out in the cold. Furthermore, a promising passenger car solution had to be abandoned, despite offering a higher CO_2 saving per euro on cost than the competing electric hybrid alternative, and a performance car programme on which Torotrak's flywheel technology was nominated in preference over a battery based KERS was also abandoned from lack of support. (KERS stands for kinetic energy recovery system, a device that recovers the kinetic energy present in the waste heat created by the car's braking process. It stores that energy and converts it into power that can be called upon to boost acceleration.) These were wasted opportunities to get more efficient new economic species into the transport mainstream.

As it is, nearly all sums raised by governments on oil fuel and vehicles are diverted away to unrelated causes. The public and manufacturers alike, while deeply unsympathetic to, even resentful of, such one-way taxes, would likely be a great deal happier about pollution levies if they could be sure their money was going towards developing cleaner technology for the benefit of this and future generations, instead of being spirited away to prop up national budgets.

Confederation of British Industry director-general Richard Lambert made this point in 2008 when he remarked that the amount of money that the British government's newly announced emissions policy, the controversial "showroom tax" (which would generate a massive £1.2 billion by the end of 2011), would *not build confidence in the government's green measures. We need carrots as well as sticks to change behaviour,*" he said.

The upshot is that under a VEL regime, manufacturers rather than drivers would be put under the cosh. They would need to get smart quickly in developing ways to improve their models year-on-year.

One way manufacturers could respond to the VEL challenge is to apply evolutionary theory to fuel efficiency and emissions. Genetic algorithms (software that mimics evolution's drive for fitness) have already been applied by computer scientists [14] to find the best tuning options for racing cars. Here a population of potential solutions would be tested for fitness and the most successful cross-bred and mutated. The less fit members of the next generation would be rejected, leaving only the fittest to go on. This could readily be applied to the fuel efficiency, emissions and performance of production cars and trucks.

Money and success speak loudest

There is little doubt where in the world combustion engine pollution is worst: according to the US Environmental Protection Agency (EPA), the US have about 30% of the world's cars and light trucks, but are responsible for about half of the entire world's vehicle emissions. Engine development there seems to have hit a "bottleneck of innovation" according to one of the senior directors of the Automotive XPRIZE (AXP) [15]. The powerful financial incentive provided by the Automotive XPRIZE, and awarded in 2010 to three contestants, has shown what can be achieved by the prospect of cash and the kudos of success.

The AXP's multimillion-dollar prize was mostly allocated for the development of a four-passenger, mass-market vehicle and a performance two-seater, each capable of 100 mpg (2.35 litres/100 kilometres). According to a poll, over 60% of American drivers would like to buy a car capable of 100 mpg, but there is considerable doubt in the US motor industry whether the public would be prepared to pay more to get it. However, *Junglenomics* would favour these cleaner colonising car species in the short term by ironing out price differentials in their favour. Manufacturing efficiencies and volume production would in due course bring costs down, as historically it always has. Sadly, it is indicative of government failure to galvanise innovation and to smooth market entry that these prize-winning developments have yet to feed through to the market.

Much the same principle applies to large trucks. In the US, the trucking industry has been remarkably disinterested in fuel efficiency despite the obvious potential benefit to profits. Trucks move about 70% of goods around the US and Europe, but despite tighter emissions regulations, temporary higher fuel prices and recession, the industry has made very little progress in getting cleaner [16]. Between 1990 and 2007 US trucks increased their daily fuel usage from 1.6 to 2.5 million barrels a day, and their efficiency is little better than it was 40 years earlier.

Yet there are technologies available that could increase fuel efficiency by a quarter. Wheel skirts, axel motors, aerodynamic fins, drag reducers, super-wide tyres, heat and energy recycling, engine design and transmission innovations – all these and more are only creeping timidly into the marketplace when they should be exploding into it. They represent a diverse fauna of technological species lurking in the fringes of the economic ecosystem, struggling to gain a foothold. Although, as oil begins to run out, some of them may eventually get to colonise in force, this could take many decades, time the world doesn't have. Our environmental problems are immediate and growing. Accelerating the colonising process by helping beneficial newcomers to sail through the usual painful process of gaining a sure position in the marketplace could significantly reduce their fledgling period and bring forward much-needed efficiencies.

Older cars cannot be allowed to escape the net because they last so much longer these days. The same levy principles need to be applied to them on a graduating basis, with strong financial incentives to scrap or upgrade them to be cleaner and more fuel-efficient. This principle is well established. After all, many governments give generous grants to householders to insulate their lofts to save energy or to install solar panels, yet not one that I am aware of helps drivers to reduce their emissions by attaching filters. The development and production of exhaust filters manufactured by pollution-free methods is an urgent priority – not just for the blighted diesel market – but for all cars.

Dirty flying

What goes for cars and trucks goes equally for aeroplanes. Taxing airline tickets and pocketing the proceeds is a favourite ploy in both the US and Europe's emissions policies. But it is not the best way to get lower emissions any more than is non-ring-fenced fuel tax. It sucks cash out of the aero industry as a supposed deterrence to flying, which doesn't work; the skies get ever busier. And even if it did work it would only impede freedom of travel and reduce the tourism that so many biodiversity-rich countries depend upon.

Reducing aircraft emissions can therefore only happen in two ways: developing cleaner, more fuel-efficient aeroplanes, and improving occupancy rates. That means raising levies on airline fuel efficiency at both manufacture and usage stages. This can only be done by making less efficient planes more expensive to buy and to use, and more efficient ones cheaper.

This is a highly competitive market. If an airline knows the seats in a particular new aircraft will have to carry lifetime environmental charges because its efficiency is below the adopted mean, it may choose a rival. In order that airlines know the costs of running an aeroplane before they buy, aircraft need to be assessed for pollution and noise levies before reaching the production stage. In the same way as for other polluters, these pollution levies can then be channelled back into aircraft design, helping to finance the next generation of cleaner and quieter aircraft. Lowering pollution and noise would then get built into the commercial loop, driving the whole aircraft industry towards reducing its external costs.

Such changes could not be brought in overnight of course, as they could bankrupt some airlines. Introducing levies gradually and with plenty of advance warning to give aircraft manufacturers time to adapt would ensure a level playing field. Absent in this strategy is most of the expensive legislation and enforcement and the inevitable accompanying bureaucracy. By creating the conditions for steady beneficial evolution, the pain of a revolution is avoided, the need for which will otherwise become more and more pressing as time goes by.

In the end, passengers will pay for all this because airlines will have to pass on their costs. But their payment would not go into balancing a national budget, but towards a cleaner and quieter future for air travel, prime requirements that will become ever more essential as air traffic volume increases. As with cars and industry, while they would certainly not be happy fattening the national exchequer, I believe the public would tolerate such levies so long as they were ring-fenced to bring about a new generation of cleaner aircraft as swiftly as humanly possible.

To summarise this chapter, in order to address the urgent problem of air pollution and carbon emissions, economic fauna within oil-fuel-based transport markets must evolve much more rapidly than at present. Above all they need to do so within a framework that is momentum-driven and self-perpetuating, and that is understood and respected by all players. Short-term adaptation and medium-term evolution is Nature's way to rebalance disrupted ecosystems, and it should be the case here too. Research and development are essential. Because R & D is expensive, and the targets we are aiming for are not a demand-led priority but an environmental one, market priorities need to be manipulated.

Under the Polluter Pays Principle manufacturers should be made to help pay for what is in effect a clean-up of their act. But robbing huge revenues from their markets is not how to go about this. R & D through the reinvestment of levies *is*. Money, just like nutrients, has not only to be raised but also recycled to enhance the pace of technological evolution. When we divert it to unrelated causes we are no better than farmers who impoverish their land by forever taking from it with no care for its long-term fertility.

I have alluded to CO_2 emissions a number of times in this chapter because the transport system is a major contributor to excess carbon in the atmosphere and hence to climate change. This is becoming the biggest issue of our age, and the next chapter looks at tackling it through *Junglenomics*.

1. World Health Organisation
2. European Environment Agency report
3. American Lung Association
4. University of Michigan Transportation Research Institute in Ann Arbor
5. The "common rail" system
6. Commissioned by Transport for London 2015
7. E.g.: "Transport 2000"; Friends of the Earth
8. Phil Goodwin of University College, London, a leading expert on traffic congestion
9. Department of Transport figures
10. Bureau of Transportation Statistics, table 3:10, National Transportation and Economic Trends
11. PowerSource: a companion resource to a weekly print section of the Pittsburgh Gazette that covers the region's diverse energy industry
12. European Parliament News 2009
13. Torotrak plc
14. Peter Bentley and Kryszt Wloch of University College, London. NS2452 p22
15. The AXP is the automotive version of the XPRIZE Foundation's aerospace prize
16. Amory Lovins, Rocky Mountain Institute, Colorado

Chapter 5
Climate Change
The *Junglenomics* Approach

Why Nature conservation demands we should redouble our efforts to reduce carbon emissions whatever our misgivings

Carbon has had a lot of bad press in recent years – evil stuff that is polluting our air and causing the world's climate to overheat, it is claimed. Yet strictly speaking carbon is not a pollutant – all life on Earth is built from it. Just as a weed is really nothing more than a plant in the wrong place, likewise climate change is caused by too much carbon in the wrong place – in this case the atmosphere. The problem is not in carbon itself, but in its changing distribution. There is a finite quantity of carbon in the Earth's biosphere and most of it is locked up in soil, rock, water and living organisms, especially vegetation. The rest floats around in the atmosphere mainly as carbon dioxide (CO_2), getting there through chemical reactions like decay and fire. This is a fluid process – carbon is continually being released and reabsorbed by earthbound matter. The rate of release versus the rate of absorption denotes whether the proportion that is locked up to that which is airborne is stable or changing.

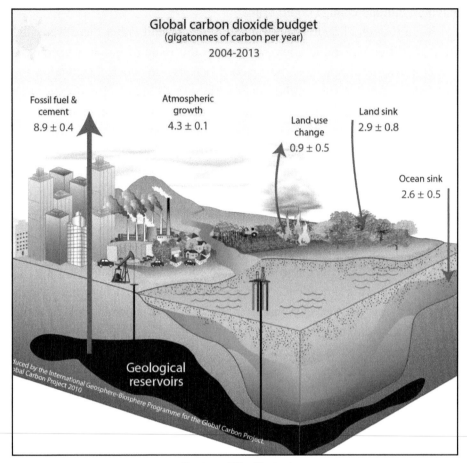

Courtesy of Cloudfront.net

Our industrial activities, especially energy generation, involve a great deal of burning of carbon-bearing materials such as coal and oil, and this has released extra carbon into the atmosphere. In excess, carbon creates a "greenhouse" effect in the atmosphere, trapping more of the sun's heat at low level. CO_2 is thus known as a "greenhouse gas" (GHG). Leading scientists have concluded that a rise in the amount of airborne carbon therefore contributes to climate change – the insidious "global warming" about which we hear so much.

It is generally agreed that an increase in average global temperatures will bring serious economic and environmental consequences. Reducing atmospheric carbon release while at the same time locking up, or "sequestering" carbon back into land, vegetation and ocean has thus become a priority for an international community rattled by dire predictions of the mayhem climate change could bring.

Yet although climate scientists and others would rather there were not, there is still considerable controversy over the issue of global warming. It is a controversy that cannot be ignored because so much depends on the credibility of the science and on the contingent ability of climate scientists to push for concerted remedial action worldwide. No one can have escaped the welter of publicity surrounding man-made climate change, but what may not be so apparent is the intense political struggle that underlies it.

Economists and ecologists, respectively representing human development and environmental conservation, have long been at loggerheads over whether people or Nature should take priority when it comes to planning. Economists have always had the ear of government, while ecologists tend to have to shout to make themselves heard. Hence, until fairly recently, the boot has been firmly on the economist foot, and consumption, growth and wealth creation have taken precedence over conservation issues. Environmentalists eventually saw that the only way to make governments and their economic advisors sit up and take notice was to present the effects of carbon release – climate change – as an *economic* cost, and therefore an obstacle to ongoing economic development.

It worked. By increasing atmospheric carbon levels in predictive models the resulting global warming provided the perfect vehicle for converting economic advisors to a new concept – sustainable economic development. A major threshold was crossed and a new creed was born. Yet as in all walks of life there were many non-believers, and there still are.

I am not for a moment suggesting that the exponents of climate change are adhering to a belief system rather than strict science as their chief opponents claim. However, the value of man-made – that is *anthropogenic* – climate change has proved immense as a lever for the ecologist cause, and has at last put this to the forefront of economic planning. Inevitably this success has given rise to a degree of arrogance in some peripheral ecologist quarters at the expense of strict scientific impartiality. Not to put too fine a point on it, intercepted inter-office communications at the UK's Climate Research Unit exposed some clumsy attempts at news management and predictably this caused a press furore.

The upshot was that in late 2009 the public perception of the credibility of the science that underpinned the case of anthropogenic global warming was severely dented. Opponents seized on what predictably soon became known as "Climategate" as confirmation of what they had claimed all along – that anthropogenic climate change was a conspiracy by ecologists and greens to set up and run a very expensive world environmental agenda based on tenuous science and maintained by smoke and mirrors.

Perverse as it may seem, at first I cautiously welcomed this setback to the climate change case in 2009. This was not because of any suspicions of my own over its veracity, but because in the previous few years this single issue had overshadowed all others. Climate change was regarded as an umbrella cause for many other environmental issues, as indeed it is, but to gamble all on it seemed to be a risky strategy because any loss of credibility on climate change science threatened to drag down the entire environmental cause with it, as indeed the Climategate furore demonstrated. I felt that water and air pollution, overdevelopment, forest clearance, the displacement, decline and extinction of species, rural poverty – all these vital and urgent issues – should not be bound to the climate issue and risk living or dying by it. It was too many eggs in one ecological basket. Direct environmental damage needs to be tackled with equal attention, equal vigour and equal resources. After all, will the curbing and sequestration of carbon help tigers, orangutans, rhinos, frogs, snow leopards, overexploited plants and all the other endangered species on the ever-lengthening IUCN Red List in the near term – the only term that can save many of them? These are localised struggles that surely need and deserve our attention every bit as much as global warming.

This at least was how I saw things in the immediate aftermath of Climategate.

I subsequently changed my mind, however. Essentially this was because I came to see that there was a peculiar and unique aspect to the issue of anthropogenic climate change and one of its potential remedies – sequestration. I began to think about what would happen if the sceptics gained the upper hand and caused essential political and economic resources to be withdrawn or withheld from carbon control tactics, and that worried me a lot. Here is why.

Climate change – the indisputable facts

Forget the hype and the politics – what are the indisputable facts about global warming? To begin with the world climate *is* warming; even many sceptics now acknowledge this, though they dispute the cause.

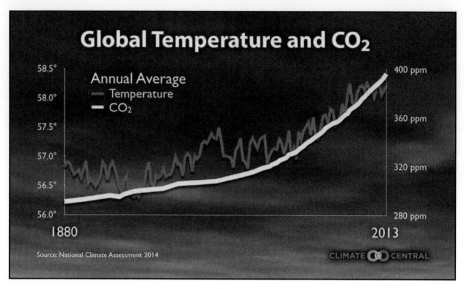

US Public Document

A joint statement by the world's most prestigious scientific academies in Brazil, Canada, China, France, Germany, India, Italy, Japan, Russia, the UK and the US stated: *"Climate change is real. There will always be uncertainty in understanding a system as complex as the world's climate. However there is now strong evidence that significant global warming is occurring. The evidence comes from direct measurements of rising surface air temperatures and subsurface ocean temperatures and from phenomena such as increases in average global sea levels, retreating glaciers, and changes to many physical and biological systems."*

The next fact concerns what is causing this. Logically, there can only be three sources of climate warming:

a) from inside the Earth: that is, if the Earth's core is radiating more heat to the surface. Most of the heat in the Earth's core is fuelled by the decaying of radioactive isotopes such as potassium-40, uranium-238, -235, and thorium-232 contained within the mantle (the outer core), and it escapes at a steady rate, expanding the inner core by about a centimetre every thousand years. There is no evidence that the rate of heat loss has altered, nor any known reason why it should have done.

b) from the sun, if the sun is getting hotter. Some data early this century did appear to show an increase in total solar irradiance (TSI) over the past century until the 1970s, but since then more reliable measurements show that it has not moved outside its normal fluctuations of 0.1%.

c) because less of the sun's heat is escaping back out to space from the Earth's atmosphere, which means it is being trapped there by something in the Earth's biosphere.

The finger is thus firmly pointed at the third alternative – making the second indisputable fact that more heat is being trapped in the biosphere.

So then, what is trapping this heat? Data from ice core samples show that high levels of airborne carbon in the form of carbon dioxide coincide with warm periods in Earth's history. Since the beginning of the industrial age CO_2 levels have risen from 280 parts per million (ppm) to 380 ppm, a rise of 35%. Coincidence? Not according to satellite measurements, which now show unequivocally that increasing infrared heat, of the specific frequencies absorbed by CO_2 and other greenhouse gasses, is being absorbed by these particulates and reflected back to Earth. So whatever the naysayers claim, all the available and measurable evidence points firmly to CO_2 as the main heat-retaining culprit. End of story. That increased greenhouse gasses (and in particular CO_2) are to blame for global warming is therefore the third indisputable fact.

The fourth indisputable fact is that this CO_2-induced climate change will have great and diverse effects on many environments, and in turn affect those species that live in them, not least mankind.

It is when we come to look at what, if anything, could and should be done about this situation that the real dispute begins. The majority of scientists hold the view that by preventing atmospheric CO_2 levels rising too far above 380 ppm, warming can be kept to manageable levels, 1.5 to 2 degrees Celsius, with less severe consequences. But even this is not guaranteed because current warming could at any moment start a feedback phase: it may begin to release the vast amounts of greenhouse gases locked up by permafrost, peatbogs and undersea methane hydrate deposits (methane is an even more potent greenhouse gas than CO_2), compounding the problem. The oceans have, up to now, been absorbing about a third of the CO_2 created by industrialisation, but scientists say they are now reaching saturation, which could also accelerate the amount of airborne carbon without any further increase in emissions at all. This is also causing the acidification of the oceans, with severe negative impacts on marine ecosystems.

There are those who argue that global warming is part of a natural cycle that could reverse at any time on its own. Others again accept the case, but believe we should not spend trillions of dollars trying to stop the inevitable, and that instead we should be preparing to adapt to the new reality. They may not understand quite how alien the new reality

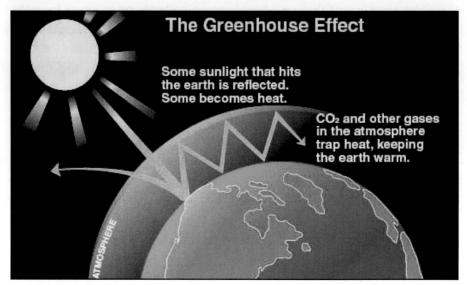

The Greenhouse Effect

Some sunlight that hits the earth is reflected. Some becomes heat.

CO_2 and other gases in the atmosphere trap heat, keeping the earth warm.

ATMOSPHERE

http://www.durban.gov.za/City_Services/energyoffice/PublishingImages/ClimateChange.jpg

could be if CO_2 reaches 1,000 ppm and above – a resulting average temperature rise of 4 degrees and more – as it almost certainly will if business as usual continues. While it is true that there are no guarantees in controlling greenhouse gasses, it is a fair prediction that without any controls things will get a whole lot worse.

So that is the choice – do nothing either because we might wake up one day and find the problem has gone away, or because it's a better use of money to learn to adapt to it. Or do everything humanly possible to clean up our act and reduce greenhouse gas emissions.

Despite the brief hiatus, my own feelings on this issue gradually became unequivocal. I will later argue a case for the conservation of whole environments rather than cherry-picking individual species to save, but what use is that if the fundamental conditions of those environments are undermined by climatic change? Existing rainforests need to remain moist and steamy, peatlands damp and swamps wet; rivers and streams need to keep flowing; savannahs need reliable seasonal rains to feed the huge mammal herds and other creatures that depend upon them; oceans need to be free of carbon-fed eutrophication. However hard we try, we cannot ourselves nurture hundreds of thousands of species through a climatic trauma in which these life-giving things cease to happen. As we know, disruption in one region can easily have knock-on effects elsewhere, which means few, if any, ecosystems will be safe. The Sixth Extinction will be well and truly upon us and there will be no going back.

But there is a second and overwhelmingly powerful reason for governments to take up the fight against climate change as never before. This is because it also provides the ideal opportunity to transform the economic equation as a whole in favour of Nature conservation. This is urgently needed. For example, despite all the efforts that have been made to save the world's great remaining primary forests over several decades, their clearance reached a worldwide rate of over *twenty-nine* million hectares

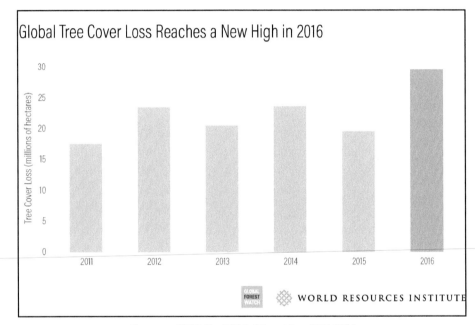

Courtesy of WRI. Total Global Forest Loss 2011-2016

in 2016 [1]. This is not only a major source of greenhouse gases (land use change together accounts for about 20% of all carbon emissions, more than the entire world transport system [2]), it is also an unmitigated disaster for biodiversity and an ongoing source of human misery. If "business as usual" were to continue in forestry markets, hundreds more millions of acres of forest could be lost over the next 50 years with incalculable and irredeemable loss to world biodiversity [3], not to mention to the livelihoods and cultures of innumerable native peoples.

One doesn't have to be a devotee of the carbon science to see that the argument for cleaning up industrial output and arresting the current destruction of wildlife and wilderness is unanswerable. It is obvious that there is an immense amount to gain by doing so, and an immense amount to lose by not. The ongoing destruction of the world's remaining wildernesses and the climate change issue are profoundly interconnected, and we therefore have the opportunity to end one of the biggest single sources of increased airborne CO_2 and protect the majority of the world's incalculably valuable biodiversity at the same time.

Unfortunately, while America may be a world leader to whom the West looks to in times of insecurity, it continues to struggle to reconcile its love affair with money with its environmental conscience. This is a major hindrance to progress. A significant proportion of the population, represented on the public stage mostly by Republican politicians, remain stubbornly myopic so far as climate change is concerned. There is a disappointing, dogged denial of powerful science that defies rationality, something that Senator Bernie Sanders among others rightly sees as an "embarrassment" to the American nation.

Climate change will become a security issue as its effects bite on populations worldwide. If the first duty of any government is the security of its people, then it is hard to see why all possible measures should not be taken in conjunction with other major states across the world to protect their people from the severe loss of security that climate change will bring.

I live in hope that one day I might wake up to find that President Trump has had a Damascene moment, and he tweets: "*this climate change thing is bad; I mean – really bad, and we're gonna stop it*". Dream on.

Revaluing Nature

I long ago came to the unqualified conclusion that for its protection Nature needs to be radically revalued by markets, a theme that recurs throughout this book. I have argued that regulations, though essential in supporting any programme, have never been and will never be sufficient on their own to halt the man-made decline of the world environment because of the irresistible power of the colonising imperative imbedded in markets. This means that we will never succeed just by ordering people not to emit greenhouse gasses, or fell rainforests, or kill tigers for that matter. *Junglenomics* prefers to harness market forces to encourage markets to evolve naturally, attracting symbiotic services and boosting compliant industries, while rendering non-compliant ones ever less viable.

Finding ecology-inspired market solutions to market failures is a central refrain of this book. Applied to the current feverish destruction of Nature, the *Junglenomics* approach requires that the beneficial exploitation of biodiverse wilderness becomes economically more attractive than its destructive exploitation. There is no middle way. The time for dithering is long past. We need as a world to embark upon a new course with a clear strategic target – an economic system that emulates natural systems.

As I remarked just now, many people seem to have given up on preventing climate change and the even more severe depletion in species that will accompany it. They have begun to talk in terms of mitigation planning instead – preparing for the worst. Yet I repeat that I believe it is still not too late; not too late for GHG emissions and climate change; not too late for the world's wildlife. For despite the gloomy prognostications there already exist two schemes that, harnessed with money-market instruments, have the potential to reduce emissions to the levels they need to be in time to rescue the situation.

One of these schemes is classic PPP – penalizing carbon either through tax or via the carbon cap-and-trade market, currently the world's only major anti-carbon initiative. The other is CCS – carbon capture and storage. Remember those three letters, because they represent an important element in rescuing our planet from climate change, as we will see.

Between them these two approaches represent the classic one-two of pollution mitigation – metabolic adaptation and symbiotic partnership. They are the near-term future. Nothing else, not even clean energy, can do the GHG business in time, for reasons that will be explained in this chapter.

But disappointingly both are in irons, their momentum lost. Carbon cap-and-trade is still nowhere near the success it was intended to (and could) be; there must be good reasons for this. And CCS, the brainchild of the future, has stalled at a time when it was poised to play a large part in rescuing the world from anthropogenic climate change.

The next sections describe CCS, carbon tax and cap-and-trade, and argues that they could be combined in a new partnership funded by private capital that along with clean energy technology could make a very substantial contribution to solving the CO_2 problem.

Carbon capture and storage – a misunderstood remedy

There is something bizarre about the world's current political attitude to GHGs (greenhouse gas emissions). Look at it this way. Not so long ago there were no sewage systems and no garbage collection services. They came about because our forebears came to the conclusion that raw sewage thrown in the streets to run down a central gutter into some stinking ditch was a health threat, and that garbage brought rats and flies and got in everyone's way.

So what did we do? We eventually did the obvious thing, the right thing. We built huge sewage systems, like the aforementioned one in London after the Great Stink, and for more remote areas we invented septic tanks. And to replace the lowering buckets into often polluted wells we laid thousands of miles of pipes across our nations to deliver drinking water to our homes and workplaces. Last century we built nuclear power stations to help power our factories and homes and the waste from that is so polluting and dangerous that we also do the sensible thing – we go to enormous lengths to keep it from escaping, at vast cost and not inconsiderable risk.

Now we have discovered that the greenhouse gases and pollutants we release when we burn carbon-based fuels (not to mention other emitters like cement factories), which we didn't pay much attention to when we built carbon-producing plants and vehicles, are actually going to cause problems to the world so serious that they could make sewage and garbage seem a minor inconvenience.

So what have we done about this? Naturally, we have followed the same logical course. We have done as we did with sewage and garbage. We have built a similarly comprehensive infrastructure to capture it at source and send it to be safely locked up out of harm's way.

Only we haven't.

Instead we have either done nothing or we have gone for "green". We have focused most of our efforts on alternative energy sources such as wind and solar, and built dams for hydropower at vast expense and considerable environmental damage. There is no doubt that these are the future, but they have no prospect of replacing the regular baseload of energy, so well provided by fossil fuels and nuclear reaction, fast enough to avoid the 2 degree warming that climate science models suggest is critical to avoid catastrophic climate change.

The unfortunate reality is that 85% of the world's energy still comes from carbon-rich fuels, and whether we like it or not that's just not going to change significantly anytime soon. In 2012 for example, the oil giant, Exxon

Mobil signed a $500-billion deal with Russia to explore new oil resources in the Arctic. They are only able to do so because climate change has thinned the ice sufficiently. While we make inadequate attempts to reduce GHG emissions in small sections of the industrial world, rising economic stars like China and India are still building hundreds of new coal-fired power stations belching out GHGs like never before. (Despite China's apparent change of heart on these, cancelling 100 new power stations, Chinese energy corporations are building or planning to build more than 700 new coal plants at home and around the world). These comprise some 76% of proposed new energy capacity worldwide [4]. Sure – we would all like green energy to replace it, but it just isn't going to happen in time. Period.

There is no time to waste now either. The consensus among climatologists is that to avoid the worst effects of global warming it is critical to limit global temperature increases to 2 degrees, but the world is already producing 80% of the GHG emissions required to reach that increase. This means the pressure is on, not just to stabilise, but to significantly reduce current GHG emissions. So far the signs are not at all good: 2010 marked another high point in CO_2 emissions, and the biggest increase on record [5], and after a short lull, 2017 emissions set a new record.

Despite supportive promises, coal-fired power stations are also proliferating in Indonesia and the US; and for some like Germany, nuclear is off the menu altogether due to popular pressure following the Fukushima disaster in 2011. Britain is betting on shale gas through fracking – cleaner than oil or coal but still a substantial emitter of CO_2 when burned. In the US, fracking is already a major industry, and hence a major polluter.

The inescapable fact is that the age of fossil fuel dinosaurs is not yet over, not for a long time, and no amount of wishful thinking is going to change this. New oil and gas fields are still being sought out and exploited by the energy dinosaurs for one simple reason – gasoline and natural gas are still the most efficient and plentiful fuels [6]. They are going to be so for many decades yet, whatever we do or say. There are new energy species rustling in the undergrowth, but they are still very far from replacing the pivotal role the fossil fuel dinosaurs play in the current economic ecosystem. Without them our economic ecosystem would collapse, and with that so would civilisation. We have to live with that and do what it takes right now with what we have.

Not only do we have massive, mostly unmitigated, CO_2 release from energy production and industries such as cement and steel, but on top of it is the tragedy that carbon-retaining natural wildernesses – including forests, wetlands and peatlands – are continuing to be destroyed at an alarming rate, releasing further vast amounts of previously locked-up GHGs into the atmosphere.

Frankly, it's chaos out there. At the present rate, under no circumstances is the atmospheric carbon balance going to be restored within 150, let alone 50 years with the half-hearted efforts we as a world are currently making. In the face of such undeniable realities our local attempts to go green are patently futile. We need other ways, we need them now, and we need them on a large scale; but our leaders are frozen in the headlights of climate change, unable to rouse themselves to face this immense challenge united.

So is the world quite mad?

I ask this particularly because while politicians argue and procrastinate, a significant part of the answer in terms of energy CO_2 emissions is right there under their noses – the science, the technology and the know-how. It's called carbon capture and storage, or CCS. People have been raving about it for decades. It is seen by many as one of the only real immediately doable answers to the CO_2 problem.

CCS has five-star *Junglenomics* credentials. Think of our friend the defecating wildebeest. Throw in some giraffe, buffalo, zebra and a herd of elephants for good measure. In this scenario, the many species of dung consumers are working overtime but there's vastly too much to deal with. We can try to get all these big beasts to defecate less, but that's the way they are made. We would have to genetically redesign all the animals – or destroy them, the first of which is not possible in the time frame available to us, and the second a non-starter. Nevertheless, with a bit of special dieting and buttock clenching we may get the dung emissions down by maybe a few per cent. In the same way, polluting factories and power stations are not changing their emissions much or closing down anytime soon.

Or we can do the obvious thing – develop new symbiotic species to help clear up the mess and lock it away safely.

CCS is in effect one such new species. It takes carbon at source, pressurises it into a liquid, which is then transported to a facility that sends it back deep underground to be locked away under impermeable layers of rock – back down where it has come from as oil and gas. As Tim Bertels, Shell's Global CCS portfolio manager told the *Guardian* newspaper, "*You don't need to divest in fossil fuels, you need to decarbonise them.*" CCS is sensible, natural and, according to its many passionate protagonists, safe. According to Howard Herzog [7], *"All the necessary components of a CCS system are in commercial use today somewhere in the economy. To be considered commercial-grade, these different components need to be integrated and scaled up."*

"All the major climate analysts agree on one thing. That CCS is one of, if not the most, valuable technologies to fight climate change. Globally, the UN calculates that without CCS, meeting climate targets will be 138 per cent more expensive," says Matthew Billson, programme director of Energy 2050 at the University of Sheffield, calling CCS *"the Cinderella of low carbon energy technology"*, overshadowed as it is by nuclear and renewables [8].

Support for CCS is widespread among the highest echelons of energy experts. For example, the International Energy Agency based in Paris has drawn attention to its importance, while the UK-based Energy Technologies Institute stated that in the absence of CCS the cost of meeting the UK's climate targets will double. And in November 2015 the Committee on Climate Change likewise stressed the importance of CCS, saying, *"It is important that the low-carbon portfolio includes roll-out in the 2020s of offshore wind and CCS given their long-term importance and the role of UK deployment in driving down costs."*

Yet having made a highly promising start, Herzog's view is that CCS has been sidelined and is now running only in second gear. In Britain it may be running in no gear at all since the Cameron government pulled out of its £1 billion support of important CCS developments in Britain, which were projected to become template CCS instalments for the world to follow.

Why? Essentially the reason was that as yet there is no market for carbon capture, and ostensibly therefore no one other than governments to pay the bills. There was no market in the past for garbage or sewage either, yet we spent billions on the infrastructure to deal with them safely. CCS too is simply a much-needed new public service. It doesn't have its own market because there isn't enough demand for it. The consumer market for CO_2, while diverse, is limited in the quantities it requires [9]. There are emerging markets for carbon capture and utilisation (CCU) [10] – new symbiotic consumer species are therefore evolving, but altogether they will still use up just a small per cent of currently emitted CO_2 unless they can radically ramp-up their effectiveness.

The upshot is that we have to make a market artificially. To do this a colonising imperative for carbon capture and reduction has to be generated with a lure of profit. The obvious way to do this is to put a price on carbon. The income this produces can then be used for national and local government investment in CCS infrastructure exactly like those for sewage and garbage.

When I frequently refer to "we" in these discussions, I'm not just referring to "we in the West", but "we the human race". When we hear that Denmark has broken the world record for wind power in 2015, generating 42% of its energy [11], and that Britain expects shortly to have over 50% non-carbon energy generation, we in the West may feel we have a handle on climate change mitigation, so what's all the fuss about CCS?

However, the reality is that the real CO_2 damage is happening in developing economies. According to the Global CCS Institute, "*Deploying CCS in developing countries is critically important. The International Energy Agency estimates that to achieve global emissions reduction targets 70% of CCS projects will be in non-OECD countries by 2050*".

The chief obstacle is the scale of capital funding needed. We're talking big bucks here, and persuading governments to part with it, while there are so many other demands, not least subsidising alternative energy, is not expected to be easy. So where governments are not either willing or able to provide the legislatory incentive or the finance to create new nationwide utility services to control GHG emissions, including crucially America where scepticism is still rife, how do we get CCS back into first gear and rolled out all over the world at the speed and scale it desperately needs?

Consulting the *Junglenomics* handbook, Nature provides a potential answer: "finance capital" – in the form of investment grade bonds, as I will explain.

Financing CCS

Remember, money is the nutrient blood of the economic ecosystem. Wherever it flows it brings economic life. We have the power to manipulate that flow to serve our purposes, and no better purpose could be to clean up our economic act and establish symbiotic balance between economic and natural ecosystems as fast as we practically can. That symbiosis can only be achieved by creating the right niche conditions for economic actors to colonise and the bottom line is that it's got to pay.

There are essentially two methods for governments to raise capital to transfuse into such highly desirable causes – taxation and borrowing. Raising capital through taxation can be difficult to pull off, even in advanced economies, as the Cameron government climb-down on CCS funding has underlined. Government debt in the developed world is enormous, and the amounts needed to redouble our efforts to counter climate change are difficult to swing in democracies. Additional taxes on the big emitters of CO_2 to encourage them to find ways to reduce it inevitably impact on energy prices, and are therefore politically sensitive. As mentioned earlier, not long ago the British government declared it was going to cut the "green crap" because of its impact on energy prices. People are all too keen for energy to be greener so long as they don't have to pay for it.

In America, virtually any new infrastructure tax is a minefield. For example, in 2014 even a nickel on income taxes to pay for essential and desperately needed national road and bridge repairs proved hugely controversial and could not be agreed by Congress. What chance would there be of a carbon tax in the US, especially when there is so much scepticism on the subject? While alternative energy technologies currently receive huge financial backing, CCS projects do not. It's time to correct this imbalance. But where will the money come from?

There is more than one way to skin a proverbial cat. During the two world wars, Western governments issued debt known as "war bonds" to raise money for the Allied war effort. The bonds paid significant dividend income but were open-ended so they never needed to be repaid. The US converted them a while back, but it was only in 2014 that the British government finally announced it was going to repay all outstanding interest-bearing war bonds, or "Consols" as they were known, some of them dating back to before the Napoleonic Wars.

The current situation bears close comparison. It is no exaggeration to say that we are (or at least we should be) in a state of emergency. We are waging a new war, one against climate change, because its social, economic and environmental consequences are going to be every bit as damaging and disruptive as invasion by hostile foreign forces would be if we were to let it happen; and it is likely that no country will go unaffected. "Climate war" bonds are therefore an appropriate and workable way for governments to raise capital for major investment in anti-GHG technology.

But the question is, would investors buy these bonds if they were open-ended, given that the climate crisis is, as yet, nowhere near as conspicuous and immediate as conventional war? We are at the early stages, similar to the "phoney war" that preceded World War II – a time of disbelief and complacency among the general public. If we wait for climate change to make itself so apparent that investors flock to buy the bonds, by which time the investment needed will be many multiples higher, it will probably be too late.

However, there is an option in which climate bonds may never need to be repaid, and that is by involving the world's capital markets to attract some of the vast sums of private, corporate and national cash that is forever looking for safe and rewarding places to invest.

In order to raise investment capital on the bond markets you need two things above all – a dependable income stream and guaranteed security. Governments already raise such an income stream – through Polluter Pays taxes, carbon taxes, and cap-and-trade (the emissions trading scheme (ETS) that makes polluters buy permits to pollute, about which I will say more).

Here is the scenario: a government issues CCS bonds in the market that yield something significant – say 3% tax exempt. This rate means that every $1bn of cap-and-trade income potentially allows the raising of $33.3bn of CCS finance capital (the annual interest payable at 3% on a £33.3bn loan being $1bn).

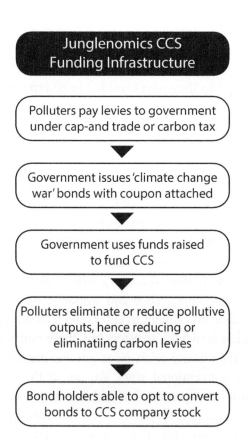

The raised capital can then be used to build a national and regional infrastructure for CCS, to include carbon capture units, transfer pipelines, distribution hubs and deep storage facilities. This can be done either by governments themselves, or by lending to the private sector, according to each government's political leanings.

In due course the bonds could be convertible into shares in the CCS companies. As each major emitter of CO_2 has its act cleaned up by adopting CCS measures, it converts from being a cap-and-trade payer (i.e. having to buy permits to pollute) to being a CCS company client, paying rent to the CCS company instead. At privatisation (if such is the case) the original bonds would become convertible into fully tradable publicly quoted CCS company stock. In this way CCS could be fast-tracked into a symbiotic role as a new "dung beetle" of major carbon-emitting industry and power generation.

CCS has powerful backers, not just major oil companies (Statoil originally proposed the idea) but also includes the International Energy Agency, which sees CCS as the most cost-effective way to produce around 20% of the CO_2 reductions needed. That's a very significant proportion. You might think – well they would say that, but in this case the facts bear it out. Many carbon-emitting industries now understand the need to cut their emissions radically in the near future. This is partly because they anticipate rapidly escalating carbon costs, and partly because of the pressure they are feeling from important customers down the line. For example, Coca-Cola, whose public image is paramount, has been giving grief to its substantially carbon-emitting plastic bottle manufacturers [12].

Teesside in Britain is the site of a concentration of high carbon-emitting industries, including the second largest blast furnace in Europe, and this makes it ideal as the home for the world's first CCS collective, where industries combine to deal with their carbon emissions together. The Teesside Collective hopes to create a template for industrial CCS for the world to follow. Its plans are impressive and well thought through. Technology is not a problem. The only real obstacle is funding, and that makes it a prime candidate for an initial issue of government-backed CCS bonds.

The EU has not been idle so far as developing CCS technology is concerned. They set up a fund, "NER 300", with an initial tranche of €1.1bn for "*innovative low carbon energy demonstration projects*", covering a wide range of CCS and renewable energy (RES) technologies. Further funding has been concentrated on the most successful projects. NER 300 has already leveraged private capital of nearly €2bn – so it's pretty clear there is a great deal of interest from the private sector and thus a lot of potential for the greater involvement that CCS bonds would allow.

The stage is therefore set for the real deal – a major commercial breakout of these technologies into the wider economy. There are, as yet, no viable alternatives for existing industries and power generators to switch to, CCS is the only option on the table and as such it needs to be seized upon energetically and wholeheartedly.

CCS controversy

It would be remiss of me not to mention that there is some vociferous opposition to carbon capture and storage. It has divided the international green movement like nothing, bar perhaps the thorny question of nuclear power generation. Two opposing camps have emerged for and against CCS within the green movement; they could be categorised variously as pragmatists and idealists.

The idealists' chief objections to CCS are twofold. Firstly, they believe that because it encourages, or at least allows, the ongoing exploitation of fossil fuels, CCS will take away from research and investment into clean energy such as solar and wind. It's an understandable view to take if that indeed were to become the case. However, under the kind of holistic, ecosystemic approach that is promoted in his book it can be avoided. Everyone knows fossil fuels aren't going to last forever, so ongoing research and development, particularly into solar energy sources, is a no-brainer, and no one is saying otherwise. But CCS could help give the world a window in which to equip itself with alternative energy sources for the long term. It is a pragmatic answer to a danger that is real and present, and that no amount of wishful thinking will spirit away.

Idealists complain that CCS is the "last hurrah" of a mature industry grasping on to existence. In this respect they are not far off being right, depending on the viewed timescales. Yet it's a very necessary hurrah. For whether we like it or not, not only is the world going to remain dependent on fossil fuel plants, cement factories, steelworks and the like for many decades to come, but some two billion more people in the developing world are due to link into the dirty fossil energy system by 2050.

To underline this, it has emerged from internal documents that the oil giant Shell, which publicly endorses moves to limit global warming, has privately dismissed any likelihood that governments will take the necessary steps to limit warming to the 2 degrees generally considered necessary to prevent extreme climate change. As a result they are aggressively continuing with oil exploration. And why wouldn't they when governments are subsiding fossil fuel exploration to the amount of $500 billion a year, which when external costs are factored in amounts to some $5.2 *trillion* a year – some 6.5% of the entire world's gross domestic product, according to the IMF's calculations?

As well-known Norwegian environmentalist Frederic Hauge, who I would place in the pragmatist green camp, was reported to have remarked: *"There is no black and white in the environmental discussion anymore"*. To fight climate change *"we need to go with whatever we can and I can't manage to do that without CCS, even if it means that our former enemies start to become our best allies."* [13]

Is CCS safe?

A rather more salient caution about CCS surrounds its safety. Large concentrations of CO_2 underground present a potential hazard were a large gaseous mass of it to escape pressurisation and leak to the surface. In 1986 Lake Nyos, a crater lake in the Cameroon, belched out an enormous cloud of carbon dioxide that killed almost everything breathing within a fifteen-mile radius in a matter of minutes, tragically including 1,746 people. This was an extremely rare natural event, but it illustrates what the potential hazards of carbon storage are.

A 2014 report by the Intergovernmental Panel on Climate Change (IPCC) claimed that *"Barriers to large-scale deployment of CCS technologies include concerns about the operational safety and long-term integrity of CO_2 storage as well as transport risks."* However, senior geologists [14] complained that the report was out of date and that great progress had been made in carbon storage and monitoring. They are adamant that carbon storage will be safe, and emphasise that safety is a central element in the CCS model.

Indeed, no one is seriously suggesting that carbon storage would not be every bit as carefully scrutinised and monitored as radioactive waste, which is a far more dangerous by-product of the nuclear power industry. That an incident will never happen cannot be guaranteed, but the risk is far less than the threat posed to people's lives, livelihoods and to the natural environment by climate change. Scientists at Edinburgh have come up with some comparisons on this, albeit somewhat quirky. They estimated that the odds of being killed by a CO_2 release are 1,000 times lower than the risk of being fatally struck by lightning in the US.

CCS conditional on responsible fossil fuel exploration

Nevertheless, although by my reckoning Nature's *Junglenomics* model strongly supports CCS, there is a strong caveat to supporting any technology that helps prolong the use of fossil fuels – one that is rarely discussed in CCS deliberations. The caveat relates to the many instances where indiscriminate fossil fuel exploration and exploitation is directly or indirectly destroying wilderness, including primary rainforest, as we will see in later chapters.

Because CCS is of such enormous financial benefit to fossil fuel companies, agreeing to its large-scale adoption provides an unmissable opportunity to impose strict limits on where and how future fossil fuel exploration may or may not take place. Not only would further wilderness degradation and destruction prolong an existing natural disaster, but without the strict protection of our priceless carbon-storing wilderness and natural forest, much or all of the emissions gains from CCS would be undermined and the benefit lost.

The bottom line of this highly important issue is that we can fret all we like about reducing GHG emissions, and criticise ourselves because we can't seem to make significant inroads quickly enough, but with a full CCS service infrastructure we could give ourselves breathing space to get full carbon-neutral and pollution-free energy sources online worldwide in an orderly manner. In the meantime, we could be secure in the knowledge that we have done what is immediately necessary to deflect an extremely dangerous threat to both Nature and us.

Securing the CCS income stream

The *Junglenomics* capitalisation plan for CCS that I proposed above is to lure in new economic actors with the resources to fund it without risk, by issuing income-yielding convertible bonds. But what about the all-important income stream needed to underwrite those bonds? To instil confidence among investors, this bond yield needs to be regular and dependable. The need for emergency underwriting in the case of shortfalls has to be avoided in order to maintain confidence in the stability of the investment, so guarantees would need to be given by the managing agency by maintaining a reserve fund.

There are two main potential sources for such regular income: a direct carbon tax, or a market mechanism such as carbon "cap-and-trade". Both have the added bonus of discouraging carbon emissions and are used to some degree in various parts of the world, but there are disagreements over which is more effective in doing so. The crucial question is – can either or both of these sources provide a reliable income stream to underwrite CCS bonds?

Carbon tax

Suffice to say that carbon tax is what it states. It is relatively easy and quick to set up and cheap to run, both virtues. It has its detractors, a main criticism being that large companies will negotiate exemption on viability and competition grounds to avoid "leakage" – carbon polluters moving abroad to less onerous tax regimes and carrying on business as usual. International agreement to levy a carbon tax even-handedly at common rates would overcome this.

A carbon tax is a classic Polluter Pays mechanism, and there is a strong argument that it is just, given that high carbon emitters are causing the problem. Its income is predictable, consistent and reliable. Although cap-and-trade (aka the emissions trading scheme, or ETS) is highly regarded in many quarters and may have a large role to play in the future, it is much more complex than a straightforward tax and has suffered a string of disappointing failures. Despite its promising credentials, years after its inception the question still hangs over it as to how effective it will be in reducing carbon emissions.

The emissions trading experiment

The fight against excessive carbon release first went global at the Kyoto summit in 1992. It was hailed by some as the turning point in our relationship with the planet. Its most significant achievements were enshrined in the "Kyoto Protocol", in which for the first time, targets were set that bound industrialised nations to reduce their CO_2 emissions by a set date (2012). Some environmentalists thought the agreements disappointingly unambitious, but it was at least a beginning. There were many effusive though inexpensive declarations of good intent, it's true, but some real beef too, most notably the introduction of a new trading arena with the potential to revolutionise biosphere management. This landmark initiative materialised in the form of a new global market for trading in carbon, and was the first instance of a major market-based solution being put forward to solve a market-generated problem.

The principle of carbon trading is ostensibly simple: industries that emit significant amounts of carbon into the atmosphere are obliged to buy an appropriate number of carbon "credits" to use as "offsets" against those emissions. In a national or regional scheme, such as the European Union's, the issuers of these credits are governments, and their recipients are carbon-emitting industries and power plants within the region.

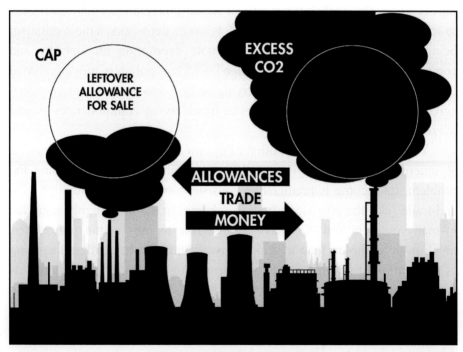

EU Carbon Emissions Trading System

On the other hand, in a fully international scheme the sellers of carbon credits can be foreign countries whose "carbon account" is in credit. This means one of two things: either their territory locks up more carbon than it releases – in primal forests and marshlands for example – or they have reduced their carbon emissions from a previously set base level and thus made a carbon "saving". They can do this perhaps by changes in land use such as altered farming methods, reforestation or new afforestation. Typically, a country with a lot of forest and relatively little industry will therefore qualify to receive most credits, which they can then sell on the open market to the highest overseas bidder. Those bidders are companies who have not, for whatever reason, reduced their target carbon output and must compensate by "offsetting" those emissions against other people's carbon savings elsewhere.

On paper at least, the international version of cap-and-trade is a three-way winning programme, or so its supporters claim. Firstly, it adds cost to new carbon emissions and thereby discourages it. Secondly it encourages the planting of carbon "sinks" in the form of carbon-absorbing biomass such as trees. And thirdly it should provide environmental security and employment for indigenous peoples.

The key to the success or failure of emissions trading lies in limiting the quantity of credits available – "capping" them so that they are sufficiently valuable yet not so exorbitant that they drive industries out of business; hence its alternative name, "cap-and-trade". Industry then has the opportunity to adapt through technological evolution rather than being forced either to pack their bags and head abroad to less stringent economic regimes, or go to the wall.

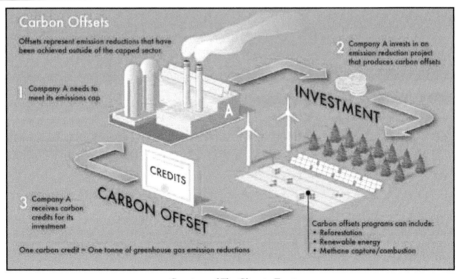

Courtesy of The Climate Trust

By reducing the available number of credits year-on-year, in theory less and less carbon gets released (carbon deflation). Industries that cannot comply or are not willing to find ways to reduce their carbon emissions will experience rising costs as the dwindling credits rise in price.

That's the theory, but how well does it work in practice? Certainly, it has detractors, for example the critics of California's proposed ETS, who claim that offsetting detracts from carbon-reduction projects and associated environmental protection at home in favour of improvements abroad, leaving polluting industries free to carry on as before.

A failed project, or a promising route to a cleaner world?

So how valuable is cap-and-trade? Has it reduced carbon emissions? And importantly in the context of CCS, can it produce a dependable income stream to underpin CCS bonds?

On the face of it the carbon emissions market appears to overflow with *Junglenomics* credentials. Recognising the service that wildernesses provide to the biosphere as carbon sinks could potentially attach real economic value to their survival. It should encourage the evolution of new, commercially motivated economic species in whose interests it is to protect and renew wilderness – potentially a classic symbiotic solution to man-made ecological problems. If successful, it would underpin the proposal put forward here that smart economics is the most effective way to protect nature against destructive exploitation.

From the start the effect of unveiling cap-and-trade was electric. Getting advance wind of it, North American energy utilities were quickly out of the starting gates as much as two years before Kyoto, which set out the stall for carbon trading. For example, a group of US and Canadian power companies backed The Nature Conservancy, an American conservation organisation, in its bid for a 14,000-acre patch of rainforest in Belize. In the process, they outbid a local group of Mennonite farmers who wanted to clear the land to grow soya beans.

This was just one of many other such promising carbon sink purchases. There were others in Ecuador, Costa Rica and Paraguay, confirming that carbon sink credits had quickly entered the marketplace as a fully fledged commodity.

The UK government showed its enthusiasm by setting up an independent

ETS, which the European Union then went on to incorporate into its own trial scheme. Although numerous national schemes have since been set up elsewhere, none has exceeded the size and complexity of the European experiment.

Unfortunately, in setting the pace for the rest of the world the European Union ETS has come up against some serious difficulties. The worst was in 2010 when a raft of major thefts, scams and frauds were uncovered. Public confidence was badly shaken at what was seen as lax standards and inept security.

Whether or not that judgement was harsh, the increasing complexity and multiplicity of European carbon trading mechanisms provided a rich breeding ground for cybercriminal activity, which appeared unforeseen and for which they were unprepared. Although robust counteraction has now been taken, from a *Junglenomics* perspective such opportunistic behaviour is merely another entirely predictable colonising scenario. It would be naïve to expect that parasitical activity in ETS markets would be any less likely to happen than in any other market – and in Nature for that matter, where opportunities inevitably lure opportunists. The simplification and standardisation of what has quickly developed into an intricate, jargon-filled system of complex financial instruments, cannot come too soon.

There are other reasons why governments are not ready to go international with emissions trading just yet. One is that they do not want to expose their home industries to potentially ruinous costs from an unpredictable worldwide market in which carbon credit prices could fluctuate wildly – a nightmare for any business needing to buy them. Another lies in accreditation uncertainties: in order for the scheme to go fully international, it must link up and trade with nations whose legal framework, contract record and political stability is less than ideal, potentially exposing valuable home industries to unfair competition.

Perhaps the best way for governments to avoid the extreme price fluctuations of the uncertainties of the open market is to lock in individual businesses to specific, well-managed and fully accredited carbon sink projects abroad. Many such conservation carbon link-ups have been created in countries such as Paraguay, Belize, Bolivia and even Russia.

However, many ecologists think this kind of arrangement fails as it is of little use in protecting threatened primary forest, and hence for biodiversity conservation. For example, offsetting carbon emissions in

North America against relatively safe carbon sink forests in Brazil is doing no one any favours. In fact, it often interferes with traditional native management of forest, now recognised as among the most successful ways to preserve this land.

Undoubtedly, some kind of fully international credit system (as opposed to offsetting against aforementioned land that is not under real threat) would be preferable because by focusing only on genuinely threatened areas it conserves wilderness and its wildlife at the same time as reducing the release of carbon through logging and peat burning. Altogether it is estimated that between 12% and 20% of the world's carbon release comes from primary forest destruction alone; and tropical forests single-handedly absorb about 15% of the carbon we release [15].

The ideal solution would be a fully functioning, international market in carbon sequestration units where common prices were determined by supply and demand like any other internationally traded commodity. Without a common international price indication for a commodity it is difficult to attract sustained demand or investment, because consumers and producers cannot make logical, educated decisions on whether to buy or sell [16]. And as we will see, *Junglenomics* likewise points to the setting up of a similar, open market strategy with its own built-in guarantees.

As ever in complex new systems, there are many problems yet to overcome. Opinions also remain divided as to whether carbon markets are even viable. Things like the accuracy of current methods of measuring carbon emissions and absorption, compliance rules, baselines, eligibility and standardised verification procedures all still need refining. The willingness of developing countries, who own most of the forest sinks, to comply is also sometimes less than enthusiastic if they see it as restricting their future development. And the EU set-up has been widely criticised for distributing far too many credits, so much so that at one point their value even fell to zero. As a result, its industry has been able to carry on polluting at minimal cost, undermining the whole concept of cap-and-trade. This is under review, and what the EU hope will be the solution is to be rolled out in January 2019, when its "Market Stability Reserve" scheme will be launched. The plan is to stabilise the price of carbon credits by bringing down the permit surpluses that have beleaguered the system. Anything would be better than the current fiasco.

The bottom line is that while the ETS has many promising attributes, it is nowhere near the finished article. The widely fluctuating price of carbon credits is a particular concern. It means that the European Union ETS is not yet in a strong enough position to provide a reliable income stream to underwrite anything, let alone the issuing of bonds to fund CCS investment. Without a guaranteed minimum price for carbon credits, governments might find themselves having to dig deep into their pockets to cover CCS bond income to their holders, and for certain they will not like that.

A carbon tax may be something of a blunt instrument, but it is a good short-term stopgap to get things moving right now in the world's hour of need, with a longer term focus on emissions trading to follow as ETS matures and its glitches are overcome.

Emissions trading in America

In the US there are plenty of problems with emissions trading too. A number of states due to participate in regional voluntary schemes from 2012, suddenly backed off. The state of Arizona, for example, found it could not justify hampering its economy and jobs market under a multistate cap-and-trade scheme in the absence of a level playing field among national and international rivals. Its governor announced early in 2010 that it would join the thirteen states and provinces that had taken up only "observer status" in the scheme, which only asked firms for voluntary monitoring of their carbon emissions. This was a blow to the Obama administration's efforts to establish a national scheme, which was already facing fierce opposition from Republicans and had stalled in the Senate.

Until the arrival of the Trump administration there was some hope for the US. In 2015 President Obama unveiled his enlightened and appropriately ambitious "Clean Energy Plan". This aimed to establish set carbon pollution standards for power plants within a set time frame, for which they would need to adopt a combination of measures. These included increasing the use of cleaner energy sources such as natural gas, or better still, emission-free sources such as nuclear, solar and wind. To achieve this, emissions trading, energy efficiency and CCS were all expected to play a role in state plans. The target date for full compliance is 2030, by when Obama hoped that 6 billion tonnes of GHG emissions would have been saved.

As could be expected, though, opposition from vested interests was vociferous, with 24 states launching legal challenges on the basis that it greatly exceeds the authority granted by Congress. They cite many of the long-held arguments – that it will hurt the coal mining industry, raise energy costs for consumers and risk electricity reliability, despite Obama and the Environmental Protection Agency's (EPA) solid assurance that it need not if states tailor the template model provided to their individual circumstances. With so much at stake it is shaping up to be a battle worth watching, though the teeth of the EPA seem to have been substantially drawn by the Trump presidency, with the insertion of an "affordable clean energy rule", which puts polluting industry back in the driving seat. As opposed to the 32% reduction in harmful emissions (from 2005 levels) that the Obama 'clean power' plan was due to achieve by 2030, the EPA says that even should all states adopt these new technology-based efficiencies – emissions will go down merely by around 1%.

So, despite all the dire prognostications about climate change from climate scientists, more than two decades after Kyoto, carbon-trading schemes in America and elsewhere are still in an emergent stage and remain under fire on many fronts. This is not just from those who do not recognise human activity as a factor in global warming, but also from politicians and business representatives trying to protect the competitiveness of their industries and the jobs of those they employ. It's a different context, but a familiar story of myopic resistance to essential progress, without which we would have remained in the Dark Ages. If the Luddites and their like had won out, industry and technology could never have achieved today's sophisticated panoply of economic fauna and the huge prosperity and health benefits that have accompanied it.

Yet there is something in the wind as I write that could become a game changer for carbon reduction: the "Energy Innovation and Carbon Dividend Act". Supported by both Republicans and Democrats, the Act proposes to raise levies on greenhouse gas emissions, and, to offset the passing of the extra costs to the public, to return it to them directly at a fixed rate ($500 per person per year). You might think these would simply cancel each other out, but despite the annual windfall, consumers will inevitably seek out cheaper energy deals, and those deals will be increasingly found in the non-levied green energy sector, leaving them with spare cash to spend on other things. The injection of so much cash is expected to boost the economy by $1.3 trillion and bring over 2 million new jobs, while reducing carbon emissions by 40% over the next 12 years.

The drawback is that under the Act, levies on exports will be refunded to businesses. This means they can continue to export carbon-costly goods to the rest of the world unhindered. The answer must be that other countries start to operate the same scheme to create a level playing field internationally. This would mean that carbon intensive US exports would be taxed abroad, pressurising them to reduce emissions while incentivising greener alternatives all over the world instead of only in the US.

A reality check for business

But despite some reluctance to fully commit, not all companies will need to be dragged kicking and screaming to the environmental way. All over the world businesses have come to realise that the writing is on the wall. Sooner or later the carbon market will take off and they had better prepare for it now. When even a captain of industry like Ron Oxburgh, chairman of the UK branch of the oil giant Shell, sees fit to publicly remark [17], *"No one can be comfortable at the prospect of continuing to pump out the amounts of carbon dioxide that we are at present... But if we don't have sequestration I see very little hope for the world"*, it is a sure sign that it is becoming accepted at the highest business levels that ecological sustainability and shareholder interests are not irreconcilable.

Eventually clean energy sources will take over. But in the meantime, levy-funded carbon sequestration gives real, tangible value to the environment the only way markets understand and respect – crisp dollar bills. It is expensive in its development stages, yes, but any scheme to reconstruct the very foundations of the Industrial Revolution worldwide is bound to be. Yet this is not a spurious expense, and it is not money wasted. It is the price for conserving essential environmental services that stabilise the climate, and for avoiding the inevitable misery that will undoubtedly ensue if we do not.

There is no backup plan. If we are to have any hope of limiting greenhouse-gas-generated climate change some method of revaluing environmental services has to be found and built into pollutive industrial balance sheets. However it comes to be funded, CCS is the only viable method on the table. And for this, or indeed for any other GHG emission remedy that costs businesses money, international cooperation is important.

Fear of handing easy advantage to overseas competitors is very politically sensitive and one of the chief obstacles to establishing any form of national carbon pricing, especially in the US. Getting a level international playing field so that companies who green up are not disadvantaged by those from non-complaint regimes is therefore an urgent objective, one that will be addressed in a more general context towards the end of this book once the other pieces of the *Junglenomics* jigsaw are in place.

The next such piece is the world's treatment of that incalculably valuable resource – the natural world.

1. *World Resources Institute 2017*
2. *Intergovernmental Panel on Climate Change*
3. *M Totten, World Resources Institute/Forest Trends: Emerging Markets for Storing Carbon in Forests*
4. *World Resources Institute*
5. *Price Waterhouse Cooper report 2011*
6. *E.g. Sullivan & Sivak 2012*
7. *A senior Research Engineer in the Massachusetts Institute of Technology Energy Initiative and an expert on CCS*
8. *January 2016*
9. *Enhanced oil recovery, urea fertiliser production, food processing, preservation and packaging, beverage carbonation, coffee decaffeination, pharmaceuticals, horticulture and fire suppression, winemaking, pulp and paper processing, water treatment, inerting, steel manufacture, metalworking, electronics and pneumatics, all of which only consumes a very small percentage of industrial carbon produced (Parsons Brinckerhoff) https://www.geos.ed.ac.uk/ccs/Meetings/edinburgh-sep-2011/Smith_ IPA_HW11.pdf*
10. *For example, enhanced coal bed methane recovery, algal bio-fixation and bio-fuel production, enhanced geothermal systems (using CO_2 as a working fluid), bauxite residue processing, power generation (with CO_2 as a working fluid), carbonate mineralisation (aggregate production), polymer processing and CO_2 concrete curing, renewable methanol and formic acid production (Parsons Brinckerhoff)*
11. *Energinet.dk*
12. *Teesside CCS Collective 2015*
13. *The Guardian, March 2015*
14. *E.g. Stuart Haszeldine, a professor of CCS at Edinburgh University*
15. *State and Trends of the Carbon Market June 2011*
16. *K Hamilton, U Chokkalingam, M Bendana (State of The Forest Carbon Markets 2009)*
17. *The Guardian, 17th June 2004*

PART 2
The Natural World:
New Ways to End the Devastation

"We cannot command nature except by obeying her"
Sir Francis Bacon (1561-1626)

Chapter 6
An Irresistible Force of Nature

The scrabble for natural resources

First the bad news. Industrial and power plant emissions, human waste and the combustion engine may be the chief sources of pollution in the world, but unfortunately our assault on the natural environment is not confined to noxious fallout. There is another major battlefront, and it too has become critical to the well-being of the planet, perhaps even to its long-term ability to support mankind. This is the rampant, ongoing colonisation and degradation of natural habitat, and it is crying out for innovative solutions.

Every year vast areas of wilderness are lost to agriculture, and agricultural land is turned to urban and industrial development. Notwithstanding climate change, this is the single greatest threat to land-based species worldwide. Things are getting bad for the natural world – indeed so bad that if you once thought you could name the world's most endangered species you now need to think again. It isn't only tigers, giant pandas and orangutans that are threatened with extinction, but the majority of life on Earth.

If you find that hard to swallow, consider this: read this book in just one day and by the time you finish it some *ninety thousand* acres of rainforest will have been felled – that's about one acre every second [1]. In those same 24 hours, somewhere between three and thirty species will have become extinct [2]. If you take a week or a month to read it – well, you can do the sums. These numbers may seem exaggerated until you consider that another study has found that between 2000 and 2012 alone there was a staggering net loss of the world's primal rainforest – one and a half *million* square kilometres of it – an area the size of Mongolia [3]. No, you didn't misread those numbers and dates – that vast-scale devastation of natural forest did indeed take place in just twelve years.

Rainforest Destruction

The truth is there is a deforestation massacre going on in the worlds' great forests, an ecological tragedy that is being repeated all over the equatorial zone where most of the world's biodiversity is found.

And there is no let-up in store. For example, official figures show that not only has over half of Indonesia's rainforest been felled in just a few years [4], but some two thirds of what remains is also due to be levelled in the near future for oil palm and acacia plantations. The rate of rainforest loss in South America slowed considerably between 2004 and 2011, but according to satellite imagery [5], in 2014-5 rates rocketed again, more than doubling the previous year [6]. Around the world in general the loss of tropical forests accelerated by 62% between the 1990s and 2010 [7] demonstrating that despite all the publicity and efforts to prevent it, forest loss is out of control. According to a recent study, one result is that nearly 150,000 orangutans had been lost in Borneo from 1999 to 2015, chiefly due to habitat loss. Unless something happens to stop it soon, it won't be long before nearly all the world's tropical forests will vanish.

To this tragedy one must add a long list of other land-based over-exploitation encompassing not only rainforests, but also savannahs, wetlands, mountains, rivers and lakes; indeed, almost every natural environment accessible to man is being degraded in some way or another.

The oceans, as we will see later, are far from exempt either. The result is that as much as 2% of all plant species are estimated to be disappearing each year, and the number on the 2008 IUCN "Red List" of endangered species passed 44,000. Those in imminent danger of extinction increased from just over 10,000 in 1995 to nearly 17,000 in 2008. Included are nearly a third of all amphibians and corals, and a quarter of all mammals. The latest figures look even more alarming (see table).

About 41% of amphibian species and more than a quarter of mammals are threatened with extinction.
About half of coral reefs have been lost in the last 30 years.
The global populations of 3,706 monitored vertebrate species — fish, birds, mammals, amphibians, and reptiles — declined by nearly 60% from 1970 to 2012.
25,821 species of 91,523 assessed for the 2017 "Red List" update were classified as "threatened".
Of these, 5,583 were "critically" endangered, 8,455 "endangered", and 11,783 "vulnerable".
African elephant numbers dropped to 415,000 in 2016, down about 111,000 over 10 years.
There are an estimated 8.7 million plant and animal species on our planet. This means about 86% of land species and 91% of sea species remain undiscovered.
Of the ones we do know, 1,204 mammal, 1,469 bird, 1,215 reptile, 2,100 amphibian, and 2,386 fish species are considered threatened.
Also threatened are 1,414 insect, 2,187 mollusc, 732 crustacean, 237 coral, 12,505 plant, 33 mushroom, and six brown algae species.
Annual economic losses as a result of deforestation and forest degradation alone may be as high as $4.5 trillion (3.6 trillion euros).

And as if all that wasn't alarming enough, we now learn that populations of the world's vertebrates have halved in size in just the last 40 years and that 60% of wildlife has been wiped out since 1970[8]. The most diverse and ecologically important regions of the natural world are continuing to disappear at such an disturbing speed that scientists say extinctions are now running at a thousand times the rate they were before we humans took over the world [9]. Predictions are that this will rise to *ten thousand* times.

This level of extinction is a singularly rare event, something the planet has not witnessed since a giant asteroid plunged into the Earth some 65 million years ago causing the great *Cretaceous-Palaeogene* extinction that famously killed off the dinosaurs. Indeed, the situation has become so bad that many scientists tell us we are causing an extinction event comparable to just five others in the entire history of life on Earth, and that to avoid extinctions on the scale anticipated by, among others, Richard Leakey and Roger Lewin [10], radical action is urgently needed.

While the economic invasion and destruction taking place in the world's wildernesses is extremely serious, according to some scientists it is nothing compared to what is to yet come as the world population rises and the demand for food-growing land and timber increases. For example, a study headed by David Tilman illustrates some of the potential consequences of the failure to develop effective, integrated international policies on the environment in the very near future. The study forecast that over the next 50 years the increasing demand for meat will mean that the requirement for new farmland worldwide will take up a new area the size of the US. This will probably result in the destruction of the vast majority of the rainforests and savannah grasslands in Latin America and Central Africa, home to a large proportion of the Earth's biological diversity.

Tilman's team also predicted that eutrophication will double or triple, and that the "marine dead zone" the size of New Jersey that has already formed in the Gulf of Mexico as a result of agricultural run-off down the Mississippi is a sinister precursor of things to come. Vast emerging cattle and pig factories containing as many as ten thousand or more animals produce as much sewage as a city, yet they are not required to treat it as cities must. Astonishingly, they fall outside legislation for both populations and industry. The report concludes that ever more widespread and more intensive farming will cause an unprecedented loss of biodiversity and cause more environmental damage than even global warming.

Another study released by the International Food Policy Research Institute [11] agreed. It shows that degraded soils, dried out aquifers, polluted waters and the conversion of natural forest to agricultural land are seriously threatening food supplies. Although we produce 24% more food than in 1961, and it is 40% cheaper, irrigation is using up supplies of fresh water and salinating farmland, affecting 1% more of farmland each year. Population growth and socio-economic development have rapidly increased water demand, especially from agriculture, which comprises 70% of world freshwater usage. Along with renewable but limited water resources and the effects of climate change this is causing an increasing number of regions to suffer water scarcity and chronic droughts [12].

With a significant proportion of the world's population already hungry or starving, predicted climate change (especially in Southern Africa) and an expected extra four and a half billion mouths to feed, will enormously exacerbate existing problems within 20 years. For example, soil degradation is already costing India between US$2.5 and $6.5 billion per year [13]. This is because some 57% of the country's land is affected by erosion and nutrient deficiency caused by poor agricultural management and deforestation.

These and other studies drive home the reality that it is rapidly becoming not optional, but essential to ensure that agribusinesses tidy up their act and that the world's remaining wildernesses are protected for the long term.

The accumulative effect of all this represents an impending ecological tragedy of epic proportions, and one could be forgiven for believing the world's oceans and land masses are teetering on the edge of an unprecedented crisis. If that isn't scary I don't know what is.

Is Nature to blame?

So who or what is at fault here?

You might say we are of course. But are we really? My initial feelings some four decades ago on discovering just how profligate we were becoming with the natural environment was the same as a great many other people – anger and despair, followed by depression. This is what later drove me to try to understand it. My anger was directed towards what I, at that time, saw as greedy over-exploiters getting rich at the cost of environments that have taken millions of years to evolve, without any regard for the future. I believed that the natural environment is something over which the human race has stewardship rather than ownership, and that generations to come have both a need and a right to inherit a planet still brimming with natural riches, not a degraded, depopulated shadow of its former glory.

Back then, direct action and retribution was my gut reaction: confiscate the perpetrators' equipment, close them down, lock them up and throw away the key. Yet at the same time I had an overwhelming feeling of helplessness that powerful forces beyond our control were playing out to an inevitable, tragic end.

However, although I haven't changed my view on our duty of stewardship, I have since come to adopt a more sanguine view on what to do about it.

Recognition of the resource-colonising imperative and its economic expression in the form of the profit imperative, had shown me that all such over-exploitation on land and sea, by humans or non-humans, is in reality entirely *natural*. In other words, Nature is to blame. That is not to say that individual greedy and callous people are not sometimes involved, only that what is happening in the whole wide world is far greater than them. Nature creates a colonising tide that is simply too powerful to be resisted by any animal, even a clever 21st-century ape like us. In the end over-exploitation happens for one simple reason – because it provides life-sustaining resources. In our special case, it is the universal resource – money – that is the lure. It is as natural as spiders catching flies. It really is as simple and fundamental as that.

Resource colonisation as a *force majeure*

It is all too easy to protest that over-exploiters ought to know better; but it is futile to do so. That they do not know better is in fact so natural that it is totally predictable. It is as predictable as the trade in heroin, Kalashnikovs, ivory, or for that matter low-grade debt. It is an anthropological *force majeure*. This is a fact not just of economic life, but of *all* life.

Over-exploitation of resources in economies is therefore a classic indicator of the all-powerful colonisation imperative at work. Where a potentially viable niche is discovered, it will be – indeed it *must* be – occupied so long as it remains viable, almost whatever that may involve. As a result, the world consumption of environmentally expensive goods is rising year after year when it needs urgently to stabilise or better still, fall.

So if it is economically viable for loggers and farmers to cut down and burn huge areas of pristine rainforest, and people discover that it is viable, then although it may not happen today, sooner or later that is exactly what will happen. If some Balkan Mountains are economically viable as sources of aggregate, or Californian rivers of water, or Australian hills of minerals, or Arctic basins of oil, then they too will be taken in due observance of the same natural process. Any legislation, quota, or taxation that may be involved is relevant only to the degree that it may affect the all-important equation at the heart of all such matters – the *viability* equation.

There is another important factor in this: it is all very well to get emotionally exercised about the ways of techno-hunter-gatherers but there is a reverse side to this coin. Even poorly managed and environmentally destructive industries can have a very important role to play – they create many jobs. As such they invaluably help fill the stomachs of the ever-increasing masses of human beings on this planet.

One can therefore see how very important it is that counteraction be constructive, designed less to destroy livelihoods than to encourage them to reform. This isn't easy, but because economies are virtual ecosystems, the answers to such conundrums can be found in the workings of the natural world.

So who is doing something to stop this merciless onslaught on the natural world? Although many ecologists and some economists speak against it loudly and clearly, in the end the buck stops with governments. It is for them alone to decide the balance between economic exploitation and environmental conservation according to their political and economic priorities. This is why those of us who care deeply have to do our utmost to bring pressure to bear on them, not in anger and frustration, but with the new, practical and proven plan explained in this book – Nature's plan.

Not long ago few governments in developed nations wanted to be seen as pro exploitation in the development versus conservation struggle. Green credentials were a must; providing that governments put their policies where their mouths were and attached high enough values to the conservation of wildlife and rural and wilderness areas, you would think that that should have rapidly become victory for conservation.

Unfortunately, it is not the way of the world as we currently experience it. There are titanic financial forces at work. Just as the brambles, nettles, rodents and destructive bugs that besiege my house and garden are no respecters of artificial boundaries, nor are their economic counterparts. All are driven by the same irresistible impulse to colonise resources – resource hunger, and today the economic-colonising imperative is as firmly in the driving seat as ever. Creating or restoring economic growth has become the priority of governments worldwide. Conservation of Nature is largely something to postpone for better times.

This is at best foolhardy; at worst criminal.

Of course, there are many individuals and organisations valiantly striving from dawn to dusk to protect and conserve the Earth's precious remaining biodiversity. These do extraordinary and noble work in the face of overpowering odds, and of one thing we can be very sure – things would be a great deal worse by now if it were not for them. But despite the billions of dollars that have been channelled their way over the decades the statistics show all too clearly that they are not winning through. They are swimming against the overwhelmingly powerful tide of resource-hungry economic forces, and rapidly losing ground. Turning that tide so that they find themselves swimming *with* it rather than against it demands a revolution in understanding and a creative new strategy like that I am proposing here.

Facing the facts

We need firstly to acknowledge the overdevelopment of land, over-exploitation of resources and overconsumption of environmentally expensive goods are the three most serious issues facing the natural world; and secondly that to solve these problems the issue must be addressed by all nations collectively. The preservation of the Earth's diminishing natural capital is a priority, and there are no forms of natural capital more important than undeveloped, biodiversity-supporting, carbon-absorbing places such as forests, wetlands and other wilderness. These are not inexhaustible, and ecologists are unanimous in declaring that they are essential to the long-term well-being of our planet, and hence of the human race.

The need to feed a growing world population and the resulting agricultural land rush going on all over the world illustrates how irreversibly entangled mankind's fate is with that of the natural environment. I am in no doubt whatsoever that the rebalancing of our relationship with Nature to ensure long-term environmental security has become a pivotal issue. Get this wrong and much of the work that so many have done will be wasted. We would take a large step backwards just at the final moment when we so desperately need to progress.

Yet any old policies will not do, for we have got it wrong too many times already. These new policies will impact on all the great areas of environmental concern to such a degree that if we fail to properly understand their implications before enacting them we may as well do nothing at all. The problems we face are not limited to specific areas of the globe or to any one area of activity. They range from priceless Amazonian rainforest to the fields, woodlands and meadows of our home countryside. There is no hierarchy of importance implied in this – all need to be beneficiaries of the global revolution in natural resource management that must come soon if we are to avoid social and economic chaos for generations to come.

That is why our rethink has to be profound, and the policies that emerge must address all these problems with equal scientific and economic rigour. I will begin with primal forests and suggest how they could be protected in perpetuity by harnessing the very forces that threaten to consign them to oblivion.

1.   Rainforest Foundation
2.   World Wildlife Fund
3.   University of Maryland Study 2013
4.   The Guardian
5.   IMAZON
6.   Philip Fearnside of INPA
7.   Geophysical research Letters: doi.org/2h7
8.   Jurriaan M de Vos, John Gittleman, Patrick Stephens et al, 2014
9.   World Wildlife Fund; Sept. 2014
10. The Sixth Extinction; 1995
11. July 7, 2001
12. Aquastat: the Food and Agriculture Organisation of the UN
13. Scientists at the Tata Energy Research Institute in New Delhi

Chapter 7
Biodiversity Markets

How the 2008 Bonn Global Conference provided inspired thinking on reforming markets to be more environmentally benign along *Junglenomics* principles

Every year about $20 billion is raised from private philanthropy and public finance to help with conservation around the world. But there is good evidence [1] that this huge amount of money is only managing to slow biodiversity loss a little. Somehow the financial resources dedicated to the conservation and repair of ecosystems needs to be increased dramatically. More and more it is being understood that the best way to get additional money to the problem is not to send it there, but to *lure* it. To this end a lot of interest is being shown in finding market solutions to the decline of ecosystems.

This interest was crystallised at an important global conference on biodiversity that took place in Bonn, Germany in 2008 [2]. It attracted an extraordinary number of experts – some 7,000 of them – from over 190 nations. Representatives from around 250 environmental, conservation and development aid organisations accompanied them. They came together to discuss something they regarded as a revolution in conservation: halting the current wave of extinctions by making the saving of biodiversity profitable [3]. The core plan was to ascribe monetary value to forests, marshes, mangroves, reefs and so on – not as commodities for consumption but as service providers essential to the healthy functioning of the Earth's biosphere, and by extension to us humans and our economies. At the time this was music to my ears because in effect it was a plan to revalue Nature.

It was not unprecedented. Some years earlier the American ecological economist Robert Costanza had estimated the annual value of the services

Nature provides for mankind at a massive $33 trillion per annum – 1.8 times the entire world GNP at the time. This was based on how much it would cost us to do for ourselves that which Nature already does for free.

Valuing natural services

However, scientists meeting at Bonn now also began to try to ascribe monetary values to individual species. Take bees for instance: for pollinating important crop plants all over the world economists estimated their worth at $2 to $8 billion per annum. And because they filter water and in doing so eliminate the need to build additional sewage treatment plants, reeds growing along the banks of Germany's Elbe river were credited with $11.9 million in annual savings. The coastal mangrove forest in Pakistan's Balochistan province is both a prime breeding ground for harvestable fish species and a primary protection against flooding. Putting these two services together produces an annual price tag of about $2,200 per acre.

Other examples cited at the conference included Scottish salt marshes at $1,555 per hectare for mussel growing, and $20 million a year for Germany's Müritz National Park. Put the whole vast array of such services together into a global network of specially protected areas and they could produce about $5 billion in annual revenue from tourism, climate protection, nutrient cycles and water supply [3].

Costa Rica came in for much praise at the Bonn conference. It was singled out as a model of conservation virtue and a pioneer at bringing market solutions to biodiversity loss. Bioprospecting, the search for new useful products from Nature, also featured strongly; it was hailed as a potential giant money-spinner for forests and indigenous peoples. Also it was claimed that billions of dollars a year could be made by selling tropical forests as carbon sinks.

The Bonn delegates also addressed an extremely important but thorny issue – the protection of the old-growth forests in which so much of the world's biodiversity is found. The Congo basin, for example, is home to the world's second largest uninterrupted forest. Not only have biologists identified more than 10,000 plant and over 400 mammal species, but it is also one of the world's most important carbon storage systems.

Just as importantly, the forests also support many human beings. Some indigenous peoples gain a living from slash-and-burn farming and from forest products, especially timber; others live in traditional tribal communities as they have for centuries. One would therefore think it not unreasonable that the world should help pay for its protection in the face of a destructive onslaught of biblical proportions.

Yet there is no defensible reason why the world should expect farmers and loggers to lay down their chainsaws and render pulp mills idle just to make up for the damage the rest of the world is doing – at least not without adequate recompense. While the current carbon offset system rewards new forestation and forest regeneration, it does not yet reward the maintenance of original standing forest; this is because, much to many people's frustration, the Kyoto Protocol carbon sink rules do not allow the accreditation of *avoided* deforestation [5]. The current Kyoto rules may be good for encouraging reforestation in once denuded countries like Costa Rica, but they do nothing to protect precious remaining old forest growth.

To my mind this is not only wrong in principle, it is also heavily prejudiced against the huge quantity of biodiversity that make its home in forests. The effect is that under this system pristine forest must first be cleared before it can earn conservation income to restore them. But as well as releasing carbon, cutting down ancient forests causes devastating ecosystem disruption and biodiversity loss. Once shattered it is impossible to recreate the complex, finely balanced forest ecosystems that have taken so many thousands of years to evolve.

Ideas to tackle this problem were also aired at Bonn. For example, the issuing of "forest certificates" by countries with large areas of forest as a kind of currency to be bought by businesses that exceed their nationally set CO_2 emissions allowance. Selling forests and wetlands as greenhouse gas sinks in this way has already lit up the eyes of governments of countries like Indonesia, Guyana, Brazil and Papua New Guinea, who still have plenty of them. The idea is that the money earned this way could go towards looking after the forests as well as providing employment. The UN-REDD Programme, which was seeded at Kyoto and which I will come to in a moment, was in due course to embody such ideas.

Harnessing market forces

There were too many promising ideas and projects in the Bonn melting pot to list them all here. What stood out for me though was the growing enthusiasm for market-based protection of the environment. Not everyone agrees with this concept and the debate about it goes on, however there seems to be a gathering momentum for what may become a global revolution in environmental management.

It certainly ticks many *Junglenomics* boxes. In particular, although it requires laws to set up its parameters, creating markets to protect Nature is essentially a systemic rather than an authoritarian way of dealing with the decline of environments. It encourages the emergence of a new set of colonising economic species to counter environmental decline as a matter of self-interest. It harnesses the power of market forces, not to destroy industry, but only to compel it to mitigate its destructive external costs.

It turns out that Graciela Chichilnisky and Geoffrey Heal of Columbia University's Earth Institute and other like-minded economists had also been convinced for years that harnessing market forces could provide better and cheaper solutions to man-made environmental problems [6]. They also advocated bioprospecting agreements like that made between Costa Rica's National Institute of Biodiversity (INBio) and the drugs giant Merck back in 1992. This gave them a substantial inducement package including a research budget, royalties on new drugs to emerge, technical assistance and training for Costa Rican scientists, as well as a promise to donate half of any royalties they receive to local conservation efforts. This too looked very much like a sound strategy for rebalancing the economic ecosystem.

So while I had been working to make a fundamental case for using the power of markets to conserve nature, had making business out of saving biodiversity already caught on to a great extent anyway? Had some form of *Junglenomics* already evolved? Could I sit back confident in the knowledge that the world had now solved the problem?

Unintended consequences

When I first read about these developments I must admit that for a moment I had doubts about whether the long years I had spent on this project been superseded by events; that perhaps the *Junglenomics* model had already been recognised and adopted under other guises. But on looking further, that moment soon passed.

I had seen that while market power can be a powerful weapon for good, it is very much a double-edged sword. To deploy it without being fully aware of its dark side is to play with fire; more harm than good may all too easily be done.

The Law of Unintended Consequences has proved the bane of many conservation efforts. Think, for example, of the results of the much-heralded biofuels revolution – the palm oil and sugar cane fiascos; and of the vast sisal fields of Madagascar planted on forest-cleared land to help fulfil the new "green" demand for recyclable packaging; and think too of the equally destructive environmental and social repercussions of mass soya planting. All were hailed as planet saviours; but through lack of foresight their negative outcomes were not anticipated. Instead of curing problems they exacerbated them or created new ones.

Time and again perverse economic incentives have emerged and caught policymakers by surprise. Once the wheels have begun to roll on any big, highly profitable market it is incredibly difficult even to change its course let alone stop it: the huge financial investment they require creates a powerful momentum. It is all very well to be wise after the event, but the fact is we need to be a lot wiser before such events than we have been.

I have long been convinced that getting new biodiversity-benefiting equations as right first time as humanly possible can only come from a thorough understanding, firstly of the real power behind markets – the ubiquitous and uncompromising colonising imperative – and secondly of the immense value of Nature's paradigm for balanced coexistence between species.

Besides, everything that was discussed at Bonn is still merely on the drawing board: the arguments may be compelling, but as yet there is little real action. So I set myself the task of discovering where, how and to what effect market economics was already being applied to rescuing and conserving biodiversity, and how it could be improved and accelerated towards short-term fruition.

1.   *Phil. Trans. R. Society B360, 255-268*
2.   *9th Conference of the Parties to the United Nations Convention on Biological Diversity*
3.   *Spiegel Online International 23rd May 2008*
4.   *Andrew Balmford et al.*
5.   *IUCN-Shell Report p.58, 2010/Science in Society Archive*
6.   *New Scientist 2172 1999*

Chapter 8
Seeing REDD

The REDD Programme

Living trees absorb and lock away large amounts of carbon, so when they are felled and decompose or are burned they release that carbon into the atmosphere. Because deforestation is taking place so much faster than new forestation (afforestation) it contributes very considerably to climate change. It accounts for around 17% of world carbon emissions, which makes it the third highest cause of increased carbon, behind energy production and industry.

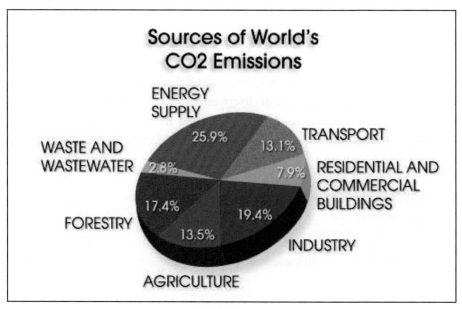

Courtesy http:www.pbs.org

Most crop forests are replanted after felling, so the chief casualty is ancient forest, which is very often replaced with cash crops like palm oil and soya that lock away only a fraction of the carbon that forests do. Tropical forests are also home to a rich diversity of flora and fauna – somewhere around 70% of known species (plus, since an estimated 80% of the Earth's species are yet to be discovered, very many more as yet unknown ones) – and provide livelihoods for more than 1.6 billion people, including some 60 million indigenous people [1] without significant harm. Including forest carbon in international schemes to reduce greenhouse gases could relieve the pressure on other schemes, halving the cost of reducing emissions globally to the target of 50% below 1990 levels. Not only that but long term it is projected that it would generate some US$3.7 trillion in welfare benefits [2].

In response to this high rate of worldwide deforestation a major scheme has been devised – the REDD Programme (reducing emissions from deforestation and forest degradation). Backed by the United Nations Framework Convention on Climate Change (UNFCCC), REDD has been around since 2005 when it was first put forward by Costa Rica, a unique paragon of environmental responsibility, and New Guinea.

No one should doubt the worthiness of REDD's intentions. Its mission is to curb carbon emissions by reducing deforestation in the world's remaining natural forests, where around 200,000 primary rainforest trees are cut down daily [3]. REDD+, as the newer version is called, also promotes and supports sustainable forest management and the conservation and enhancement of forest carbon stocks. Loggers and ranchers only cut rainforests because it pays handsomely to do so, the REDD reasoning goes, so paying them not to do so and to plant more trees would neutralise that economic pressure, stop people destroying rainforests, and so help stave off climate change.

REDD has certainly captured imaginations. More than a hundred countries have signed up to it in principle, and it enjoys the support of many non-governmental supporters, including green organisations, forest scientists and aid experts. It has also excited the interest of a new breed of "carbon capitalists" eager to make money from it, as intended.

Undoubtedly REDD has admirable aims. But can it achieve them? While there is no doubting the motives or the importance of REDD's objectives, or its ostensibly sound premise as a market solution for market-led problems, from the outset there have been credible doubts as to whether it will work without significant adjustments [4]. In 2010 the Cancun Climate

Change Conference went a long way towards addressing these concerns. The upshot was that for the first time an international agreement stemming the loss of tropical forests with financial backing from the industrialised world was signed.

Where in 1992 Kyoto had allowed only for reforestation and afforestation, not protection of primary forest, and then only in developing countries and for individual projects, now under REDD+ entire countries could be contracted into mitigation schemes. Reduced forest felling and degradation, good conservation and management techniques, and afforestation would now all be eligible for financial support. Transparency and safeguards for the rights and knowledge of indigenous communities as well as their participation in schemes were also agreed.

REDD's deficiencies

These were certainly considerable improvements on earlier proposals, but was it enough? The big question for me was, does it tick all the *Junglenomics* boxes if it is to succeed as a long-term solution to wilderness loss? Unfortunately, I do not believe it does. REDD looks a lot like sound *Junglenomics* reasoning at first, but not once you get down to the principles that underlie it. Through the *Junglenomics* lens a number of serious deficiencies show up.

The first is a problem of tenure: who owns the land that REDD is supporting – indigenous peoples or big business? The answer is that in a too many cases it is the latter, and that all too often has perverse consequences. By paying existing commercial landholders *not* to fell forest, REDD is effectively rewarding economic predators – those who would otherwise clear-fell those forests. That holds potential for dangerous unintended outcomes. For example, because it rewards hanging back from forest clearing, it generates a financial incentive to create a threat of rainforest destruction, and does so over larger areas, even among landowners who might otherwise never consider doing so, and in areas that are considered relatively safe. After all, if you pay me not to scratch every itch I'm surely going to find a lot more itches that need scratching. REDD-assisted logging companies and others would therefore be encouraged to acquire more and more sensitive land "not to harm" for reward. That's protectionism by any other name.

And because the high world demand for timber will always find ways of being satisfied, unless loggers were to stop logging and restrict their activities to milking REDD subsidies (extremely unlikely given the vast and highly lucrative timber market) they would need to find timber elsewhere to fill their order books. This would raise pressure on other forests for substitute logging and farming – "leakage" as it's called.

On top of that, even if much of this leakage were successfully controlled, permanently removing large tracts of forest from potential timber production would cause a reduction in supply and raise timber prices. This would not only put ever more pressure on unprotected forest, but also escalate the cost of REDD payments, which to remain competitive need to stay greater than their "opportunity costs" (the economic value of alternative opportunities that are foregone – in this case actual logging – when any particular choice is made).

Then there is the enormous opportunity for corruption; especially now that the scheme is to be operated at government level in order to answer sovereignty questions. The huge sums potentially available from selling REDD carbon credits into the voluntary international carbon offset market to pay off erstwhile loggers would generate a honeypot that would be irresistible to the good and the bad alike. Because poor available data on the extent of current forest cover means that accurate accounting is tricky, the temptation to falsify claims would be powerful.

History bears this out. For example, when the EU began handing out agricultural subsidies, the activities people were prepared to carry out to make illicit claims, including such things as moving entire crops between fields to make multiple claims on the same crops, were legion. There were loopholes everywhere. Billions of euros were fraudulently claimed. As we have seen, fraud became rife even in the sophisticated European carbon trading market, so how will it not be so in Third World countries which lack even the the less than adequate level of oversight of the EU?

The potential for corruption among officials managing the scheme locally is also substantial. For example, REDD creates an incentive to bribe officials to grant new logging licences to landowners so that the forests the licences applied to would then qualify for REDD payments. Little wonder that logging companies queue up with their hands out for a share of the cash bonanza. This cash has given rise to land grabs and disputes, in which wealthy companies, able to brandish substantial legal brawn and political clout, have an enormous advantage over the poor local populations the scheme was intended to benefit. Ten years on this is still a major challenge for the scheme.

There is yet another major prospective problem with REDD; it doesn't distinguish between old and new forest. This means that corporations can chop down old forest in one country and plant new forest on land that has never been forested in another country to compensate. Quite apart from the obvious disastrous ecological implications, inappropriate planting can easily result affecting local ecosystems and local people alike.

Canada has provided a classic example of this [5]. In order to get at its massive Alberta oil-bearing tar sands, which incidentally release nearly five times the carbon that conventional crude oil production does, Canada needs to cut down huge swathes of ancient forest and destroy wetlands. To get away with this environmental decimation and the resulting very high GHG production, Canada planted eucalyptus and pine as a carbon offset thousands of miles away in Uruguay – a vast 1.2 million acres of it over the past 35 years. Furthermore, to the disgust of many of that country's inhabitants, this tree planting has been taking place on land that used to be fertile pampas, not woodland at all, absorbing excess water and drying the ground.

Conifer Monoculture

The loss of such grasslands upon which indigenous peoples are dependent is a real worry. With good reason, some view this as a new form of neocolonialism, in which industrial countries exploit Third World countries so that they can continue polluting at home. Others label such practices "biopiracy".

A detailed 2018 report from the Rights and Resources Initiative (RRI), a Washington DC-based research group, bears out these observations and reservations about REDD+ in the context of the Democratic Republic of Congo (DRC), home to 50% of Africa's tropical forests. Backed by the DRC government and international financing, private companies that manage huge tracts of forest under REDD+ have ignored the land rights of local peoples, engineered displacements, and avoided prior consent requirements, the report says. They have also failed to share the windfall such programmes are designed to bring. *"Unfortunately, REDD+ projects in the DRC – as currently structured – are channelling money to private sector actors who do not have the same incentives to protect the forests,"* according to Alain Frechette, RRI's director of strategic analysis.

The Costa Rica experiment

Although REDD's well-intentioned ambition is to transfer the success of the much-lauded Costa Rican experiment to a global scale, its proponents don't seem to grasp that it is fundamentally different. In Costa Rica landholders are rewarded for restoration *and* guardianship [6]. Farmers are paid through national taxes to maintain and enhance forest on their land for the environmental services they provide. They receive payments, not for putting away their chainsaws and sitting on their backsides, but for active restoration and ongoing management. Aided by a major coalition of national agencies working together in the

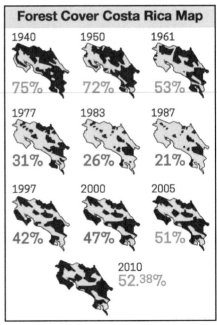

Courtesy Pax Natura Foundation

same direction, the visible result is that Costa Rican forest cover, having diminished to 26% in 1983 making it one of the most deforested countries in the world, had risen again to 52% by 2010, a remarkable and heartening achievement.

The Costa Rican system may not be perfect, but if results are anything to go by it is a lot better than any other. Costa Rica is not only helping itself, it is also helping the fight against carbon release and species loss. It therefore also has real value for the rest of the world. The core reason for this scheme's success is that forested and reforested Costa Rican land now carries a significant financial yield that recognises its contribution to national wealth and well-being. This is a simple and environmentally benign financial equation that everyone understands and from which everyone benefits whether directly or indirectly. As such it embodies a *Junglenomics* gold standard as a balanced economic ecosystem: make a resource more valuable conserved than depleted to those that control it, and ninety-nine times out of a hundred that's exactly what you'll get.

Of course, you could try to argue it the other way. You could say that Costa Rican farmers are being paid to replace forest they have previously cut, and likewise are paid *not to* deforest further. You could also argue that, whether logging companies or ranchers are the landowners, the principle is the same, for under a REDD system they too would be paid for using their land in an alternative way. If large companies then went after more forest in order to receive conservation subsidies from it, you could reason that more forest would thus be protected, however expensive that may get.

But while the differences may seem subtle, to me they are monumental in both social and *Junglenomics* terms. With a benign and conscientious Costa Rican government deploying internally raised funds there is little to find of fault. Local farmers do not have the wherewithal to buy up thousands more hectares and form a financial hegemony dominating vast tracts of forest. But scaled up to a point where billions of dollars will be crossing the globe in complex REDD arrangements it is a different matter altogether. The biggest forest destroyers, the huge and wealthy pulp mills of Sumatra for example, are a very different economic species to farmers and they have an entirely different world view. They will receive billions of dollars only because they have been such ruthless destroyers for massive profit, not because they had no other way to maintain even a subsistence living. Meanwhile the poor and mostly environmentally benign forest dwellers, the nearest equivalent to Costa Rican farmers, may get nothing, and find themselves as pawns in the middle of a vast corporate game, as the DRC example shows all too clearly.

Paying Danegeld

Not only is this morally unacceptable, but it would build a stranglehold by large corporate interests on the world's forests that may eventually be difficult or impossible to escape from. Power would have shifted, and the entire edifice would balance on the mathematics of uncertain yields far into the future. Any failure of the system and out would come the chainsaws again; only by then their owners would have gained control over even greater swathes of primary forest. After a temporary hiatus, recent substantial increases in the rate of rainforest destruction clearly illustrate how in the end markets dictate almost everything.

The biggest difference here lies in motivation: a REDD-type plan doesn't change the parameters of forest valuation permanently to protect it; it just holds the rampaging predator at bay for as long as prevailing market conditions allow. In the meantime, it attracts scavengers and parasites. To maintain an economic balance for forests, a permanent "environmental service value" has to be ascribed to it. And that yield value has to be the same or greater at the point of enlistment than that which the rampager can get from devouring it. Few would doubt this principle because it resets the economically optimum behaviour.

So then why not get the poacher to turn gamekeeper by making it worth his while, which is essentially what REDD is about? In answer it is because of the poacher's, or rampager's, very nature. He is not like farmers who invest their capital and lives in their land and whose priority is keeping it productive. The logger takes, but does not put back (or if he does it is greatly impoverished because its biodiversity is disrupted). He has invested massively in being a rampager. He is to all intents and purposes an asset stripper, an economic predator, and he will continue to follow his predatory instincts. Under REDD he becomes like a wolf thrown hunks of meat to stop him eating the village goats. He will grow fat on meaty carbon sequestration revenues, and more of his kind will be drawn to the free meal. And when the party's over and the plates are licked clean? You can guess the rest.

Under REDD vast areas of forest are given over to be guarded in effect by their worst enemy, trusting that if given enough they won't touch them. Because these predators have the control it makes forests ever vulnerable to unforeseen circumstances, creating a precarious economic ecosystem always under threat of collapse. REDD appeases without profoundly and permanently changing the allegiance, as it should, of would-be forest consumers.

This is exactly what happened when the Madagascan government was overthrown in a coup in 2009. There was no international, legally enforceable obligation for the new government to continue to protect the forests. Where the previous regime had done its utmost to protect important regions, back came the loggers in force and the forest devastation resumed. Desperate for revenues, the new government turned a blind eye to the blatant felling and open trading of valuable rosewood trees.

This insecurity of vulnerable regions is ongoing. For example, although the oil company Soco has now pledged not to drill for oil there, the government of the DRC has not ruled out reducing the size of the Virunga National Park – the first in Africa and home to more than 3,000 species including endangered mountain gorillas – by up to 40% to allow oil exploration. It is a simple battle between the commercial value of environmentally benign economic activities such as fishing and tourism, and of oil revenues. A judgement of financial opportunity costs by the government may well decide the fate of this important region one way or the other. There are dozens of other examples in sensitive regions all over the world where lucrative commercial offers forever tempt susceptible governments.

Until we find a way to permanently redesign such destructive colonising parameters on a worldwide scale, we will continue to have to firefight individual threats of economic colonisers naturally pursuing profitable resources, either by trying to enforce the unenforceable or by paying Danegeld [7].

REDD+ has brought the world's attention to the plight of the world's forests and their invaluable biodiversity and should not be abandoned. But these fundamental flaws need addressing immediately if it is to succeed in its vital work.

What I am now going to propose is a potential long-term solution to primary wilderness destruction that draws on Nature's model – a *Junglenomics* solution.

1. *Secretariat of the Convention on Biological Diversity, 2009*

2. *Eliasch Review, 2008*

3. *E.g.: see NS2648. F Pearce pp.36-39*

4. *Shell/IUCN Report 2008*

5. *Alexander Kelly, Investigate West (17/12/2009). https://www.grain.org/article/entries/255-uruguay-s-destructive-plantation-model*

6. *E.g. see: Independent Evaluation Group (World Bank): Costa Rica: Forest Strategy and the Evolution of Land Use*

7. *A tax raised in 10th and 11th century Europe to pay Viking raiders not to pillage the country, a policy for which the Anglo-Saxon King Æthelred was notorious*

Chapter 9
Winning the Battle for the Forests

An economic power struggle

In Nature, when it comes to getting and maintaining control over scarce resources, everything boils down to an equation between value and power – the value of the resource in question to a species (i.e. how much it contributes to their survival) and the power of the species to capture them in competition. Rarely does one species get absolute control in Nature though, because there are always opportunities for others. A pride of lions may prey on local antelope herds, for example, but hyena, wild dog, vultures, insects and microorganisms may take their share afterwards. Lions do not bother to chase rodents, birds or insects because the nutritional return – the profit – is so small for the effort invested. But they will defend their territory with extreme force to maintain control over its highly profitable population of large game. The general rule is that the bigger the profit the more ardently the resource is sought, and the harder it is to dislodge the incumbent species.

The same applies in the economic world. The degree of viability and the degree by which a major resource, in this case natural forest, is pursued and captured by big economic predators is a function of the excess of return over effort, in other words the size of the profit.

This may seem a complicated way of reiterating that the profit motive drives both natural and economic colonisation, and the bigger the profit, the more powerful the coloniser will tend to be; but I want the comparisons between Nature and economics to be clearly drawn because the design of the solution depends upon fully understanding the context and underlying natural parameters of the problem.

Thriving primal forest is an indispensable resource for innumerable species, and competition for living space within it is fierce. Unfortunately, three economic species are in pursuit of it as well, two of which are extremely powerful, while the third, the indigenous human population, is relatively weak and thus largely pulled along by the economic tides sweeping around them.

On one side of this economic power struggle are a number of economic species, or actors that value forest as a consumable commodity and want to exploit it via logging and agriculture. That's not unnatural – to them it's much like grazing grass or hunting prey – a question of economic survival in their chosen existence. Competing strongest with them, inadequately at the moment, are much greater numbers of species in the guise of people who want to exert protective control over wilderness so that the whole world can continue to benefit from its benign properties. Meanwhile the indigenous human species, who depend upon forests for their day-to-day existence, tend to be ignored because they lack legal rights and political clout. On the whole they are the natural allies of conservationists, who value much of what they do to manage forests sustainably.

Leaving aside aesthetic values, which Nature doesn't recognise, we – the current self-appointed "protector" species – have taken a global view of the value of forest that embraces qualities such as carbon and soil retention, climate regulation, food production, biodiversity, tourism, and as a source of medicines both now and in the future. This is a broad, long-term, intellectual view which only we humans are capable of, and providing we heed it and win the struggle with our competitors this view could be the saving of the planet.

The chief problem is that, despite our endeavours, we forest protectors don't have sufficient power to dislodge the presently more powerful "rampager" species. We are still losing on most fronts simply because the financial rewards for their destructive activities are just too great, and they will go to any lengths to secure ever more foraging territory, causing the forests and their precious species to continue to vanish at alarming speed, as earlier figures so starkly showed.

The bottom line is that we are in a war – an economic war – over the world's great natural wildernesses. A vast amount has been lost; yet as Tennyson wrote, "*Though much is taken, much abides*" [1], so there is still everything to play for. In essence, this war is just another primeval struggle for the control of resources like millions of others throughout natural history. But we have reached a critical point in this power struggle. We are so close to the point of no return that from now on every misjudgement, hesitation and inadequately thought-out scheme enacted not only causes yet more of this precious and limited resource to disappear, but also gets us nearer to the unpredictable watershed, the tipping point of climatic and world ecosystemic stability.

The wilderness and biodiversity conservation side therefore needs to get much more sophisticated about how it goes about this critical fight to conserve resources. We cannot allow ourselves to die wondering why we did not act when we still could.

So what do we have to do to win the war for the planet's vital natural resources, to provide security for its biodiversity, and to retain its carbon-sequestering properties for the long term?

Nature, pointing the way, tells us that if we, the conservationists, want to win we must dominate the marketplace – not by devising yet more inadequate rules and regulations, but by outcompeting forest destroyers at the market economics game. At present, there is no real competition; destructive exploiters win most of the time because the market demand for conserved forest is weak as it is not value led. Meanwhile, the market demand for timber and agricultural produce is powerful and prices are strong. To rescue rainforests, we have to play the economics game the natural way and reverse the value balance using market instruments – by attaching financial rewards to forest conservation that are significantly bigger than those rewards for destructive exploitation. We need to shift the power balance.

The only effective way to save vulnerable forests must therefore be to make them more valuable intact than felled. That means the world must do more than just talk about the vital environmental services that it enjoys from primal forests, it must also *pay* for them. This is Nature's way to protect ecosystem services – by establishing their true value in the economic marketplace. It is the only way to secure the safety of natural environments for the long term.

Paying to conserve forests will not be enough by itself though. We have to go further. Since it is the dominating drive to acquire universal economic resource – money – that has created the problem, only a greater opposite economic force can stop it.

To create this economic force, we must unleash the formidable power of the economic-colonising imperative – resource hunger – on behalf of forests and other important wilderness; and to achieve this, we have to construct a real time market mechanism that links conserved natural forest with powerful economic actors – international investors – so that they can thrive on a diet of forest conservation as a profitable, everyday financial activity that is safe and simple. In this way, we can convert forests into a capital asset that is financially as well as ecologically priceless, so that no timber company, no soya farmer, no oil or mineral prospector can ever again tempt forest owners into destroying them.

A new bond market to protect and manage wilderness for the long term

I suggest that the best way to achieve this would be via the issuing of an entirely new type of investment bond – an "Environmental Services Investment Bond" (ESI bond) where each bond is linked to the permanent conservation of a specific parcel of natural wilderness.

As it happens, the two principal potential components for ESI bonds already exist – green bonds and the Green Climate Fund. At the moment, the two are not linked; nor are they directly connected to the object of their activities – climate and biodiversity conservation projects – in anything like the radical way I am proposing here. I shall look briefly at each of them before suggesting how they could be tied into wilderness conservation and management on a worldwide scale.

The green bond market only took off in 2014 so it is still a new and largely untapped force, but already they have expanded substantially. Green bonds are investment bonds issued and sold through financial markets to provide finance or refinance capital for a range of environmental projects. These projects include climate change adaptation and biodiversity conservation, which immediately qualifies them for an ESI bond market. As bonds, they are essentially debt, and like any other bond issuance they are able to be bought and sold on financial markets. Some bonds can have a limited lifespan, at the end of which the bondholder is repaid, while others are open-ended, passing *ad infinitum* from investor to investor much as company shares and stocks do.

Green bonds are attractive to investors for two main reasons – they are ethical, and they produce an income. Just like a share or stock in a company, their price may rise and fall according to various market influences, including prevailing interest rates, risk assessment and supply and demand. To create the incentive to buy their green bonds the issuers need to pay interest on them – creating an investment yield, known as a "coupon". ESI bonds will similarly need to provide a significant guaranteed income to investors. This is where the Green Climate Fund enters the picture.

The Green Climate Fund (GCF) is an arm of the United Nations Framework Convention on Climate Change (UNFCCC). Its function is to raise and channel funds from the developed to the less developed world, with a target of $100 billion per year by 2020. Its 2015 income was only a bit over $1.75 billion, so there's a long way to go. Yet if used to provide income to bond markets it could potentially raise (at an average 2.5% coupon) 40 times this figure – $70 billion to spend on capital projects in return for permanent wilderness protection. Just a quarter of the hoped for $100 billion income per annum ($25bn) could potentially be geared up to raise $1000 billion ($1 trillion) on the bond markets. To put this another way, every $100bn capital raised at a coupon rate of 2.5% by selling forest bonds in the international markets would cost the GCF $4bn a year, so although it only has $1.75bn a year income to spend at present, it could still potentially raise 1.75/2.5 x $100 = $70bn. Every extra $1bn income the GCF manages to achieve can thus raise an extra $40bn on the markets. That could secure a lot of wilderness.

This is not out of the question for the GCF, because although the fund's approach has previously been disappointingly centred on action at state level – with all its potential pitfalls (especially corruption) – many of the developed counties represented on the GCF board, including the US, the UK and Japan, have persuaded it to get involved with private capital markets, in particular, institutional investors such as pension funds, which control trillions of dollars through Wall Street, London and other financial centres. The GCF's new Private Sector Facility makes it the ideal vehicle for ESI bond funding.

There are other revenue options to underpin ESI bonds. For example, governments could dedicate some of the climate change taxes they collect to it, rather than losing it in their general budgets. Raising a special carbon levy is another option, as is a modest levy on higher incomes, given that the richer one is, the greater one's consumer footprint on the world. Governments fear that increasing the price of planet-costly goods with taxes will lose them votes. We need to show them vociferously that the better off *are* prepared to accept paying modest levies, so long as the money raised goes directly to subsidising the development and support of environment-friendly technologies, businesses and wilderness-conserving financial instruments such as ESI bonds.

How ESI bonds can lock in wilderness conservation

The target for an ESI bond market is less wealthy nations with important natural environments. At present these nations are caught between, on the one hand, demands from rich nations to conserve their natural capital assets in order to ameliorate problems (especially high carbon emissions) that those rich nations have themselves created, and on the other hand, the lure of large amounts of ready cash from environmentally destructive business interests. They frequently, and understandably, say that if rich nations are so desperate to put a stop to the commercial development of wilderness they should replace the lost income of doing so. How else can their people ever hope to climb out of poverty?

Under an ESI bond scheme, countries that sign up would in effect enter a partnership with wealthy nations that realises the true value of their natural capital assets by providing substantial amounts of capital to be apportioned between conservation projects and environmentally benign development to create employment and relieve poverty.

In return these nations would agree to lock in, or "bond" important government-owned wilderness by offering it up in parcels as assets to the ESI bond market. Each bonded parcel would represent, say, ten square kilometres of natural wilderness, with rainforest as a priority because of its high biodiversity and carbon sequestration value. This means that when an investor buys an ESI bond and commits his capital to a host nation, he or she is not only financing approved projects as green bonds do, but at the same time securing the future of a specific chunk of wilderness in perpetuity. ESI bonds thus recognise the value of wilderness ecosystems in the only way markets can – by endowing them with substantial market value.

For this to work, ESI bond investors' confidence would need to be absolute. They would need to be confident that their bonds are safely underwritten and operate within an enforceable legal framework in respect of their income yield, of their ability to be bought and sold freely in world markets, and of the protection and good management of the underlying security – the wilderness. If the World Bank were to underwrite ESI bonds, then there is a real prospect of creating an energetic new market that is triple A-rated and dedicated to protecting wilderness in poorer counties in perpetuity, helping them build their infrastructure to support environmentally neutral employment.

That high rating would also be essential to ensure that while bond yields should be generous to attract investors, they do not need to be so high that they would absorb too much Green Climate Fund or other income. This is because the lower the rating the higher the perceived risk, so the greater the interest yield has to be to attract investors, as we saw with Greek and Spanish bonds in recent periods of financial crisis.

Finally, for any secondary market to flourish, bonds must be able to change hands freely. For this to happen there has to be sufficient liquidity for a critical mass for trading and price discovery to take place. These are conditions that can readily be fulfilled with multinational support from developed countries and respected institutions like the World Bank and the IMF.

Bond grading

Natural environments vary greatly, so there should be a number of different categories and grades of ESI bonds each with its own apportioned "environmental services" yield reflecting the ecological and carbon capture value of the underlying asset. They would range from premium, high biodiversity, high sequestration and therefore higher income-yielding parcels, down to low-priced, degraded, low income yield parcels ripe for restoration. Holders of these "cheap" bonds could if they wished group together to invest further capital into their bonded land parcels to upgrade them ecologically, thus raising both their value and yield while simultaneously spreading wealth among local communities involved in the work and encouraged by recipient nations whose income and asset value would likewise increase.

There could therefore be low yield, potentially high growth bonds as well as high yield, pristine wilderness bonds. Revised grade and yield assessment could be carried out by an independent panel of specialists working for the international ESI bond market administrators. In this way, such a market could rapidly develop its own variety of investment opportunities, the driving financial motivation for which would be the restoration and conservation of high-quality environmental service provision and biodiversity. Furthermore, national governments with large and important areas of wilderness would be incentivised to contribute funds, facilitate restoration, and police degraded wilderness in order to offer these areas up to the ESI bond market.

Under this scheme, not all the still vast areas of natural forest would require bond market protection. If the bonding of more easily accessed forest regions were to be prioritised, an encircling buffer zone of bond-protected forest could be created which would prevent access to the more remote regions contained within. This "bond belt" would work the opposite way to urban green belts, preventing destructive development from getting in.

This plan is an attempt to guarantee that aid funds given to developing countries, most of which have resources of their own, be properly used for the greater good and not diverted or misappropriated. It sets out to develop a partnership between host country and a supranational organisation as a conduit for wealthy governments. Markets then can be harnessed to make it worthwhile for the host country to be a good global citizen. The incentive is the prospect of substantial amounts of private capital which can be used by host nations to generate employment, greater tax revenue, and revenues from wilderness-friendly economic activities.

Private land

Private landowners would also be able to participate. In their case, bond capital would be used, perhaps under the oversight of the highly respected International Bank for Reconstruction and Development (IBRD), to relocate wilderness-degrading activity, such as pulp mills and soya farming, to designated less sensitive land elsewhere. Governments could even be incentivised to initiate land swaps with wilderness-degrading landowners for less sensitive land to allow them to sell ESI bonds to fund its restoration. Meanwhile, some significant proportion of the bond capital raised from sale could be retained in a trust fund in order to generate income for management and restoration of bonded land in perpetuity. Being permanently attached to specific parcels of land, such attached income would in itself impart significant capital value to healthy wilderness areas.

This borrows from so-called "stewardship schemes" that have run for many years in Europe. Land managers large and small were paid an income to maintain environmentally sensitive land to certain standards and refrain from destructive or degrading actions such as tree felling, ploughing, spraying and fertiliser use, an obligation that transferred with changed ownership. In this way land exploiters can be converted into land protectors.

The difference is that stewardship schemes were merely fixed term, allowing the land manager to do as he would after it was over, while for ESI bonded land the key words are "in perpetuity".

Involving the locals

Participation in management by indigenous inhabitants (over a billion of the world's poor are dependent on wilderness-oriented livelihoods [2]) could also qualify for additional ESI yield points. Studies [3] have shown that indigenous peoples are more effective at conserving forest and wildlife, and that the most effective formula for successful forest conservation is joint control and management by government and local people rather than by outside agencies. This would also help secure the traditional position of indigenous people as rainforest guardians and help them to retain their ancestral ways. Such people should be able to keep all proceeds of wilderness-friendly commercial land use, especially traditional use, and where appropriate, sensitive tourism and medicinal plant harvesting.

Host nations could be entitled to invest capital received from bond sales in a number of ways approved, distributed and moderated by an independent body acting as trustee – again perhaps the IBRD. Examples of such investment could be urban regeneration, education, healthcare, poverty alleviation and essential infrastructure projects like green energy, as well as wilderness restoration for the purpose of offering it up for further ESI bond sales.

A world market in accredited ESI bonds could have the added benefit of helping prevent the scam of developed countries offsetting carbon emissions through irresponsible foreign offset schemes as per the previously mentioned Canadian example. Such countries could instead offset emissions by purchasing ESI wilderness restoration bonds to be held by dedicated trust funds, thus enabling the conservation of vast areas of bonded wilderness in perpetuity. In such cases the bond yield could be forfeited and retained by the IBRD to commit to further restoration and conservation projects, including CCS and green energy.

Avoiding leakage

There is another positive aspect to bear in mind about such a scheme. Making it worth more for landholders to conserve forests may appear attractive, but vast swathes of wilderness that are already in the hands of loggers and planters are earmarked for clear-felling. For just one example among many, Indonesia is all set to clear three million hectares of rainforest in New Guinea (4), and almost 21 million hectares of its forest is included in existing or proposed logging concessions, which mostly means old-growth hardwoods. This is driven by a strong worldwide demand for good-quality timber.

Because it will not go away anytime soon, the destruction demand for this timber needs to be assuaged, something that can only happen through an alternative supply of timber. This suggests that to avoid "leakage" – shifting the resource rush for timber from one rainforest to another – large areas of land need to be dedicated to growing new "crop" forests. To date such afforestation has largely taken place on land first stripped of its primal forest. This needs to change. Similarly, soya and palm oil need dedicated cropland that does not involve wilderness destruction and keeps clear of regenerating forest.

One possibility to solve this is to facilitate land exchanges. Swapping designated crop and forestry land for primeval wilderness currently owned by loggers and planters could remove the immediate threat of their destruction, and over the longer term, remove the temptation to renege on conservation agreements and recommence logging. It may well be that the ability to submit such wilderness to the ESI bond market would be incentive enough to part with control of them anyway. And the fact that even forest wilderness, whose large trees have been removed, have potential value on an ESI bond market, should encourage loggers to minimise collateral damage to surrounding vegetation (and biodiversity) to maximise its potential rate of recovery, and hence its potential bond market value, whereas at present these lands are nearly always denuded in the logging process.

Maintaining sovereignty

Governments receiving aid are understandably sensitive about maintaining sovereignty; no one likes foreign powers meddling around in their backyards. But the beauty of an ESI bond scheme is that sovereignty and territorial integrity would be unaffected. While the issuing of ESI bonds on land parcels would be legally binding, as is any international treaty, it would have no effect on the ownership of, or sovereignty over the underlying asset – the land itself. While the conservation commitments that ESI land bonding brought with it would remain, the underlying "freehold" could change hands at any time by being bought and sold in the normal way in compliance with local laws, just as one can do with private property that is let on a long lease or covenanted for some purpose.

So, both the bond and the underlying asset could be freely traded, much like company stocks and shares. The beauty of the scheme is that bonding a land parcel would commit both existing and future landowners to its appropriate management, though in many cases that may mean merely leaving it alone.

Oversight, law, breaches and coups

For their part, in return for the massive inward investment that ESI bond market participation would bring, national governments would need to preserve the market's fundamental requirements in national law. Without binding laws, internal scrutiny and guarantees of compliance by international treaty, there will not be sufficient confidence among investors – a critical component – to enable them to participate in the scheme.

Among participating governments' obligations would be a legal commitment to protecting bonded wilderness from destructive activities, such as illegal logging, in coordination with a dedicated population of forest rangers, managers and indigenous peoples, whose incentive would also now strongly favour conservation for the benefits it brings. Should a government or private landowner be found to have failed in its duty by the overseeing body [5] then the ESI status of affected land could be removed and capital grants converted to debt. At this time, any income would cease, the bondholder would be compensated from a reserve fund, and the government held responsible for repaying the debt unless and until they took steps to restore the affected land at their own cost. Any such debts remaining unpaid could be subtracted from their ESI bond capital account by the overseeing body. This would give recipient nations a strong incentive to police bonded regions effectively.

To ensure their integrity, bonded wilderness could be monitored by satellite (such as NASA's 30-metre resolution "Landsat 7", which has now spent over 17 years mapping forest loss, and Satellite Imaging Corporation's 15-metre "ASTER" satellite) or drone imagery relayed to computers, a technology that is becoming increasingly sophisticated, making fraud difficult even in the remotest places [6]. The World Resources Institute's "Global Forest Watch" is a hub for such information and is followed by people and organisations all over the world.

As to bankruptcies among forest landowners, ESI bonded land would be unaffected because the legal commitment to conservation and attached income would remain in place whoever came to own the underlying asset. And in the case of coups or insurrections, all national income would be suspended and bonds become technically repayable unless or until lawful conservation management is shown to be ongoing.

REDD involvement

At the moment, there is no long-term formula to provide funds for REDD schemes. It is currently funded hand to mouth from national pledges that vary immensely from country to country and have no correlation to those countries' carbon footprint. There has been interest in harvesting income from the carbon offset market, but as already discussed, the future of carbon trading remains highly uncertain due to lack of large-scale uptake and the oversupply of carbon credits in its largest operation in Europe. A price of 60 cents or less per tonne goes almost nowhere to meeting REDD's costs, which are apparently not covered even at $5 a tonne. At current prices carbon markets are clearly neither sufficient nor reliable, funding REDD long term depends upon securing a reliable source of income. However, with a share of the resources raised by an ESI bond market at their disposal, things could be very different for REDD. Its sophisticated mechanisms would be given free rein to carry out their remit to reduce emissions by protecting, restoring and conserving wilderness for the long term.

Don't mistake me – despite my criticisms I believe that REDD could become the genuine article in forest conservation. But its failure through inadequate design would not only be disastrous for Nature, but would disillusion those who have provided billions of dollars to back it, making a subsequent scheme very much harder to set up. It must succeed at first attempt, and to do that it needs, above all, to be designed to succeed, not as at present, to fail. I have shown how this can be done based on the workings of ecosystems, and we ignore these lessons at our and the natural world's extreme peril.

Environmental Services Investment (ESI) Bonds

FIRST WORLD POLLUTERS

ASSESSED FOR AND PAY CARBON
TAXES AND/OR POLLUTION LEVIES TO
INDEPENDENT ESI AGENCY

ESI MARKET AND AGENCY

ESI AGENCY CATEGORISES BONDS
ACCORDING TO ES CRITERIA.
PROVIDES RECEIVED FUNDS FROM
VARIOUS SOURCES TO ESI MARKET TO
PAY COUPON ON ESI BONDS

SALES PROCEEDS HELD IN
DEDICATED ESI TRUST

REDD++ MANAGES COMPLIANCE
AND REPORTS BREACHES TO HOST
GOVERNMENTS, WITH POWERS
TO ORDER SUSPENSION AND/
OR REPAYMENT OF TRUST FUND
ALLOCATIONS AND POLICING
CONTRIBUTION, ENFORCABLE UNDER
INTERNATIONAL LAW

INVESTORS

BUY FULLY TRADABLE, OPEN-ENDED
ESI BONDS, UNDERWRITTEN BY
THE WORLD BANK, ATTACHED TO
SPECIFIC LAND PARCELS, PRICED
ACCORDING TO PREDETERMINED ES
VALUES AND HUMAN PARTICIPATION
CRITERIA

RECEIVE GUARANTEED TAX FREE
COUPON (INCOME) OF 2.5%

MAY INVEST IN UPGRADING BONDED
LAND TO HIGHER CATEGORY, AND
HENCE RECEIVE COMMENSURATELY
HIGHER YIELD

ESI TRUST

TRUST FUNDS ALLOCATED TO
EDUCATION + HEALTH + SUSTAINABLE
DEVELOPMENT PROJECTS IN
RECIPIENT NATIONS, INCLUDING
WILDERNESS RESTORATION UNDER
REDD++ OVERSIGHT FOR FURTHER ESI
BOND OPPORTUNTIES AND SOCIAL
INCLUSION

INCENTIVES TO RESTORE DEGRADED
LAND FOR INCREASED COUPON

Environmental Services Investment (ESI) Bonds

(CONTINUED)

NON-GOVERNMENT
LANDHOLDERS

```
SUBMIT WILDERNESS PARCELS TO ESI
MARKET IN PERPETUITY
```

```
SALES PROCEEDS HELD IN DEDICATED
ESI TRUST
```

```
TRUST FUNDS ALLOCATED TO
BUSINESS RELOCATION, WILDERNESS
RESTORATION AND SOCIAL
INCLUSION
```

```
INCENTIVES TO ESTABLISH
DEDICATED CROP PLANTATIONS ON
LESS SENSITIVE LAND
```

ENVIRONMENTAL SERVICES
INVESTMENT BONDS SUMMARY

Aims:

1. To achieve no-net-increase in CO_2 emissions from developing nations
2. To achieve no-net-loss of biodiversity in the world's most biodiverse nations
3. To stabilise and secure the future of indigenous populations through participation
4. To fund infrastructure development in biodiverse nations without further recourse to destructive exploitation of their natural capital

Mechanism:

1. **Finance:** international ESI bond market affiliated to existing bond markets. Participating nations with extensive important biodiversity issue ESI bonds to the market, each relating to specific parcels of pristine, or degraded but restorable land within their borders.

   Such nations then receive payment for these bonds, but do not have to pay interest (or coupon) on them to the purchasers (investors) as they normally would if they issued standard government bonds. Instead, others pay the coupon on their behalf: wealthy nations that emit the highest amount of CO_2 and other undesirable gases, pollutants and particulates (e.g.: Europe, China, Russia, Canada and the US). Along with the Green Climate Fund and others, these nations have to contribute annual income via a carbon tax or emissions trading scheme to supply the coupon to these ESI bonds, guaranteeing that income.

2. **Security:** participating nations underpin the value of the bonds they offer in the market by attaching them to specific grid areas of, say, rainforest, which are placed in trust under international agreement, attaching certain conditions as appropriate to good conservation and management practice, overseen by the REDD organisation.

3. **Sovereignty:** participating nations do not lose sovereignty over bonded land, as they may buy back the bonds at any time and release them from the terms of the bonding if they so wish, or otherwise retain them in trust and receive the coupon themselves (as they grow wealthier this may be their preferred option as it provides ongoing income from their natural capital assets).

4. **Categorisation:** bonded land is categorised according to its natural capital asset value by an independent board of valuers. Lower value land such as degraded forest will yield a lower coupon and therefore carry a lower bond price. However, by restoring such land, reassessment by the board can raise it to higher categories and hence improve its coupon. Bondholders can club together to provide capital to

restore degraded land and hence improve its categorisation, thus raising its coupon and capital value. Bonds may be bought and sold in the market, as in any other.

5. **Oversight, management and enforcement**: the issuing of ESI bonds will only be available to nations that sign up to a convention obliging them to abide by certain rules, including conferring legally enforceable ownership or occupation and participation rights upon indigenous tribal populations. This is to ensure that they can benefit from all legitimate, non-destructive commercial use (for example tourism, sustainable small industry and drug development), overseen and upheld by one of the established international organisations such as the UN-REDD scheme organisation, who will be charged with monitoring bonded land using satellite or drone information, and will report to a central "court" that will investigate alleged breaches of trust.

Nations that allow the degradation of bonded land will be held responsible either to restore it or repay the bond and ongoing coupon to the bondholders. Investors' funds will be underwritten by the World Bank and IMF jointly, which will hold recalcitrant nations to account using their leverage as lenders.

6. **Infrastructure investment:** the proceeds of bond sales will be held in trust by an appropriate arm of the UN and released to ESI bond issuers to spend only on essential, non- or low-pollutive infrastructure, for example schools, hospitals, social care, social housing, low carbon energy production, roads (avoiding biodiverse areas), bridges, sensitive tourism, green industry, and low emissions transport.

7. **Termination:** ESI bonds will be open-ended, in that they will never require repayment (other than in cases of default), allowing poorer nations to develop without accumulating debt, but instead by benefiting financially from the ongoing integrity of their valuable but as yet undervalued natural capital assets.

Benefits:

1. Personally involves investors of all shades in direct biodiversity conservation
2. Creates a major green investment focus for investors and charities
3. Locks specific areas of wilderness into a conservation programme in perpetuity
4. Creates a financial incentive to restore and then maintain degraded wilderness
5. Allows private landholders to exchange actual or potential destructive commercial income for a conservation-associated income
6. Revalues wilderness as a worldwide asset providing essential ecosystem services
7. Permits non-destructive, non-invasive economic development
8. Helps governments with immense wealth of wilderness to regard it as a national asset
9. Allows financially strapped governments to develop social services and sustainable, economic development without incurring debt

A *Junglenomics* overview of ESI bonds

By being permanently bonded to benign economic actors whose interests are aligned with their well-being means that valuable wildernesses could be conserved in perpetuity – a state that would be underwritten by international agreement to which participating countries would be irrevocably committed in return for substantial inward investment. In *Junglenomics* terms this means that the viability of remaining pristine and restorable forests and wetlands would be assigned to a new economic species – financial investors – backed by law and enforceable property rights.

The important element to this arrangement is that, although motivated as ever by the pursuit of the universal resource – money – this new investor economic species is independent of logging interests and irresponsible carbon offsetters. It sees ESI bonds as an asset class, and its interest is entirely in maintaining or improving the status and value of the underlying asset. Under the ESI bond scheme the investor becomes in effect a "forest guardian" species, a niche created specifically to compete with "forest consumer" species. To the guardian species, forests and other wildernesses are only valuable if standing and healthy, and this therefore becomes his prime economic imperative.

Furthermore, a soundly set up *Junglenomics* conservation economy such as this need be neither exclusive nor elitist. REDD++ (as it might be called) would hand presently undervalued and undefended natural wildernesses of the world a formidable economic weapon with which to begin at last to fight its corner. It would provide wildernesses with a real chance to survive the current economic onslaught against them, and with diligence enable them to thrive long into the future. Instead of a consumed, finite resource forever lost once exploited, wildernesses would become a permanent source of revenue and wealth for countries. They would find their living natural resources a blessing, not just for short-term financial exploitation as they mostly do now, but as something to be cherished in perpetuity.

There is certain to be some issues surrounding the details of an ESI bond market as envisaged here, and there is much more to work through, but the bottom line is that, for any scheme to be effective in protecting wilderness and biodiversity and controlling atmospheric carbon levels, *Junglenomics* principles need to be paramount.

Up to now this book has been all about evolutionary behaviour and economics. It has said little about the subject of all this – people. *Junglenomics* would be a poor system if it was only about Nature and ecosystems and didn't have the welfare of people at its core – not in the general sense of rescuing the planet from a decline that will clearly impact on everyone, especially the poor, but in the quality of their everyday lives.

So, before I attempt to spread the golden cloak of *Junglenomics* over more puddles in the path of mankind, here is a chapter on how it could be used to help raise millions of people out of poverty.

1.   *from Tennyson's "Ulysses"*

2.   *The World Bank 2004*

3.   *E.g.: Isager, Theilade, Thomson: People's Participation in Forest Conservation: Considerations and Case Studies – FAO – post 2001*

4.   *Wetlands International and remote sensing institute, Sarvision, & Greenomics Indonesia 2011*

5.   *The present state of forest governance varies from one country and culture to another according to historic local factors. Accordingly, the World Resources Institute has initiated the Governance of Forests Initiative to try to bring widely accepted principles of good governance into effect to manage the varying challenges of profitable forest maintenance. The initiative is intended to provide a practical tool for countries to systematically analyse, diagnose and initiate governance reforms tailored to their particular circumstances*

6.   *NASA's satellite, the Orbiting Carbon Observatory, for the first time provides a global overview of carbon emissions and sinks. Other private companies (e.g.: DMC Imaging) also offer high resolution surveillance service for remote regions*

Chapter 10
Participation and Property Rights

Environmental decline, property rights
and the alleviation of poverty

The continuing prevalence of extreme poverty, even in this era of great industrial wealth, is a mark of the human race's failure to properly adjust to its post-hunter-gatherer, property-owning culture. Looking at the world economy as a whole, despite centuries in the making, it remains chaotic in relation to its natural environment. It is still a long way from maturing into the fully balanced economic ecosystem it needs to be if it is to achieve long-term stability.

Symptoms of this economic immaturity are highlighted not only by the fact that we continue to wreak havoc on other species and the environment they inhabit, but also that such a high proportion of people remain excluded from its benefits. It is a sad but unavoidable fact of economic life that lucrative new markets always attract the economically powerful, and in the mêlée, the poor all too often miss out. Without particular care the oncoming boom in carbon and biodiversity markets might be no different. Economic inequality is arguably a natural state of affairs, reflecting the many and varied pulses of wealth that pervade any economy; but its extent and extremes indicate gross market failure, which in turn indicates that there are fundamental flaws in current economic paradigms.

Perhaps this economic immaturity is not so surprising. After all, our economic ecosystem is still young, just a few thousand years old, and arguably it has barely even reached puberty. The natural flow of events since its inception has seen colonisation, competition and natural selection do their business as surely as in any other ecosystem, and this evolution has been variously bloody and benign as humans have gone about the aeons-old routine of establishing lineages as best they can. Left to itself, things would continue much the same for perhaps thousands of years to come, though the inevitable environmental fallout hardly bears contemplating.

Short-circuiting this evolutionary process through economic instruments in order to prevent catastrophic environmental repercussions is an important goal. But even this is not enough. Why? In addition to the obvious humanitarian aspect, if extreme poverty is not addressed *in conjunction* with environmental issues it may undermine the entire restructuring process. Unreconstructed industry breeds pollution and biodiversity loss; but so does poverty. Political instability, civil war, mass migration, land degradation, illegal logging, water pollution, bushmeat hunting and so forth – all are direct challenges to biodiversity conservation and all stem from poverty. The drugs trade likewise thrives on it.

So how can poverty be addressed through *Junglenomics*? Just like the environment, widespread economic exclusion can only be tackled effectively in a systematic manner on an international scale.

It is a natural principle that activities which provide viable niches will inevitably attract species to occupy them. And it is because this principle also applies to economics that I have advocated creating the conditions to make beneficial environmental behaviours pay and therefore attract economic species to them. But the growing will to protect environments and biodiversity also presents a golden opportunity to address the poverty associated with these protected lands. To succeed, biodiversity management needs to attract big investment and if properly set up this will generate wealth for the operators as well as the investors. So who will those operators be?

Much of the new wealth will be created from actively sustaining environments that hitherto have been economically almost worthless and thus expendable – rainforests for example. This opens up the opportunity for allocating a reasonable share of the proceeds of such newly valuable property to those that need it most. To watch the already wealthy engage in a new gold rush while millions remain impoverished would surely be more than right-minded people could endure; yet the wagons are already rolling. To make saving biodiversity profitable would be fantastic. But the secondary outcome – to ensure the very poor also receive a fair share of this new wealth – would be not far short of ecstatic.

Stewards of biodiversity

Which brings us to the question – who should the environmental stewards be? Should they be governments, companies and consortiums as in the REDD Programme? Or will accreditation authorities demand a more populist ownership system that could achieve two aims at once?

There is only one way to be sure to benefit the third competitor in the triangle of economic species – poor forest dwellers – and that is to insert them into the new economic loop by design. I discussed earlier how it was the invention of private property that gave rise to the new economic paradigm: so long as you could obtain resource-yielding property you were in a strong position; but for those with none, in the absence of welfare, the outcome is exclusion and poverty. One solution would be to create and allocate new resource-yielding property in the form of rights and responsibilities in biodiversity management; in other words, to pay the poor to be stewards of biodiversity.

Acting on their own initiative, some enlightened individuals and organisations have already done this (the Africa Foundation for example); however, their experiences show what an uphill struggle this can be under present conditions, and few undertake it. History shows us that it is entirely insufficient to rely on goodwill and charity. Big business is the force that needs to be harnessed; and big business focuses on numbers. Those numbers therefore need to make it worthwhile for business to include the poor in both their logistical and financial calculations. I don't mean the poor should simply be given assets that can then be bought off them for small sums, leaving them back where they started, as has so often happened in the past. I mean making their *ongoing* involvement profitable for investors. That way there is little incentive to buy or sell participation rights. They become the permanent, non-divestible property of local communities engaged in biodiversity conservation.

In this way, and in innumerable different scenarios, the poor can establish what they so badly lack at present – viable, long-term economic niches. The ESI bond market could be one major source for this, but it is confined to particular areas of high conservation value; and as such it represents only a small proportion of the rural poor. Yet the same principle can be applied everywhere, so that protecting the natural world pays the poor wherever they may be.

One may legitimately ask if that means poor communities could simply collect the money without doing their jobs properly. Not if the set-up is right, so that they are acting under contract to provide essential environmental services and are rewarded for quality. Such arrangements would not be poverty relief but economic inclusion; which means local communities would have to meet performance targets to receive benefits like any other economic sector.

Sounds simple enough perhaps, but to underpin them any such arrangements would rely entirely on one vital element – a solid legal framework. This is essential for creating market-conducive conditions because citizens and investors alike need the surety of enforceable legal rights to protect their interests, validate contracts and ensure fair participation in markets. Property rights are going to be especially important for carbon and biodiversity markets because land values are going to alter dramatically due to their new-found income-earning potential as offsets. Such value increases will make land a tempting target to national regimes that are less than scrupulous about minding the legal rights of citizens. For example, REDD+ is said to be "evolving in a context of rights abuses, displacement and dispossession, threats and harassment over territories, and the repression and assassination of environmental activists by state and private forces." [1]

In fact, legal rights are so important that the accreditation of biodiversity markets needs to encompass binding commitments on these rights by participant countries. And the only way the rigour and permanence of those commitments can be guaranteed is if an international accreditation body oversees them. Such a body would need to be accessible by citizens as well as commercial interests, and have powers to suspend or even withdraw accreditation if necessary.

Additional difficulties arise where existing land titles are tenuous. In countries like Costa Rica the problem is generally solved because most of the landholders have legal tenure of specified land areas – mostly farms. But it is not so easy in, for example, the Amazon basin. Who there has the right to the vast tracts of forest inhabited only by local populations and subsistence farmers – governments or indigenous peoples? Loggers or prospectors?

A sense of natural justice might encourage one to select indigenous peoples. But if carbon sequestration is going to be big business, generating huge potential revenues, who will fight for the rights of the poor unless it is made profitable to do so?

Some politicking will be inevitable; but because it will provide the funds, the developed international community could exert a powerful influence here. Should funds be paid to wealthy companies *not to* destroy biodiversity as some argue? Or should they be paying the poor who live there for benign stewardship of their ancestral lands, free from the threat of destructive exploitation?

It is a question that I have little trouble answering, especially as, quite apart from political and moral issues, community-based land stewardship is probably the most effective way to conserve biodiversity. The reason I say this is because, although local market economics is becoming ever more widely recognised as an essential ingredient in successful conservation management, surprisingly it is still all too rarely applied. Perhaps this is partly because of the popular image of local farmers and hunters being primary destroyers of the rainforests. But according to a major review [2] presented to a UN meeting on the world's tropical forests, this is deeply flawed. In reality forest dwellers are far more knowledgeable about and efficient at management [3] and even spend more money on forest conservation than government agencies. The ownership of land rights allows them to protect springs, sacred sites, medicinal herb supplies, and to keep out logging companies, hunters and land speculators. Yet it speaks volumes about the lack of science and coordination in conservation matters at the highest level that, despite the fact that local people are successfully conserving more than 370 million hectares of tropical forest worldwide, the UN's International Tropical Timber Agreement, whose signatories comprise around 90% of the world timber trade, has resulted in just 2% of rainforests being managed sustainably – a miniscule proportion.

Free-market environmentalism

I have found that in developed countries private property rights are also widely acknowledged for their environmental benefits, mainly through their association with the more efficient management of natural resources.

In the US, for example, the market approach to environmental problems is known as Free Market Environmentalism (FME). FME supporters believe that while government subsidies often result in degradation of the environment because of the perverse incentives they produce, property rights encourage good stewardship [4]. In fact, there are numerous examples of how market dynamics combined with property rights have been used in the US to solve diverse environmental and resource problems and protect environments. One of the best known of these involves the "water capture" function of upland forests lying upstream of public water supply systems. In such a situation, the city of New York paid for purchases of land, concessions and maintenance contracts in the Catskills in lieu of a water treatment plant that would have cost billions of dollars to build. Restoring, enhancing and maintaining this natural resource under contract made both economic and environmental sense.

The good effects of private stakeholding are apparent in many different contexts, but it is perhaps nowhere better illustrated than in the startling contrasts thrown up in the immediate aftermath of people gaining a stake in property for the first time. Britain in the 1980s provides a classic example: when the British government gave public housing tenants the right to buy their homes, it was soon obvious which occupants had taken up the offer: smart new front doors, gleaming paintwork and well-tended gardens quickly replaced often shabby and unkempt ones.

Another stark contrast was provided in a conversation with a tenant of a state-owned farm near my home. It soon became clear that because the tenant's son would have no right to take over the farm when he retired, his farming policy was geared to getting the most out of it now with little or no attention to the future condition of the land or its buildings. One can hardly blame him. After all what incentive is there to keep the farm in good order at his own expense just for someone else to take it over when he retires? Ownership or intergenerational tenure would make all the difference to his attitude and actions, he told me.

Another example involves a friend who owns salmon angling rights on a stretch of the River Exe in Devon, England. When he found that its waters were being polluted by effluent from small industries upstream he went through the appropriate official channels to try to stop it. However, probably due to divided loyalties, the local authorities proved completely ineffective. In frustration, my friend adopted a different course: he took the offenders to court, successfully arguing that his fishing rights were being impaired by the rafts of contaminated foam floating down the river.

This was a victory not just for his enjoyment of his fishing rights and for their capital value, but more importantly for the mistreated river environment and its biodiversity. No public money was involved; just a private individual protecting his personal stake with his own resources. That he owned such rights and that they were legally enforceable was of course the key to his successful restoration of a clean river environment.

None of this is exactly rocket science. But even though the property rights principle has time and again proved effective, and in the USA the application of FME policy is increasing as news of its successes spreads, even there such "enviro capitalism" is still far from universal acceptance. An entrenched culture of central control and inefficient management is said to be the chief obstacle, something also familiar to most other nations.

To my mind such politically based resistance to change needs be broken down in the face of so much evidence that enviro capitalism works. It does so simply because those living on the land with a proprietary interest in it are best placed to manage its resources efficiently and protect its ongoing asset value.

However, despite widespread official reticence there are reasons for optimism. Such is the interest in enviro capitalism that the World Bank and other international organisations are already supporting some enviro capitalist systems, Costa Rica's for example. The latter's Ecomarkets Project ensures that rural landowners receive payment for four key services in addition to food production – water capture, biodiversity protection, scenic beauty and carbon sequestration. Consumers that benefit from these services include the burgeoning tourist industry, which picks up the bill through a government intermediary. The beauty of it is that these services all stem from the same hectare of land. This land consequently gains greater value intact than pillaged of its trees and plants. As in Nature, so in economics – what provides survives. It is classic *Junglenomics*.

If they can be invested with high economic value intact, then coastal ecosystems, rivers, lakes, forests and vast tracts of wilderness will not only continue to provide essential services to the planet, but if appropriately managed could also put food on the table for some of the poorest people of the world. This theme lies at the heart of the *Junglenomics* ethos, and it applies wherever we see Nature under stress, not only in terms of entire environments, but also of individual species whose corpses are currently valued higher by markets than their living flesh, as the next part of this book explains.

1.   *Centre for International Forestry Research review of academic literature, 2017*

2.   *'Who Conserves the Forests?' by the Washington-based, Forest Trends Group, which includes organisations such as the World Bank, WWF and companies like Mitsubishi with large tropical logging interests*

3.   *Excluding slash-and-burn techniques. Indications are that forest fire frequency is considerably higher in partly cleared (i.e. slash-and-burn) forest areas than on farmland or in pristine forest (Daniel Nepstad and colleagues)*

4.   *E.g.: T Anderson, R L Stroup, the Property and Environment Research Centre (PERC). PERC is dedicated to original research on ways to use market principles to solve environmental problems, and the issue of property rights features strongly in their argument*

PART 3
The Wildlife and
Wilderness Conflict

Chapter 11
Expanding Human Populations
and the Natural Environment

Wildlife and markets

Many great colonisations of the Earth have taken place in the past, but ours has been far more relentless, pervasive and destructive than any other. Expanding human populations and industry continue to demand ever more water, food and territory. Innumerable reports of ecological damage emanating from all corners of the world confirm over and over again that in the face of these demands the natural world nearly always comes out second best.

The ability to exploit Nature's gifts in such a wide variety of ways is, after all, our trademark. It is one of the chief reasons for our phenomenal success. We have become adept at creating new markets, including for species and their body parts gathered from the wild, and this frequently poses a threat to their continued existence. This has become a grave global problem demanding to be addressed more effectively. National policies on wildlife vary according to the prevailing convictions and priorities of those who impose them. This sometimes results in them being not just at variance, but on occasion even diametrically opposed to each other.

The unsustainable exploitation of wild resources for economic gain is consequently rife. Technology has seen to it that sea and land-based organisms alike are highly vulnerable to overcropping. Wherever they become imbued with that extraordinary magnetic quality we call "market value" they are rarely spared economic exploitation. Indeed, the exploitation of wildlife and environment is so widespread that it adds up to an event of global scale. It is estimated that as a result of human incursions we are losing some 27,000 species worldwide each year [1] from a possible total of just ten million. According to the world's first comprehensive, evidence-based assessment by the Intergovernmental Science-Policy Platform on Biodiversity and Ecosystem Services (IPBES), compiled by more than 100 of the world's top experts and released in 2018, over 75% of Earth's land areas are already substantially degraded, undermining the well-being of 3.2 billion people. Wetlands have been hit hardest: globally, 87% have been lost in the last 300 years and some 54% lost just since 1900. And the destruction continues, mainly in Southeast Asia and the Congo region of Africa.

The upshot is that the world is on course to lose a staggering *two thirds* of its wildlife by 2020, from 1970 levels [2]. Furthermore, in addition to the well-publicised systematic deforestation of South America and Asia by loggers, developers and farmers, the deliberately set fires in Indonesia in the late 1990s are estimated to have destroyed some two million hectares of virgin forest alone with untold environmental and biological consequences.

But shocking as these events are they represent merely a few headline examples of what is a remorseless resource-colonising phenomenon taking place in scores of countries worldwide. It is a fact that the closer you go to the equator the greater the number of species you find. Because most Third World states are clustered around equatorial regions the pressure on wildlife from their expanding populations tends to be more intense than in richer economies. Poaching, bushmeat hunting and land competition are all endemic problems. But Third World governments are often severely hampered in their attempts at sound conservation policy by their lack of national wealth. It is much easier to be ecologically sound when you are affluent.

Consequently, it is perhaps unsurprising that there is considerable resentment directed towards those who advocate policies that in effect mean ecology first, people second. This is compounded by the fact that those who do so are mostly wealthy westerners from nations whose own record on pollution and conservation over the past 200 years is among the worst of all, and yet they now rail at other peoples to economise when there is no more opportunity for further cutbacks. One extreme view is that such policies are part of a deliberate ploy to deny emerging nations the wealth they deserve and keep them in powerless penury.

Hopefully most people's cynicism is not quite so deep-seated. Such economic myopia is more likely to be a consequence of the narrow perspectives typical of the antiquated brand of economics almost universally still pursued. Yet there also appears to be a distinct tendency among some Western ecologists to put the welfare of species and ecosystems before that of indigenous populations, who often seem to be regarded as obstacles to healthy ecosystems.

Viewing human populations as little more than pieces on a board to be shifted and manipulated according to prevailing environmental doctrine only increases resentment. As such it is deeply counterproductive. History shows that policies with economic ecosystemic apartheid at their core are useful as emergency stopgaps but not as long-term solutions. They are yet another attempt to dam the human-colonising tide rather than manage it. As such they do nothing to alleviate the build-up of ultimately irresistible colonising pressures and only postpone the inevitable day on which long-lasting solutions have to be devised.

The poaching menace

Large-scale poaching is among the most destructive and pervasive manifestations of this colonising pressure, and it urgently calls for more successful solutions. Poachers are claimed to be bad guys, and undoubtedly some are, but theirs is essentially an economic activity like any other, and as such it requires an economic solution.

Take the illicit trade in rhinoceros horn as a classic example. It originally came about because of the demands of two economic genera: the first is medicinal use – in the Far East it is used as an anti-convulsive and for reducing fever in children; the second is for the Yemeni tribespeople of the Middle East to make greatly prized ceremonial dagger handles. (Rumours about its value as an aphrodisiac are apparently greatly exaggerated.) Little or no farmed supply of rhino horn is available because at the time of writing selling it remains illegal, so this demand is met from wild stocks, with obvious dire consequences.

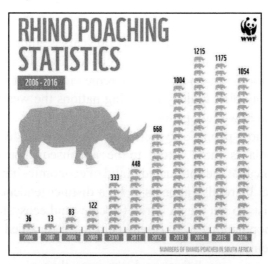

Courtesy WWF RhinoGraph-2016Stats-2-use

How do you protect the rhinoceros in the face of this determined onslaught for the sake of one tiny fraction of its body mass? Had innumerable articles, books and gory film reports not told us otherwise, we might easily be forgiven for thinking that this dense, inedible matt of hair stuck on the end of its snout could be of no possible interest to any creature other than the beast itself, any more than, say, a dingo's testicles. But that would not reckon with the sometimes exotic divergences of resource-hungry economic colonisation that frequently converts otherwise innocuous pumpkins into golden carriages of prosperity.

We humans have hunted a large number of species to extinction during our ascendancy. The dodo and the passenger pigeon are amongst the best known of recent times, but long before that we were responsible for the demise of not only virtually all the large mammals of Pleistocene Europe [3], but also probably the Americas as well. In addition to meat, they were killed for their hide, horn, tendon and bone. These creatures fell foul of an uninhibited arch-coloniser – *Homo sapiens* – that forced them into liquidation.

But unlike the rhino today, in antiquity it was a question of sheer survival, and so that kind of killing now seems to us to have been natural and therefore acceptable. The fact that the rhino is today hunted for so little of its body mass is in truth irrelevant; for were it but a single cell of its body that gained market value the situation would be the same. This is because markets have the potential to absorb almost anything, living or not, into their sphere, which is both the beauty and the tragedy of the new economic dimension. It is also why, though numerous attempts have been made to disrupt the trade, wild rhino numbers still continue to decline, their population graph descending as steeply as a rift valley escarpment.

To address the poaching problem in terms of *Junglenomics* one needs to fully understand the fundamental reason why it happens, not just the obvious one. What really draws people to poach? Is it poverty, excitement, financial gain, opportunity, or perhaps resentment? And where should efforts be concentrated to reduce it?

As in ecosystems, the riskiest, least rewarding or least attractive economic niches will naturally tend to be the last to be occupied – when there are no better alternatives. After all, how many people would choose to empty garbage bins for fifty dollars a day if they could work in a sports hall for two hundred or run a property business for a thousand? At the extremes of poverty, desperate need drives the exploitation of desperate niches, ones that might otherwise be deeply unattractive when easier options are available.

As it happens, the rhino-hunting niche can be a coveted one not least because it involves the use of expert hunting skills that are still very much part of local tradition. For the more adventurous it is also an exciting challenge made doubly attractive by its extraordinary potential rewards (a single horn can now bring up to $300,000 on the black market, up from only around $760 in 2006, and though the poacher himself may receive as little as $100, to him this is a large sum). It is therefore each person's assessment of risk versus reward that must lie at the heart of their decision to engage in the poaching chain. *"Look how well Ndoro's family have done by it. True, my cousin was shot and killed last year, but there are only twenty rangers to cover thousands of square miles and they'll never catch me"*, and so forth.

Crime and punishment

Although authorities can easily create artificial risk to try to discourage such activities using fines, imprisonment or even execution, the effectiveness of these in deterring this kind of criminality is dependent on individual perceptions of risk and reward which, being individual, are relative. So, to magnify the risk of an undesirable niche sufficiently to close it down, the standard reasoning goes, "make the punishment fit the crime". The punishment must be seen to be worse than the alternative – perhaps the ongoing abject poverty endemic in so many parts of Africa, South America and Asia – to the risk-taker. Yet sometimes even the threat of death may not be enough to deter if the reward is high enough or the fear of dying low enough, because there is so little to lose.

The response could be to increase the punishment to, say, the hanging, drawing and quartering of the offender's wife and children. This only goes to demonstrate how absurd the weight of the risk factor alone really is in controlling ecological criminality in the presence of economic deprivation alongside high potential rewards. Such problems therefore need to be tackled concertedly from several angles with established economics principles in mind, in particular by redirecting resource hunger.

The reward side of the equation is also measured on a sliding scale because it too is dependent on many local factors and therefore has potential to be manipulated. I would not normally enter the Zambezi river for a casual swim for fear of being eaten by crocodiles. But with a hungry lion close on my tail I may well be willing to chance it. The one risk is a near certainty, the other at least only an as yet unseen menace. The reward, with luck, is survival. The risk of swimming was about the same whether I swam casually or in desperation. The reward was in the one case just the pleasure of a cool dip on a hot day – certainly not worth it – and in the second a better chance of survival – definitely worth a try.

To prevent me opting to take a dip in the river and disturbing the dozing crocs then, the best bet is surely to lock up that famished lion. The tragedy is that innumerable people all over the world still find themselves and their families stalked by a just such a lion – that of poverty, deprivation, disease, and starvation. It is hardly surprising then that, as they feel its hot breath on their necks, some will choose to take on the warden "crocs" that patrol in search of them. It is not hard to see why the dangled lure of horn, ivory and pelt, promising relative riches, even status, can be tough to resist, and bushmeat practically impossible to leave alone when you are poor and your family is hungry.

A prime example concerns the long border between South Africa's Kruger National Park, with its large population of white rhino, and Mozambique, home to a burgeoning and impoverished human population to whom rhino horn is like gold bars. South African rangers have had a shoot-to-kill policy for poachers who cross the border for some years now. In 2011 alone they shot 26 poachers dead, but so great is the temptation that even this radical deterrent has had little or no effect. We would do well to remember that these poachers were human beings, cherished sons of fathers and mothers and possibly with wives and children. This kind policy is not only a failure, it is inhuman. It is a clear sign of desperation in the face of catastrophic market failure.

It is a sad fact of market economics that the scarcer a target species becomes the more valuable its product and so the more threatened are its few remaining numbers – an accelerating route to extinction. Further along the chain of supply, the middlemen tend to stand the least risk and reap the greatest rewards. While the demand exists, one can be sure that these individuals will always find others to do the dangerous work for them. But the truth is that by taking advantage of the bureaucratic corruption, endemic in so many species-rich countries, to smooth the working of supply routes, they too are nevertheless quite simply and naturally fulfilling a demand. They are colonising a powerfully beckoning niche in time-honoured fashion.

Their efforts can be hampered to some degree by policing and education, which the Convention on International Trade in Endangered Species of Wild Fauna and Flora (CITES) determinedly promotes and supports; however, while policing and education will continue to play an important support role, it is clear that conserving wildlife is not solely a policing and education issue. How much confidence should one have that they alone will be any more successful in the long term than the same policies have been on, for example, drug trafficking or prostitution? There is simply far too much money involved; too much demand. The plain fact is that confronting illicit niches head-on may limit them to a degree ("damming" was the analogy I used earlier), but barring exceptional circumstances it nearly always fails to destroy them. Sooner or later they simply find ways to counter the measures taken against them.

There are innumerable examples of this failure. For a headline example, scientists working for the Wildlife Conservation Society with extensive experience in the rainforests of Indo-China [4] reported that, despite all but one of the six countries covering the range of the Indo-Chinese tiger signing up to the CITES agreement, tiger parts are still sold openly in the marketplace, along with the dismembered remains of their prey species – in itself also a major threat to tiger survival.

The elephant ivory quandary

Disagreement, indecision and disunity in matters of wildlife conservation policy are problems epitomised by that other headline case, the ivory trade. Arguments about how best to conserve elephants against the pressures of this unhappy trade rock back and forth, and policies accordingly oscillate between directly opposed positions – licensing and banning. The trade ban lobby believes any lifting of the ban for licensed sales will only stimulate a greater demand and hence increased poaching. The pro legal trade lobby argue that a legal market will lower prices and so reduce demand for illegal supplies. Neither side seem to have anything but selectively biased, historical anecdote on which to base their arguments; science doesn't enter the frame.

Occasionally, controversial auctions of national stockpiles take place, which the trade ban lobby sees as highly undesirable. Making minor enhancements to an ivory market now and then without providing it with a regular and reliable supply is a sure way to generate a black market to fill the supply-demand gap, they say. While it is true that only countries that can prove their anti-illegal ivory credentials are allowed to bid at these auctions, when a country with 1.3 billion people joins that group – China – you don't need their tea leaves to predict the likely future of thousands of wild elephants under the pressure of such massive new demand.

The demand from China for ivory is not just a domestic affair though. Much of it is carved and goes to tourist markets throughout the Far East. Here even the Western tourist seems to have forgotten the former taboo on ivory. An ivory trade ban was imposed back in 1989 by CITES after poaching radically drove down the population of African elephants in the 1970s and '80s. Coupled with a public awareness campaign against ivory products the desired effect was largely achieved, and the price of ivory plunged to just £1 or so per kilo.

However, it was not surprising to learn that this ivory trade moratorium didn't last long. In June 2002, the six tonnes of illegal ivory that was seized in Singapore *en route* to Japan was an ominous sign. These were levels not seen since the ban was introduced and confirmed suspicions that the trade was again accelerating. The Elephant Trade Information System (ETIS), set up by CITES to monitor global trends in ivory seizures, cited greatly increased demand from a newly affluent China.

Nevertheless, ETIS did not blame, as some do, a general market appetite revitalised by the licensed sell-off of ivory from culled stocks by Botswana, Namibia and Zimbabwe. These African nations have decided that the ban on trade is not working and that they are being penalised since their own elephant populations are healthy. They say, with considerable justification, that the money raised by legal sales is urgently needed for conservation projects. Namibia auctions up to five ageing rhinos a year for culling, fetching up to $350,000 each. This is far more than tourism could ever generate, and it goes straight into wildlife protection and breeding programmes. The result is that, despite more than 1,000 rhinos a year reportedly being poached in South Africa, both Namibia's and South Africa's rhino population have been rising steadily since limited cull hunting has been permitted.

But diametrically opposed to this policy there is a concerted attempt to stamp out the ivory and rhino horn trade altogether, with stockpiles of confiscated ivory and horn being publicly burned in tragicomic rituals in America, China, France, the Czech Republic, Madagascar and elsewhere, on the prompting of CITES and others. Yet these tusk treasures belong to Africa, and it could be argued that it is for Africa to decide what is done with them, not ecologists in foreign countries. Far from killing the trade, destroying illegal tusks and horn is a purely symbolic act, and counterproductive as it only increases market scarcity and raises prices further, making the remaining elephants and rhinos even more of a target. As an "educational" gambit this burning of tusks has had little or no effect either.

The tragic side of it is that, despite these albeit well-intended actions, the price of ivory remains so high that in parts of Africa quasi-war has broken out between rangers and heavily armed, well-equipped and trained militia working for unscrupulous criminal organisations. This is an entirely different prospect to the usual stealthy poach-and-run strategies elsewhere. This is taking place in broad daylight in the Democratic Republic of Congo, in Africa's oldest national park, the Virunga, where 180 rangers have been killed in the last ten years, and in South Sudan, the Central African Republic, Congo and parts of Uganda, Chad and Tanzania, these well-armed and well-trained militia target whole herds of animals rather than one or two, killing as many as possible in a single attack. They need an army to counter such actions, and without one, the war is being lost [5].

Virunga National Park, DRC

In Brazil the chief target is anti-palm oil activists. A growing assassination toll among those brave souls who dare to speak out in defence of forests testifies to the desperation, determination and contemptuous lack of morality among those making big bucks from forest clearance. Nazildo dos Santos Brito – a leader of a Quilombo Afro-Brazilian community formed by runaway slaves – is the latest victim at the time of writing.

Elsewhere things are more under control. In Kenya for example, a conservation body called "Tusk" works with the Northern Rangelands Trust, which employs nearly 700 rangers in an amalgamation of 26 community wildlife conservancies. Here, 3 million acres of land has been dedicated to wildlife conservation, and the rangers perform multiple roles as conservationists, wildlife guardians and peacekeepers. Poaching has been halved since 2012, but this takes plenty of money, and not everywhere is conducive to earning the big tourist dollars needed to pay for it. It is therefore argued in some quarters that levies raised from legal sales could perform the dual benefit of supplying the market and funding the protection of wild populations for any species unlucky enough to have attracted the attention of markets [6].

South Africa is considered a world leader in elephant conservation, and not without reason. A member of the republic's delegation to CITES, Moshibudi Rampedi, once remarked, *"The controlled sale of ivory will in fact assist in the elimination of illegal trade, as the commodity will be available on the legal market."* Indeed, many conservationists now agree that reopening the ivory trade and involving local communities would give them the incentive to protect elephants. *"The reality is that if people don't have some incentive, they will not tolerate these animals"*, according to Paul Funston, a conservation expert at Technikon, Pretoria, one of South Africa's leading research institutes. He sees tourism, trophy hunting and tusk sales as the only way to enlist the army of local protectors needed, especially if the regular destruction of their crops by the great beasts is to be tolerated [7].

The principle of community conservation is being invoked here. Yet there is a powerful opposing lobby that argues strongly that it is dangerous to stimulate demand with legal ivory sales without supplying enough to satisfy big new markets like China, otherwise prices will rise and poachers will step in to fill the shortfall. It is a valid argument.

Notwithstanding those arguments, however, Funston's view in principle represents sound *Junglenomics* thinking. What he advocates is Nature's own remedy – a healthy symbiosis between suppliers and consumers. Science deals in realities, and if we really want positive results in wildlife conservation we can't just point a disapproving finger at the problem or burn tusk hoards in disgust; we have to act according to the realities. You have to ask this question: does burning ivory raise or lower its price in the market? Raise it and you also condemn more elephants to death by poaching. I myself would never wish to shoot an elephant, nor do I relish the thought of elephant ivory farms; but we cannot allow sentiment to stand in the way of conservation. Ultimately, no species subject to poaching will ever be safe until they are worth more alive and thriving in healthy numbers than as victims, and this is all too often not the case. Once again it's all down to markets and value.

This is the heart of the matter. Whether we like it or not tigers, rhinos, elephants and innumerable other species are fully and irrevocably caught up in our economic world and are perceived to be worth less there alive than dead as things stand. There is no point in bemoaning this – it is a fact of life. Equally there is little point in relying on "damming" the economic forces that detrimentally exploit them via policing alone because time and again it has been proven not to work beyond the short term. In the end the market always rules. If my journey to this point has taught me anything it is that all such exploitation is an inevitable consequence of the colonising dynamic of markets and ecosystems alike. Instead we need to find ways to manipulate our economic ecosystem to be kind to conservation. We need lasting *market* solutions to what are essentially market-generated problems.

So it is that, while economics is fast becoming the nemesis of many species, paradoxically it is also their chief hope of recovery. For if the demand for animals to live free in protected wilderness is more financially rewarding than that for their body parts, then the power of markets will automatically be enlisted to help protect them. We consequently need to set good, powerful markets to overwhelm bad ones.

I will return to this subject a little further on, as there are other considerations involved that will become apparent in the meantime.

Can *Junglenomics* turn this destructive economic tide?

What would Nature do about a drastic loss of species and environment to the rampages of such a resource-hungry supercoloniser as *Homo sapiens*?

The literal answer is of course, nothing at all. After all, throughout the history of life innumerable species have died out; indeed, some 99% of species that have ever existed are extinct. Nature is not in the business of saving species; instead she creates new ones and reconstructs ecosystems that include them. So, no one or thing is going to throw us a lifeline. We are on our own and have to solve these problems ourselves or suffer the consequences. This means that we have no alternative but to learn how to re-engineer this malfunctioning economic ecosystem of ours to make it more compatible with the global environment and its species, upon which this ecosystem is entirely dependent. Business as usual is not an option.

A fully developed economic ecosystem is exactly like an ecological one. Its participants interact in ways that permit coexistence and survival. At heart it is dog eat dog in both of course, but the balancing formula is ultimately one where the survival of essential participants is assured, not so much through compulsion but through the powerful, universal dynamics of self-interest. Ecosystems only reach a state of balance, therefore, when the power of the self-seeking participant organisms to overconsume remains below that needed to upset the balance. Currently our economic ecosystems are in a state of imbalance in their interactions with the natural world because certain influential economic actors are too powerful. It is not yet too late to change this: realignment is still possible.

The key lies in creating systemic counterbalances that do the business of conservation and are self-perpetuating. The *Junglenomics* approach to reducing poaching and environmental over-exploitation to sustainable levels would therefore be achieved by nurturing and empowering counterbalancing economic entities in whose economic interest it is to protect and restore threatened species and environments. Conservation programmes would therefore need to focus on finding ways to make vulnerable species and environments worth a lot more alive than dead to financially (and legally) powerful groups. That means raising their "alive-and-wild" financial yield (and hence capital value), while simultaneously reducing their carcass or consumer value.

One good way to help with the latter is to substitute cheaper, easily available alternatives, by farming or synthesising them for example. Another is to increase deterrence measures (the costs) for the consumers of wildlife contraband, who are the primary catalyst of such markets. However, while these methods can sometimes contribute usefully for a while (like the 1989 ivory ban), in this case they have not proved effective on their own. Something more is needed to complement them – a broader economic solution.

What does this involve in practical terms? There are some interesting projects that fit the bill. Although these projects exist already, to date none receive the scale and intensity of international support they could and should if their true value were more widely appreciated.

Community-based conservation

The first of these projects was highly successful in its 1990s heyday, but through loss of support, since declined. It was called the "Communal Areas Management Programme for Indigenous Resources", or CAMPFIRE. The context in which CAMPFIRE came to be set up in Zimbabwe in 1989 is interesting because it is typical of much of postcolonial Africa.

Under colonial rule indigenous people had been banned from hunting the wild animals on which they had previously depended for food, clothing, tools and ritual practices. The result was that, where once they had lived in harmony with wildlife, these now subsistence farmers came to regard it as a nuisance. It destroyed their food crops, raided livestock and threatened their safety, and at that time they received no compensatory benefit to sweeten the pill [8]. There was also widespread resentment that others, mainly safari tourists and big-game shooters, had taken over what they regarded as *their* wildlife and were exploiting it for their own financial gain.

It is perhaps little wonder therefore that poaching became rife. As numbers plummeted, colonials were replaced by conservationists and tour operators. These saw the exclusion of indigenous people from national parks and the deployment of armed rangers as the only answer to the decline in species. Tribespeople were shipped out from their ancestral territories *en masse* and forbidden to return. But growing populations, poor agricultural practices, and intermittent droughts began to put pressure on the lands surrounding the national parks to which the local people had been banished. More land was now needed for them to cultivate.

By the 1980s, expanding cultivation and poaching had become two of the biggest problems facing wildlife in Africa. Valiant game rangers, always far too few in numbers, fought a running war against poachers entering the parks to hunt valuable ivory, rhino horn and bushmeat. It was a losing struggle. Wildlife numbers went into a downward spiral. Another solution was sorely needed. It was with inspired inputs from ecologists, economists and sociologists alike that CAMPFIRE came to into being [9].

CAMPFIRE's remit was to bring wildlife and local people back together again, to put them on the same side once more. By involving rural communities in conservation and sustainable development the hope was to alleviate poverty and protect wildlife all in one. The plan was to harvest natural resources for profit, not least by tapping into the lucrative international market for game hunting. Foreign hunters have long been prepared to pay substantial sums to hunt elephant, buffalo, giraffe, lion, kudu and other wild animals, and soon over 60% of CAMPFIRE profits were being derived from elephant hunts alone. The new inflow of funds brought schools, power, water and roads to the poorest Zimbabweans. There were other benefits, for example the sale of excess animal stocks to national parks, and the sustainable harvesting of natural resources. Tourism was another important element [10].

This imaginative project was for a time well supported by international charities. For example, USAID, the primary American conduit for Third World project funding, was a leading contributor. But USAID became infiltrated by animal rights pressure groups whose campaigns bore an undue influence on policy. Despite CAMPFIRE's evident benefits they remained vehemently opposed to all forms of hunting, unmoved by the argument that hunting had always been a fundamental and natural part of the African way of life. Although I would not consider big-game trophy hunting myself, I would not begrudge it to others so long as it is performed in a lawful, humane, ecologically sensitive and socially inclusive manner with demonstrable environmental gain.

If wildlife populations are not damaged by carefully controlled game hunting (indeed those involved vigorously maintain the reverse is true, and the evidence supports it) it seems incongruous that affluent foreigners who don't begin to understand the complexities of wildlife management should seek to impose subjective, sentimental and elitist Western morality on those who struggle to feed their families. Some animal rights campaigners like to point to Kenya as a paradigm for successful non-hunting conservation, yet anyone who knows Kenya knows that poverty, conflict, poaching and exclusion remain endemic there.

Perhaps I am being unduly harsh towards these activists. They overflow with that most noble of human sentiments – empathy. But when empathy towards individual animals overtakes empathy for fellow human beings and for wildlife in the round to such a degree that they actively obstruct constructive programmes that clearly benefit both, then perhaps they need to re-examine both their consciences and their philosophy. If they had their way everywhere they would surely preside over the destruction of our great wildernesses and their wildlife.

CAMPFIRE was perhaps the nearest you could come to an example of a socially responsible commercial project for wildlife conservation. It was also hugely successful in its main aim – to re-engage local people with their wildlife. As revenues were distributed, local people soon began to view wildlife in a different way, as a result of which poaching levels plunged.

Yet in 2000, all outside aid to CAMPFIRE ceased and the project was on its own. But the problems that later arose were not from lack of funds, for it had by then generated substantial commercial revenues. Instead they were political. A combination of the ending of the charities' oversight of accounting practices and spiralling political turmoil in Zimbabwe resulted in the corrupt inveigling of revenues by local chiefs and their comrades [11]. Democratic processes were subsequently undermined; payments to local communities fell to pitiful levels, further diluted by opportunist incomers joining the bandwagon to milk the revenues.

Nevertheless, while CAMPFIRE's political structure was in disarray, many of the pre-2000 benefits, such as reduced poaching and better resource use, seem to have become engrained in local behaviour – for the time being at least. Ongoing hunting revenues also ensure close attention is still paid to conserving trophy game species' numbers. Despite the current hiatus, CAMPFIRE's benign influence is not in doubt. At independence from Britain in 1980, just 12% of Zimbabwe's land was devoted to wildlife management, all of it in state-managed protected areas. But since the establishment of CAMPFIRE this has increased to 33% through the inclusion of communal lands and private conservancies [12]. The principle of community conservation thus remains intact.

Functioning as it did pre-2000, CAMPFIRE's credentials within the local economic ecosystem were not in doubt; in fact they were classical. In effect the system nurtures economic species, among them hunters, tour organisers, conservationists and, most importantly, local people. They promoted the welfare of ecosystems and wildlife for the most pressing and dependable of reasons – economic and social benefit.

Hunting holds an extra-special place in conservation. This is because you can breed many kinds of animals for the table in controlled farm environments, but you cannot do so for hunting. For that, animals need not only to be wild, but also to inhabit wild places. Therefore hunting encourages the conservation of wilderness and wildlife together, and leaves great tracts of land virtually undisturbed. In fact, hunting safari parks in South Africa have resulted in huge areas of land being "re-wilded" – that is, turned from farmland back into natural wilderness. This is to the benefit not only of the large species, but to the tens of thousands of others, of all types and sizes, that have been able to recolonise their old habitats after centuries of exclusion. It is truly a win-win situation.

This is not to suggest for a moment that there should be a hunting free-for-all; just sensitive cull-hunting programmes like those that have operated successfully on Scottish sporting estates and elsewhere for centuries – for the benefit of the species for which it is in everyone's interests to conserve. Regulated hunting needs to be carried out only under licence as part of a legitimate conservation programme monitored by conservationists and run by experienced personnel. Done in this benevolent way, more rural Africans will be given the opportunity to re-engage with their priceless heritage in a constructive and mutually beneficial way, producing a potentially rich and productive symbiotic relationship that could stabilise the loss of land and wildlife, and endure long into the future.

CAMPFIRE is once again thriving, and along with its undoubted success in wildlife conservation, its claim that it *"has a combined 2.4 million beneficiaries, made up of 200,000 households that actively participate in the programme, and another 600,000 households that benefit indirectly from social services and infrastructure supported by CAMPFIRE income within districts"* is testimony to the benefits of its model.

Tourism and community conservation projects

What goes for game hunting goes equally for game viewing. The involvement of local people in tourism and wildlife conservation projects is an essential means to ensuring that protection, something at which the CAMPFIRE Association also excels. It is the only sure way to balance local economic ecosystems. You cannot expect wildernesses and wildlife ever to be safe while financial exclusion, resentment and poverty lurk hungrily at its gates.

Frustrated by the failures of recent years, elsewhere conservation thinking has likewise turned towards exploring alternative approaches to controlling the over-exploitation of wildlife and plants. It is encouraging to see that some of these approaches also have the hallmark of *Junglenomics*, and it is perhaps no coincidence that they too are showing considerable promise. In Nepal, for example, villagers were encouraged to reclaim and replant more than six square miles of degraded forest on the edge of Chitwan National Park. They were then allowed to keep half the proceeds from visiting tourists eager to see the wildlife. In the first year alone they earned $308,000 from entrance fees, and, even more excitingly, not only did a family of tigers and two transient males soon move in, but also at the time of writing twelve rhinos have also given birth there. A charity called Eden Reforestation Projects has taken up the baton, and by partnering with the national park system, is helping to protect and create a reforested buffer zone that is vital to protect animal habitat while at the same time benefiting the local economy.

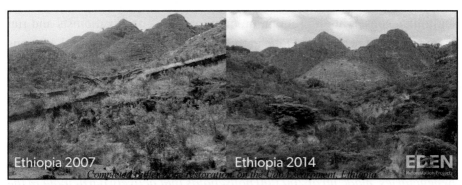

(courtesy of Eden Reforestation Projects)

Meanwhile in northern KwaZulu-Natal, Dave Varty and Alan Bernstein began a remarkable project with 17,000 acres of low-grade agricultural land. They transformed it into a game park containing all the "big five" – leopard, lion, elephant, rhino and buffalo. With luxury lodges for ecotourist guests the project returned a substantial region to the use of wild animals and plants; it also increased the return on the land from about $13 per hectare per year to $280.

Even more importantly, they had what was then a new ethos in tourism. Recognising that local economic development and successful conservation are inseparable, they resolved to revert substantial revenues to local people. This not only brought more and better paid jobs for local people but in

1992 the company, CC Africa (now called "&Beyond"), went a leap further by founding Africa Foundation, dedicated to empowering communities through conservation.

This not-for-profit organisation focuses on education, healthcare and income generation in areas adjacent to conservation areas across Africa, using over US$6 million [13] on projects for local people that have transformed their lives. Through pure common sense, Varty and Bernstein recognised and acted on what is a fundamental *Junglenomics* truth: that those granted a significant economic stake in wildlife survival will naturally help to protect it. Economic forces were imaginatively redirected towards a creative exploitation of wild flora and fauna.

African Parks is another outstanding not-for-profit organisation that is making inroads in this respect. Also using a business model, it takes on complete responsibility for the rehabilitation and long-term management of national parks in partnership with governments and local communities. It currently manages 15 national parks and protected areas in nine countries covering 10.5 million hectares: Benin, Central African Republic, Chad, the Democratic Republic of Congo, Malawi, Mozambique, the Republic of Congo, Rwanda and Zambia. African Parks only began in 2000, but it has proved that it too deserves to be fast-tracked by the international community rather than left to its own devices.

However heartening this may be, such enlightened investment and management is still far from widespread. Elsewhere, ongoing economic exclusion has continued to cause some tribespeople to resent wealthy tourists, for whom their ancestral tribal hunting country is exclusively reserved. As a result, it is unsafe for travellers to visit large parts of Kenya, for example, as well as many other African countries.

Through the Africa Foundation, "&Beyond" has shown what can be achieved. But it has been a tough road for them and others like them. Only hard work and loyal shareholders have seen it through a number of crises. Such indisputably valuable enterprises should get a substantial financial leg-up from the international community if they are to colonise the ecotourism market as we would all surely want them to. They are a benign new economic "start-up" species struggling to get established, and they need and deserve help to survive and thrive like any in the wild. As it is they have to rely on generous donors, not public funds, and cannot yet dominate the marketplace because they are up against tough competition from tourist companies unburdened by such responsible financial commitments to local people. With better funding and a level playing field they could thrive and colonise the market in time to help save species, reduce poverty, expand education, and conserve wild regions far into the future. Whenever that happens, it will not be a moment too soon.

I should add that this is emphatically not intended to belittle the magnificent efforts of the numerous charitable wildlife conservation organisations, take the Wilderness Foundation for an outstanding example. With charitable support, they carry out invaluable work protecting wildlife, educating, building trust and cooperation. But still they are just fingers in the dam, making recognisable progress locally, but only at best temporarily checking the onslaught of destructive commercial exploitation of their beloved wildlife and wilderness. The unavoidable truth is that this onslaught will only be broken and the pressure on wildlife and environments lifted for the long term when the economic equation favours it.

A virtual experience

Of course, there is a limit to just how many tourists can visit sensitive areas without causing them harm. However, technology is throwing up exciting new and potentially lucrative opportunities for greatly expanding "wildlife experience" among people, without any increased footfall – from the comfort of their living rooms. Live camera set-ups are already out there and you can log on to watch them from your armchair any time you like, but I'm referring here to "virtual safaris", in which wearers of virtual reality headsets will be able to experience live safaris daily from the comfort of their living rooms thousands of miles away. The potential market is huge, and it will surely motivate millions of people to empathise with and learn more about wild animals, nature and ecosystems. It will engage them in the real time stories about real places and their struggles to survive, and that can surely do nothing but good.

There are technological hoops to go through, especially the problem of broadcasting sufficient resolution for 360-degree vision, but if this can be overcome, and "virtual safari" businesses were to raise pay-per-view revenues from subscribers to go towards wildlife management and local development projects, the outcome could be good for all.

Diversionary farming: protecting wild populations through farming

As mentioned earlier, another way to reduce market pressure on target species and environments can be to make cheaper and more easily available alternatives available by farming or synthesising them. Such "diversionary" farming is an important, yet underused tool for conservation that in principle has sound *Junglenomics* credentials.

Quite a few wild species are already farmed, notably marine ones, with which considerable progress has been made. Included are the Atlantic salmon, catfish, carp and various shellfish, crustaceans and molluscs such as mussels and oysters. Some undomesticated land animals are farmed for their highly valued products too – ostrich, crocodile, deer, bison, water buffalo and mink for example. Ranches, many in South Africa, also breed a selection of game, including buffalo, sable and roan antelope, and wildebeest, both for trophy hunting and to provide stock for burgeoning wildlife parks in newly affluent countries such as Vietnam and China.

The relative security of the wild populations of many such farmed species demonstrates how the farming of appropriate wild animals and plants can be a sustainable way to take the pressure off wild stocks, create local wealth, and satisfy market demand all at once.

Bob Murphy of the Royal Ontario Museum in Toronto is one of those who spotted the principle some while ago [14]. He proposed that the commercial breeding of tokay geckos in Vietnam, hunted to scarcity because of their supposed medicinal properties, might save the species from becoming endangered. His common-sense solution was that once commercially farmed, these easily bred creatures would take the pressure off the wild version. It would also increase wild geckos' value as replacement breeding stock, further helping to protect them. A thriving gecko farming industry now flourishes in Vietnam.

However, hunting tokays from the wild still continues because demand outstrips supply, and farming is more expensive than wild sources, so the latter get passed off as legitimate. Clearly, farming needs to be well regulated and monitored, which isn't currently the case, making it relatively easy to smuggle wild geckos in with farmed ones.

Nevertheless, diversionary farming is another classic *Junglenomics* tactic. Outlawing the hunting of wild geckos would be difficult and expensive to enforce, which is probably why it failed beforehand. It would struggle against the economic tide and could not be sustained forever. But the development of an alternative economic niche – farming – to satisfy the demand for geckos keeps the price low and relieves the pressure on their wild relatives. The financial resources used on policing, law courts and prisons would also be much better used on subsidising farming to keep its prices down.

The farming of wild animals and plants is after all no different from what our ancestors did so successfully 10,000 years ago with wild fruits, grasses, goats, sheep, pigs, cattle, horses and fowl, the wild versions of some of which would otherwise almost certainly be long extinct.

There are other notable examples where farming has taken the pressure away and thus protected wild species, allowing their numbers to recover – among them the South American vicuña, alpaca-like animals whose wool is some of the finest and most expensive in the world, and which before range farming came into being was severely endangered [15].

Breeding for the wild – the ranching industry

Breeding wild animals specifically for release into the wild is another way in which farming contributes to wildlife conservation. Few could object to this form of species "ranching" because captive breeding programmes, whether commercial or funded, can help to restock wild populations of endangered species. Bengal tigers, for example, have powerful economic pull because tourists will pay handsomely to see them in the wild, just as they do Africa's "big five".

However, where poaching is still a problem, reintroduction to the wild can be difficult and disappointing for those who invest so much energy only to see the progeny slaughtered by poachers, as so often happens. For example, with rhino horn now more valuable than gold it has become extremely difficult to protect rhinos once released into the wild. It therefore needs to take place in coordination using programmes like Africa Foundation, CAMPFIRE and Chitwan. Even in areas where it is not safe to release endangered species, captive breeding programmes still play an important role in increasing public awareness and raising funds for conservation projects.

The trapping and transporting of excess stocks of species among its ranches is also a thriving business among South Africa's numerous commercial game ranches. The market in game and predator species is strong and animals can fetch high prices at auctions. These markets, generated by ecotourism, overseas safari parks, hunting and meat production, are carried out under licence to ensure standards. They also ensure that for the foreseeable future all the species involved are safe from extinction, even if not in the wild.

The scourge of traditional medicine

At least a quarter of the world's population, including Japanese, Vietnamese, Koreans and ethnic Chinese use medical practices based on traditional Chinese medicine (TCM). TCM pharmacopoeia lists more than 11,500 different plants, animals and minerals, and the effects of this on wildlife has been devastating despite a plethora of international laws to regulate their supply and use.

The reason for TCM demand is case specific. Mainstream TCM now rejects the use of endangered species for medicine, but millions of Asians still demand traditional cures from a medical tradition stretching back 3,000 years or more. TCM prescribers are well aware of the plight of many of the species they exploit, but they also feel a duty towards their patients. Chemical and farmed alternatives have made some inroads, but the problem here is that the whole ethos of TCM rests on the perceived "naturalness" of its remedies, which may have some placebo effect. Many consumers and prescribers therefore prefer wild ingredients, believing them to be more potent. But even if they did not, TCM plants cultivated in China only supply less than 20% of the required 1.6 million tonnes per annum.

Pangolin

Similarly, China's demand for animal products such as musk and pangolin scales (a kind of anteater) far exceeds the supply available from farmed sources. Because nearby stocks are limited, suppliers search for new markets in other continents, buying eagerly offered wild supplies from as far afield as Ecuador and Mozambique [16]. Consequently, the TCM merchant network has spread worldwide.

The demise of wild stocks of herbs through over-exploitation resulting from the increasing commercialisation of this market threatens their very survival. It also threatens the livelihoods of many poor rural communities that currently depend upon harvesting them. If appropriate intervention is not forthcoming soon, many more species will suffer the fate of *Prunus africana*, the African cherry, the bark of which was popular as a remedy for prostate enlargement. It was in such demand that whole trunks were stripped, killing the trees wholesale and with them the lucrative market they had enjoyed [17]. The problem is so bad that, it is estimated, somewhere between four and ten thousand of the fifty thousand medicinal plants still harvested in the wild are now endangered [18].

Some see this as being a failure of farming as a remedy for wild exploitation, but as a generalisation this is surely mistaken. Clearly farming is successful in other arenas, and successful at supplying the TCM market and reducing the pressure on wild stocks at least to some degree.

Undoubtedly this penchant for wild ingredients is a difficult problem to solve – like trying to stop Americans eating hamburgers or Germans sauerkraut. Changing engrained culture, even in an authoritarian society like China's, is never going to happen overnight, and it will take a range of measures. To this end, along with the subsidised expansion of farming there are at least four good ways to attack the medicinal, culinary and cultural market demands that the trade in endangered TCM species thrives on: education, substitution, policing and consumer deterrence. Education is probably the least effective method in this unique case because, according to experts, consumers are incorrigible: TCM's popularity and long tradition of use among educated people means that trying to convince them that it is unprovable nonsense is doomed to failure – in the short term at least.

Substitution for alternative, non-endangered animal sources is sometimes possible. For example, the bones of a common Asian rodent, the sailong, are said to be a good alternative to those of tigers [19]. However, consumer deterrence is of special importance in curbing the demand for wild TCM supplies. It goes to the heart of the matter. Consumer demand is after all the power, directly or indirectly, behind all markets. Without it the motive to supply dries up, dissipating the economic-colonising imperative. It is practitioners' prescriptions on the one hand and demand from their clients on the other that fuel the poaching problem. Those who poach are reacting to the eternal drive to colonise viable economic opportunities, so in the end the economic equation is about as simple as it gets: if there's no money from the activity there's no incentive to do it and it won't happen [20].

Driving the trade in unsustainable TCM supplies underground is the quickest way to ensure its survival. *Junglenomics* requires that such unwanted economic species are driven to extinction by competition from benign sources rather than mutated into a pernicious, hard to eradicate, illegal market. For this reason, the trade in wild sources needs to remain legal, visible and monitored, but also to carry substantial levies. Ring-fenced, these levies can then be used to support farmed products by increasing the price differential between them and wild sources. All practitioners should be licensed and forbidden to buy illegal supplies on pain of financial penalties and even disbarment (similarities to the drugs trade are legion).

The older generation may be stuck in their ways, but a new generation of educated and aware Chinese youngsters may yet shame them into mending their ways. So at the same time a loud public information campaign for the younger generation, endorsed by respected role models such as pop and film stars, against wild TCM supplies needs to be launched. The Chinese pop star Angelababy has already blazed the trail in defence of pangolins.

Asian government investment and market management have so far been woefully lacking in these areas. The sooner resources can be diverted to economic remedies, licensing, education and deterrence, the sooner the profitability of such destructive niches will be undermined. In the absence of such a concerted programme of management it is beyond doubt that the ongoing growth of human populations will ensure that all wild flora and fauna that provide an economic niche (or that are dependent on ones that do so) will continue to be endangered. Undoubtedly many will disappear altogether.

In Vietnam, a new twist to the TCM story is playing out, one that is causing a double tragedy. Rising pollution has inevitably followed in the wake of rapid economic growth, and cancer rates have soared to near Western levels. With a dire shortage of radiotherapy units, quack doctors have reportedly turned to prescribing exotic and highly lucrative "cures". Powdered rhino horn is one such, even though it has no place anywhere in TCM pharmacopeia. These charlatans' newly affluent, often desperate patients can hardly be blamed for being tricked in this way, but it is yet another devastating exploitation for rhinos and it needs to be addressed urgently.

Wild animal farming controversies

Gecko farmer, Bob Murphy, was not the first to practice the commercial breeding of endangered species specifically to take the pressure off wild populations; but obvious though the idea may appear it has been surprisingly slow to get off the ground. Lack of expertise and capital investment may have something to do with it but, to be fair, farming may not be not practicable in some cases because some species do not lend themselves well to commercial farming. Farming wild animals can also be controversial for ethical reasons. A large number of people are particularly against the farming of higher species, especially mammals. But criticism of bear farming for bile, a popular remedy in TCM, puzzles Chinese officials who regard it as a triumph of balancing conservation and commercial needs. You don't have to be an activist or conservationist to believe that animal welfare is an important issue in any kind of farming, and concern over bear farming methods in particular seems well justified. The extremely cramped living conditions and painful bile extraction process via permanently connected drip tubes defies any reasonable definition of a humane farming procedure.

Bear farming for bile raises another important issue that needs to be addressed before any big expansion of wild animal farming can be encouraged. Can the commercial exploitation of animals be ethically sanctioned where the medical effectiveness of their products is based solely on superstition and palliation? Furthermore, does this kind of farming not feed the growth of frivolous markets that will inevitably also claim ever more victims from the wild, where they are seen to cost nothing?

To illustrate this, consider the tiger again. Currently the price of supposedly medicinal tiger parts is high and only wealthy Chinese can afford them. Mass tiger breeding programmes would bring down their price and expand their trade to unprecedented levels, especially in a vast and newly affluent continent. However, there is little doubt that wild tiger parts will still hold a premium over reared, being considered "more potent". What is more, as wild tiger parts are impossible to tell from reared ones, once in the market they cannot be identified, making policing extremely difficult.

Tiger farming cannot therefore realistically fulfil the crucial aim of reducing the corpse value of wild tigers and making them more valuable alive than dead, a primary objective of *Junglenomics*. So on this count alone it is clear to me that a non-farming solution has to be found, one that either destroys the market for tiger parts or makes wild tigers far more valuable alive than dead and well protected by those endowed with a financial interest to protect them – local communities engaged in tourism, for example.

So when it comes to higher mammals, not everything is as clear-cut as one might like it to be. There is also a lot of sentiment involved. The French eat horses, which upsets the British. In the Far East, they eat dogs, which upsets a lot of people everywhere. And, is it just me, or is there something about the African elephant that makes them a special case? Do we really want to see these magnificent beasts farmed for the frivolous ivory market? Is there really no other way to protect them other than shooting poachers dead, day after day, far into the future? Killing the market by direct means is proposed in some quarters as the best solution, and the Chinese have instituted a ban on the ivory trade to that end. But is this not just another example of the failed "damming" of unwanted markets that I referred to earlier as historically and evidentially ineffective?

Here I am uncertain what to think, so I will say no more and hope that just the once damming works, though I fear the worst. I fear that ivory bans will not only mean that the trade will continue underground at even higher prices, but also that some ivory poachers will turn their attention to other species, putting even more pressure on remaining rhino, tiger or pangolin populations for example, moving the problem from one trade to another in classic "economic avatar" style as described at the start of this book.

The problem with taking a high-minded or sentimental approach to any and all wild animal inclusion in the economic ecosystem is that it may easily have the opposite effect to the desired one. When markets are untameable by any other means, farming must be the preferred option, even if only as a stopgap mechanism while more palatable, long-term solutions are pursued. Sentiment must not be allowed to usher species to their extinction.

Clearly one size doesn't fit all when it comes to farming and domesticating wild species. Decisions over which wild species should be farmed need to be taken on a case-by-case basis and policies chosen accordingly. Making wild animals and their environments valuable to governments, and most importantly, entire local populations, and equipping the latter appropriately to defend them, must be the first choice *Junglenomics* option. Farming is beneficial only where an expanding, long-term market is supportable and justifiable, and where farming methods are humane and safe. Reversing such decisions later will be difficult once markets and supply lines have been established, as the oil palm industry has so clearly demonstrated.

The "commodification" argument

Unfortunately, there is a core of people, some of them ecologists, who object to any commercial exploitation of wildlife, which they see as a "commodification" of the natural world.

While instinctively and emotionally I cannot help but sympathise (I would love nothing more than if wild places and their species could be left entirely alone), my pragmatic *Junglenomics* head tells another story. Much as we might dislike it, commodification has been a fact of life long into prehistory. We humans have wanted to acquire animal parts and plants for hundreds of thousands of years, ever since we began wearing hides to keep warm, perhaps earlier. Indeed, the exploitation of animals helped make us who we are. Just look at any stock farm, or at the milk you just put in your coffee.

Today's legal trade and illegal poaching for parts and pets is really nothing new, therefore; it is but a modern-day manifestation of the age-old practice of commodifying species for our use. The only difference is that, where once people hunted and gathered their own animal parts and plants, farming has multiplied our numbers exponentially, and economic specialisation means that others now supply them to order. It is thus a market supply and demand equation like any other, and as such it is an integral element of economic life that we cannot wish away and that demands economics solutions.

Today, vast population increases have ramped up demand for ever-diminishing wildlife resources to unprecedented levels. It is a toxic combination. Nature also suffers badly because far more of its products have been translated by the modern economic world into commodities than ever before, including the very land wild species need to survive on. This is so whether it is something like rainforest being exploited destructively, or a food resource like marine life, or a "free" sink for waste and pollution. There is no escaping this. We cannot vanish the natural world off the radar of economic demand by edict. History shows us that regulations – the instinctive shield that the traditional conservationist reaches for – have not and will not work on their own over the long term because of the deep fallibility of enforcement methods; which is why we find ourselves fighting the same old battles just a few years after we thought they were won. Because like all others, ecologically destructive markets are powered by the irresistible natural imperative to colonise resources, the economic pressures are far too great, too widespread and too shifting to police indefinitely.

On the other hand, projects that are run on a socially inclusive principle represent an economic counterculture, which by valuing living, thriving wildlife as an economic asset gives it its rightful place in the economic ecosystem that we have constructed.

In the end, if we really want to protect species from destructive markets we have no alternative but to fight fire with fire by empowering ecologically benign markets to displace destructive ones. One day we may live in a world where ethics dominate all markets, but we cannot wait for that impossibly idealised day to save threatened species – they will be long gone by then. The realities of the economic world we live in, and the power of resource hunger that drives it, need to be recognised and accommodated if they are to be contained. Anything else will only add to the record of abject failure, condemning the natural world to continue its slide towards oblivion.

1. *According to Edward O Wilson*

2. *World Wildlife Fund 2016*

3. *Anthony J Stuart. Mammalian extinctions in the late Pleistocene of Northern Eurasia and North America. 21 Jan. 2008.*

4. *Amongst them George Schaller and Alan Rabinowitz*

5. *Guardian May 2016*

6. *Guardian May 2016*

7. *New Scientist 2365*

8. *TED case study 1999, Amanda Hilligas*

9. *http://www.resourceafrica.org/documents/1993/1993_campfire_bg.pdf*

10. *http://www.globaleye.org.uk/archive/summer2k/focuson/mars_pt1.html*

11. *Dr. Judith Mashinya, 2007: Participation and Devolution in Zimbabwe's CAMPFIRE Programme: findings from local projects in Mahenye and Nyaminyami*

12. *Bond 2001; Khumalo 2003; Murphree 2001*

13. *According to its own online literature*

14. *New Scientist 1994*

15. *Vicuña poaching problems are again on the rise, but this is largely because of extremely lax enforcement regimes towards trafficking. Without farming, it is certain they would long ago have ceased to exist in the wild*

16. *New Scientist 2115*

17. *Study by Kristine Stewart of consultants Keith & Schnars NS2429 pp10-11*

18. *Alan Hamilton, a plant specialist from the global environment network, the WWF*

19. *For a comprehensive overview of animal use in Chinese medicine see: Scienceline.org: "From Beijing to New York: The dark side of traditional Chinese medicine" Rachel Nuwer 2011*

20. *Professor Rosaline Duffy's article in NS 2777, p28, makes a similar point*

Chapter 12
The Population Time Bomb

Malthus revisited

Whatever policies are adopted to rescue the world's environments from over-exploitation, many of them are sooner or later going to come up against perhaps the greatest obstacle of all – mushrooming human populations.

Population planning is a thorny issue. In 18th-century Europe the idea was to increase numbers to cope with labour shortages. But not everyone agreed with this – most famously the British clergyman and economist Thomas Malthus, who made a name for himself proclaiming that the benefits of greater access to resources brought by economic development would be counteracted by growing numbers of people, keeping millions in poverty instead of helping them out of it as intended. Population should therefore be kept in check, he argued.

Although Malthus's views have long been discredited (due in no small part to the failure of his predictions to materialise in Europe), population growth has once again come to be regarded as a sure recipe for resource depletion and the perpetuation of poverty, this time in some of the least developed regions of the world. Essentially this is Malthus revisited. Of added concern today however, is that growing numbers of people also means growing pressure on biodiverse regions such as rainforests, savannah and wetlands for materials to sell and land on which to grow food.

Up to now it hasn't been rising populations of the poor that has been the main driver of decline in world environments, but runaway demand from wealthy developed countries. From afar, the developed world has been consuming vastly more resources per capita than *in situ* Third World inhabitants. This insatiable consumption, from oil and gas to minerals, timber, rubber, beef, paper, soya, palm oil and so forth, continues to be the greatest destroyer of wilderness and diminisher of biodiversity, for which China, the US and the EU carry the greatest responsibility. To make matters worse though, the developing world has now joined the party. As a major recent report from the Intergovernmental Science-Policy Platform on Biodiversity and Ecosystem Services (IPBES) concluded: *"underlying drivers of land degradation are the high-consumption lifestyles in the most developed economies, combined with rising consumption in developing and emerging economies."*

So just when most of the developed world is at last waking up and looking for ways to clean up its act by reducing pollution and conserving biodiversity both at home and abroad, the negative consequences of rising populations in the developing world have become a highly unwelcome extra burden on an already besieged and declining natural world. Increasing consumption, along with rising numbers of subsistence farmers, poachers, and bushmeat and pet trade hunters in sub-Saharan Africa, Asia and South America, is rapidly heading up the charts as a driver of biodiversity loss – the demise of the orangutan and the pangolin being flagship examples. As the IPBES report goes on: *"high and rising per capita consumption, amplified by continued population growth in many parts of the world, are driving unsustainable levels of agricultural expansion, natural resource and mineral extraction, and urbanization."* In other words: more people consuming more stuff at the expense of the natural world. Familiar?

Should we worry? Is this burgeoning of populations merely temporary? It seems not – in sub-Saharan Africa at least. New studies based on advanced methodology predict with 80% certainty that, although over the next few decades birth rates will stabilise in most continents, including the Americas and Europe, and while Asia it is expected to rise by around 10% before falling back, Africa is the standout exception: its population is predicted to rise from 1.2 billion today to between *4 and 6* billion by the end of the century. That's around a *fourfold* rise or more in just 80 years in a continent already struggling to feed its people.

If this predicted problem isn't resolved in Africa in particular, then feeding such a huge number of new mouths is inevitably going to have dire consequences for its wilderness and wildlife. It will greatly exacerbate an already tense human-wildlife competition for resources, especially for water, timber and territory.

This could hardly happen in a more sensitive place. Africa is home to eight of the world's 34 biodiversity hotspots, including a quarter of the world's mammals and a fifth of all bird species, so there's no doubt that this glorious array of biodiversity will be hit hard as ever more wilderness is lost to human incursion.

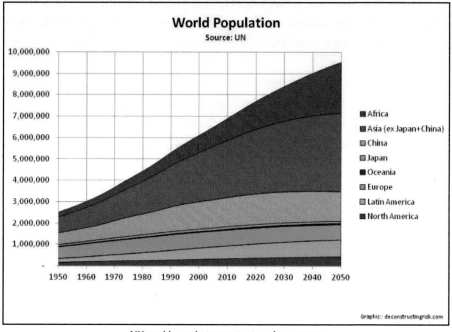

UN world-population-projections-by-continent

This is the main reason why the emphasis is once again on population control. But why are Malthus's worst fears resurfacing for the developing world when they were proved false two centuries ago in his home continent, and indeed everywhere else in what is now the developed world? It's important to answer this because where Malthus's predictions went wrong in Europe ought to provide a good view on how to make sure they do likewise in Africa.

History again delivers the perspective. I explained in chapter one how farming allowed individuals to specialise in producing products like pots and carts and tools, and then exchange them for food. Yet while farming made way for specialisation and freed some from the production of food, specialists naturally still needed to get food – it was just that farmers now produced enough to go around – so long as you had something to trade in return of course.

At first this all took place in a local context much like the African subsistence scene today. However, as over the centuries European economies developed, food supplies could gradually come from ever further afield. Rome's dependence on grain from its far-flung empire is legendary for example, releasing ever more people from farming to take up specialist trades and congregate in cities. Today, vegetables may travel all the way from Spain or Mexico, fish from Indonesia, Chile or Canada, meat from New Zealand or Argentina, and fruit from China or the Caribbean. Indeed, so great is the international trade in such staples that in most developed countries local produce is the exception rather than the rule.

The world trade in food is important to this issue because the food trade allows people *not* to have to grow stuff in their backyard and destroy more and more wilderness in the process. They can do something else clever and then trade the proceeds for food, just as those first specialists learned to do thousands of years ago. Yet in the poorest regions of the world this is still not so to any great extent – particularly in remote areas adjacent to or within wilderness where, despite the passing of centuries since their exposure to Western agricultural methods and markets, the development of high-tech, modern trading economies has still to even get out of bed.

The result is that in the absence of technologically smart, specialist-filled economies and sophisticated divisions of labour, rural people are still far too largely dependent upon locally grown produce, and most are therefore subsistence farmers or menial labourers scraping by in tough circumstances. Whereas in a developing Europe more mouths translated into more specialists, here in the African hinterland more mouths therefore translate into more subsistence farmers. Here, ill-equipped agriculture and ill-informed agricultural practices exhaust soils and drive desertification, encouraging ever greater incursions into wilderness and ever more cattle into bush, depriving wild animals of essential habitat and grazing; and here, droughts bring food shortages, and in the worst cases, periodic famines, a grim reality that may be experienced by more and more poor people as climate change bites deeper into local weather patterns.

These problems are already bad enough, but the predicted huge population increase in sub-Saharan Africa is set to exacerbate them beyond our, and their worst nightmares. The point is, we are not talking about encroachment on African wilderness by exploding numbers of chartered accountants, lawyers, shopkeepers or insurance salesmen. Here it is a primary equation mainly involving that first rung in economic development – agriculture. In a developed and diverse economy, specialists need land measured merely in square metres to live and work in, and of no agricultural quality. But a farmer needs acres to subsist, acres that are all too often converted from valuable wilderness once housing precious biodiversity and providing valuable ecosystem services, such as rainfall, ground stabilisation and temperature control. And to cap this, extracting and selling Nature's raw materials is the easy option when other jobs are scarce. True – developed countries have already converted a high proportion of their land to agriculture, destroying much of their own wilderness in the process; but as advances in agricultural technology have allowed land to become vastly more productive they have been steadily increasing their forest cover. With plenty of previously degraded land ripe for regeneration at their disposal, it is this high level of agricultural productivity that sub-Saharan African nations need right now.

A developed agricultural economy thus allows much higher numbers of people to live together without necessarily invading ever more wilderness to feed themselves, especially where the conservation of that wilderness and its biodiversity carries an economic benefit to them as it should.

However, the more advanced agriculture becomes, the less labour it needs; so the largest proportion of a growing rural population still gravitates towards towns and cities looking for work, which then carry the brunt of rural population increases. All too often though, all that awaits these urban migrants is filthy slums and overcrowded shanty towns. This has to change. Apart from its blatant inhumanity, the misery it causes breeds discontent and potentially dangerous outcomes for social stability. For any large-scale move to towns and cities to happen sustainably, new incomers need jobs, houses and money in their pockets, just like they might in most American, Canadian or European cities, for example.

This was where Malthus's calculations went wrong in Europe – in underestimating the impact on national wealth of the compound economic development that was to flourish in cities, especially from the service industries that are now such a major part of any advanced economy. And it is exactly this kind of revolution that needs to happen in Africa if Malthus is to be proved wrong once again.

First World hegemony

So what is proposed to combat the predicted population explosion and urban spread in Africa? Incoming investment? Incentives to farmers to protect biodiversity rather than destroying it, enabling them to buy in food rather than having to grow ever more themselves? Is there international collaboration and support from the developed world to bring jobs and wealth to Africa?

It seems not; at least to nowhere near the degree necessary to diffuse the coming population time bomb. The two major Western powers that should be doing the driving – the United States and the European Union – have made trade deals that, although they may on the surface appear to be cut in favour of developing African nations, look about as hard-nosed and self-serving as they could be. The deals they offer maintain the pressure on African nations to increase agricultural production for staples such as coffee, soya and cocoa for export rather than in feeding themselves (sub-Saharan Africa imports 80% of its food), or in developing the manufacturing and services sectors that it needs to evolve into modern economies.

The trade deals that the EU has brokered with most African nations on low or zero tariffs mainly serve to keep them as primary raw materials suppliers, just as in colonial days, in order to preserve more lucrative, secondary product development for themselves (think chocolate bars, for example). In return it demands open access to African markets. But rather than exporting manufacturing plants to Africa as say, Ford and Nissan cars have done almost everywhere else in the world, at most they only assemble them there. Even then there are only a handful of assembly plants, mainly in South Africa. The only home-based car manufacturer of (potentially) mass-market cars in all the vast expanse of sub-Saran Africa that I could find on the Internet is IVM, a Nigerian company that appears to survive only thanks to Nigerian government discouragement of importing wholly assembled automobiles. For African companies to compete with foreign behemoths like Hyundai, Porsche, and say, Cadbury and Nestlé is impossible.

The EU is not above coercion to maintain this comfortable hegemony over trade with Africa, threatening Kenya for example with swinging tariffs on its vital cut flower exports to Europe if it didn't sign up to its Economic Partnership Agreement (EPA), which forces African countries to open 80% of their markets to European imports, exposing them to a flood of imports against which they have little or no home-grown products to compete. In exchange, African states supposedly receive customs-free access to the European market. Yet the EU is not above suddenly raising tariffs by swingeing amounts to protect home-growers, such as the whopping 16% it slapped on South African oranges for Spain's benefit in 2016 regardless of what was best for EU shoppers, let alone South African growers. So much for 'free trade'.

Consequently sub-Saharan Africa is kept as a vassal economic system. To grow their economies, African nations are therefore incentivised to encroach on ever more wild land to expand exports of cash crops, just as they did in the 19th century, with decimating effects on wildlife.

Meanwhile the United States' trade relationship with sub-Saharan Africa remains severely underdeveloped. In fact, US trade with Africa has been declining since 2011 [(1)]. Most US trade is anyway restricted to oil imports, which is diminishing as it becomes more energy independent. If sub-Saharan Africa is to haul itself into the 21st century, one key part is to accelerate economic growth and development through increased participation in international trade with the US. This represents a major opportunity for the US that is very much in its national interests, if only to keep the fast-growing influence of China at bay. To this end, the US needs to embark on major new initiatives to engage much more robustly in trade and capital investment in Africa.

Yet, though others can do a lot to help, the main route to economic development with population control lies squarely in the hands of leaders of African nations. They cannot go on living on sympathy and aid. Each African nation contains a distinct economic ecosystem comprising a wide diversity of "species", but these are heavily biased towards ones that have little or no spare employment capacity to cater for population growth, nor can even begin to provide successful economic niches for their existing populations (over 40% of Africans still live in extreme poverty, numbering around half the world's total). Every African nation needs to reassess its assets and opportunities, and to instigate an overhaul of policy to provide new economic niches, especially in urban areas, to create the depth, diversity and volume of jobs that will prove Malthus wrong once again.

To this end they could do a great deal worse than studying the widely acclaimed and highly influential, *Making Africa Work: A Handbook* written collaboratively by Greg Mills, Chief Olusegun Obasanjo, Jeffrey Herbst and Dickie Davis [(2)]. Ex-president of Malawi, Joyce Banda, is one who wishes this book had been around when she led her country from 2012 to 2014.

There is another important area in which African nations need to act decisively. The number of failed African states is already the highest in the world, so if at the same time as reforming their economies, African leaders do not also move briskly towards democracy, accountability and the eradication of institutional corruption, revolution and social collapse most likely awaits them as their populations skyrocket and civil resentment grows. Corruption in particular eats at the soul of a nation.

When a nation's economy implodes it is an ugly event with ugly outcomes for many, especially the poor; but when its leader's intransigence to essential change is absolute, then the results can be horrific, as events in Syria, Iraq and Libya have so graphically demonstrated. The best survivors – in economics and politics as well as in ecosystems – are the best adapters.

Africa's catch-22

This is not to suggest that fertility doesn't need to be tackled as well. A fourfold increase in population in such a short time is going to stretch any system to the limit, whatever economic actions you take. Measures are being introduced to this end by some sub-Saharan African leaders, who have finally woken up to the fact that exploding numbers doesn't by itself mean exploding economies (a surprisingly commonly held fallacy).

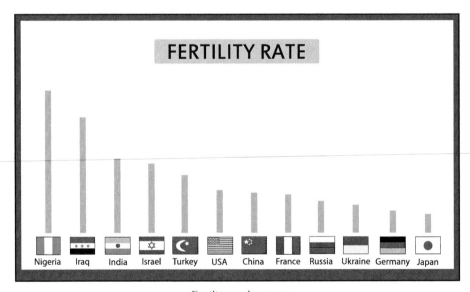

Fertility rate by country

This may seem like interfering with the natural order of things to the Catholic Church perhaps, but controlling fertility in times of need isn't unprecedented even in Nature. Surprising as it may seem, some animals practice family planning to match available resources. Female ground squirrels, for example, appear to be able to shut down their reproductive abilities in order to improve the chances of their own survival [3]. The Arctic skua and great egret have a rather more ruthless way of keeping down their numbers when food is short: the strongest of their chicks simply kills the other. Kookaburras, however, are altogether more civilised: they live in hierarchical social groups of up to five or six, but only the dominant top pair breed. The others are far from redundant because they help in incubating eggs as well as the feeding and protection of chicks as they grow up [4].

We humans generally go for broke though, continuing to breed liberally as if there were no tomorrow, just when you'd think we should know better and hold back. The trouble is that extreme poverty tends to come with its own set of self-perpetuating cultural traditions, trapping people in backward and ignorant ways that are hard for them to break out of. Tragically, extreme poverty almost always comes hand in hand with high child mortality, which encourages people to have more children to compensate, helping to perpetuate the cycle of poverty and suffering.

Population control may be on the cards again in parts of Africa, but how to achieve it against these odds? Robert Engelman is one who believes that education lies at the heart of population control, and that the central need is for women to be *"empowered educationally, economically, socially and politically"* [5]. Part of that empowerment is to have easy access to affordable contraceptives, and to be able to use them without pressure from menfolk, or stigma from religious and cultural mores.

There's plenty of evidence that such strategies do work. For example, Mauritius managed to plunge its national fertility rate from 6 to 1.5 children per family over a relatively short period, and Tunisia managed a drop from 7 to 2. In fact, there's evidence of a significant effect on birth rates merely from improved education: on average, African women with no education have 5.4 children, while women who have completed primary school have 4.3. An even bigger drop to 2.7 comes with the completing of secondary school – that's a 50% drop overall. And for those that go on to attend college, the figure falls again – to 2.2, much in line with the US and Europe [6].

That's all well and good, but it is unwise to underestimate the role of wealth-making in fertility control because education is wasted if it doesn't go hand in hand with economic opportunity. Free choice, good health and education only become universal in the presence of prosperity, social services, and above all – tax revenues, which is how the developed world got to pay for its own social and healthcare infrastructures in the first place. A two-pronged approach is therefore needed – direct measures to reduce fertility need to take place hand in hand with job opportunities – new economic niches worthy of newly educated people, and an economic climate that nourishes the entrepreneurial spirit.

Optimists see good things unfolding over the next century [7]. They envisage a renewed and thriving natural world and a human population that has learned to live within its means. I share this optimism, but I can't see it coming about until the world starts to get much smarter in its thinking, beginning with reviewing and renewing its entire relationship with the natural world.

Migrate to survive

Nowhere is the urgency for smart and innovative policy from within and without greater than in sub-Saharan Africa, because increasing loss of wilderness and biodiversity isn't going to be the only downside of a population explosion. Africa's population is already very young – more than half the continent's nearly 1.2 billion people are children or teenagers [8]. This makes them potentially far more mobile. As the carrying capacities of African nations in terms of sustainable resources and economic opportunities are exceeded ever more, mass migration to other continents is inevitable.

As Europe knows all too well, this migration has already begun, with frequent, tragic consequences as refugees take to leaky boats to escape to its haven. In the absence of concerted action from the developed world to make their African homelands stable and prosperous, this is going to get a lot worse. Already as many as 37% of young adults in sub-Saharan Africa say they want to move abroad [9], mostly because of a lack of jobs and insecurity. So if they are to avoid political instability and backlashes from reactive, sometimes violent forces of the kind already being witnessed in some places in the US and Europe, wealthy nations need to pay full and urgent attention to this looming migration crisis for their own sakes, let alone for that of Africa's priceless natural environments and its peoples.

The things that such migrants seek, we in the developed world take for granted: personal safety, housing, secure jobs, social services, and not least – freedom from corruption and oppression. It is not just morally wrong that the poorest in the world do not enjoy these things, it is an imperative for the economic and social stability of our world too that they get to do so as soon as possible – *within their own countries*.

A prospering Arica will have added benefits: it will bring the continent into the 21st century, creating new, environmentally sustainable wealth, and new markets to boost international trade. The great bonus is that it can reduce its birth rate by peaceful, respectful and natural means.

Junglenomics for Africa

The case for generating prosperity in Africa is overwhelming; but how can it be kick-started *Junglenomics*-style?

Where species aren't able to self-help, as ground squirrels, skuas and kookaburras are, Nature's immediate solution when they exceed the carrying capacity of their environment is migration. The alternative is brutal competition, with mass die-offs of the less fit. To avoid such unthinkable consequences, along with fertility control the human carrying capacity of Africa has to be sustainably increased by intelligent design. Africa's economic ecosystem has to be transformed into one similar to those of America and Europe, but without the environmental toll.

To achieve this, wealth-making opportunities need to be on show: inward, job-creating investment in ecologically friendly industry needs to become an attractive proposition to powerful international actors, enabling and encouraging Africa to be colonised by legions of opportunistic new economic species. Not predatory or parasitic species though – benign, symbiotic ones. To this end, manufacturing, IT and service businesses need to be incentivised – not to send most profits back the motherland as they mostly have done – but to plough profits back and open up further enterprises in Africa itself, employing Africans – and not just in menial jobs.

And to avoid exploitation all this needs to take place within a framework of justice, regulation and human rights. Africans want no more than what most westerners have, and if they can't get it at home, then inevitably they will come searching for it the West in numbers that may overwhelm already stretched infrastructures.

The *Junglenomics* principle of attracting powerful, resource-hungry economic actors to create a healthy and vibrant, self-sufficient economic ecosystem provides the key to making sustainable economic development an attractive – even *exciting* – investment opportunity in Africa. No doubt it will take tempting incentives to draw in that investment, but that is not beyond the abilities of African nations if the rewards are sufficient and the risks sufficiently mitigated.

Cost is ever a central issue, of course. But assessing the likely costs of *in*action is equally as important in any economic equation as assessing those of action. It's time for Africa to declare itself ready and open for business.

The next challenge for *Junglenomics* involves over two thirds of the surface area of the globe and the greatest ecosystem on Earth – the oceans. Once a seemingly permanent and limitless resource too vast to be touched by Man, they too are now suffering steep decline at his hand. Finding ways not just to halt this decline but regenerate them has become a priority every bit as urgent as any, as the next chapter explores.

1. *Brookings Institute*
2. *Hurst & Co, London, 2017*
3. *Tim Karels, Rudy Boonstra*
4. *Veronica Parry*
5. *R Engelman (Worldwatch Institute): "Six Billion in Africa". Scientific American 2016*
6. *International Institute for Applied Systems Analysis*
7. *E.g. Ronald Bailey, Chris Thomas*
8. *International Institute for Applied Systems Analysis*
9. *R Engelman (Worldwatch Institute) 2016*

Chapter 13
Rescuing the Oceans

The marvel of the oceans

Although some half a billion years has passed since our distant ancestors first crawled out from them, we are still as dependent on the oceans as ever. Not only does their vast ecological biodiversity help feed the world, but the services they perform are critical to the Earth's, and hence to our, well-being. We have them to thank for the rainfall that waters the land and for helping purify the air we breathe, producing more than half of atmospheric oxygen and absorbing huge quantities of nitrogen. They also regulate the climate by absorbing more CO_2 than everything else put together, cushioning its effects on climate change. Ultimately the very existence of life on Earth is dependent upon them, for without them it would be as barren as the Moon.

The oceans are also invaluable to us in economic terms. In addition to the seafood on which billions of people around the world depend for work as well as nourishment, we rely on them for the transportation of 90% of world trade, for leisure pursuits, and increasingly for energy generation. About half the world population lives within a coastal region, and ocean-dependent businesses contribute over £350 billion ($500bn) to the world's economy.

The oceans are both a marvel of Nature and an immensely valuable economic resource that in a well-managed world would be cherished, protected and nurtured. Yet we do none of these things. On the contrary, we are systematically denuding them of their biodiversity, contaminating them with pollution, and destroying the delicate seabed environments that are the nurseries for their perpetuation.

So why are we wantonly destroying the health of the oceans, and what can we do to change this?

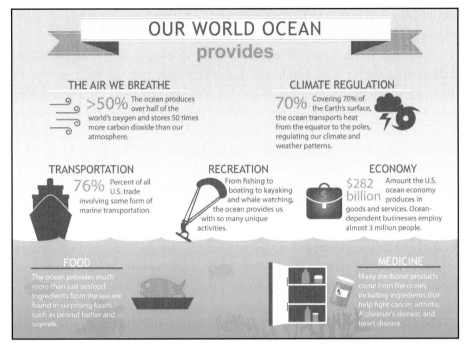

Courtesy of NOAA NATIONAL OCEAN SERVICE (US)

If we again step back and look at the big evolutionary picture – who we are and how we got to this point in our history – the answers are clear: the root cause of our degradation of the oceans is exactly the same as for every other case of economic overdevelopment. It stems from a combination of our unique intelligence, our unprecedented versatility, and our implacable resource hunger.

Critically, these combined elements have not just enabled, but actively encouraged us alone to completely do away with something important – one of Nature's primary equations for keeping its ecosystems in equilibrium and free from ecological turmoil. This important something is the relationship between predators and their prey. Here's why.

Nature's benign inefficiency

As a fully interconnected and finely balanced system with almost everything recycled and nothing wasted, it is perfectly reasonable for us to associate Nature with supreme efficiency. However, it is also true that to achieve a balance between species Nature also relies on a significant degree of *in*efficiency – of less than perfect outcomes – particularly in maintaining the all-important food chain.

After all, if sea lions for example were to evolve to be such efficient hunters that they could catch and kill every last fish on their menu, or anteaters so adept that they could catch every last ant, then for a while they would thrive and their numbers explode; but eventually their prey would diminish and the food chain would break down. The hunters' populations would then crash and they would disappear along with the hunted.

In the balance of Nature therefore, it is not those that are caught and eaten by hunters that matter most, it is those that get away. These survivors are after all the breeding stock for the next generation that will sustain not only themselves but also the other species with which they are interlinked. As Richard Dawkins pointed out in the opening chapter of *River Out of Eden*, you and I are only here to read this page because we are the descendants of survivors, survivors that go back in an unbroken chain to the beginnings of life billions of years ago. That chain has depended on every link – every single one of your and my direct ancestors – escaping the attentions of their predators long enough to procreate the next generation all the long, long journey from amoeba to ape.

So despite Nature's wonderful achievements in designing fabulously efficient creatures to feed on other creatures – from stealthy cats to sublimely agile birds of prey – more often than not they fail in their efforts. Lions, for example, mostly find their prey too alert or too fast to catch up with; attentive gazelle safely bound off in a cloud of dust leaving even the fastest land mammal, the cheetah, panting in the hot sun; vast shoals of small fish swarm into dense "bait balls" to reduce their losses to hunting dolphins, and small birds dive into the depths of dense bushes leaving the marauding sparrowhawk frustratedly grasping at thin air.

Dawn hunt: cheetah in pursuit of antelope

For the most part, land hunters therefore have to rely on catching unwary, disadvantaged and otherwise vulnerable prey – mainly the young, the sick and the old; meanwhile marine hunters, big and terrifying as some are, simply don't have enough energy to hunt their elusive prey to the last one. What's more, by generally weeding out the "least fit", this predator-prey equation carries the added bonus of contributing to natural selection and evolution, honing species to peak "fitness". It is all part of what is commonly referred to as the "balance of Nature" – populations in stable ecosystems finding equilibrium with each other at optimum levels.

So far, so good – this is all classic Darwinian stuff, and what a jolly good system it has proven for populating the world with such a magnificent plethora of species.

But then *Homo sapiens* came along and changed the game.

We humans once operated within the same equation. Our hunting abilities were likewise imperfect, so that our prey too very often got away to breed. True, we were probably responsible for eliminating nearly all the larger mammals of the late Pleistocene epoch (before 10,000 years ago) merely with traps, spears and arrows. These included such exotic species as giant wolves and ground sloths, sabre-toothed cats, woolly mammoths and giant wombats. But this was only a foretaste of what was to come. Over just the last few centuries we've developed into a different creature altogether – an extremely dangerous one - easily the most dangerous this world has ever bred.

We humans have become so dangerous principally because we have learned to break out from this benign inefficiency in predation. Through the evolution of sophisticated technology, we can now use guns to shoot birds and animals, chainsaws to clear forests, gigantic nets to catch fish. This can happen (and indeed is happening) all down to the very last one if we so choose because there is almost nowhere that is out of our reach. Our predatory methods have become so efficient that they are more than a match for any species we care to set our sights on. And crucially this means people are able to prey on the young and fit every bit as easily as on the old and weak.

Nothing is safe from us any more.

Humanity has thus become far too efficient for Nature's good, and as it is turning out, for our own good too; for some of us have no hesitation in preying on living, natural resources in unsupportable quantities, nowhere more so than in the seas and oceans. The impulse to colonise all such resources is too strong to resist and because thanks to technology we can now take them at will, we do so without compunction.

And yes, for the time being we are thriving on this bonanza; but at this rate it will not, indeed it *cannot*, last much longer.

The devastating effect of modern technology on the oceans

While land animals and plants have long been within our grasp and have suffered accordingly, until very recently the oceans have been a far greater challenge: we simply didn't have the means to even dent their vast diversity. But in just the last few decades all that has changed. Rapidly developing technology has allowed marine hunter-gatherers – fishermen – to exploit the oceans on an industrial scale. Their role has evolved from the ancient art of gathering the bounty of the seas in quantities that Nature could comfortably replace, into a rampant, wasteful and remorseless plundering of the oceans' wild populations.

The staggering scale of this pillage has only recently begun to be fully appreciated. The demand for seafood has doubled over the past 30 years, and is increasing steadily every year [1]. The result is that some three quarters of commercially important marine and most inland water fish stocks are now either overfished or on the verge of being overfished [2]. Since 1950, 29% of commercial fish species have suffered a collapse of 90% or more [3]. And the rate of loss is accelerating to such a degree that the last currently commercial fish species may be lost by 2048.

Put into context, what is happening in the oceans is ultimately no different than would be the wholesale netting of wildlife from the forests and plains to supply the world's meat markets. While we would be horrified to be offered mongoose terrine or leopard's tongue pizza at some fashionable restaurant, most people think nothing of tucking into sushi made from skate wings or bluefin tuna, both of which are critically endangered.

Another result from this ocean free-for-all is that around the coasts many delicate sea floor gardens are being ploughed to oblivion. The hunt for scallops using technologies designed for maximum return irrespective of collateral damage, or even the welfare of the target species let alone the uneconomic or inedible ones, is insatiable. The reef at the mouth of the Exe Estuary in Lyme Bay, England provides a vivid example of what can happen without protection. Years of dredging for scallops transformed a complex marine landscape into a featureless plain [4]. It has taken eighteen years and a lot of money to create a marine reserve for this nationally important marine environment. But for much of it, this has come too late.

Courtesy of httprenaissanceendeavour.blogspot.com

The tragedy is that despite many alarms being sounded, the over-exploitation of the oceans and seas continues largely unchecked. Future generations may be justifiably astonished that wild hunting and gathering on such an unsupportable scale should have persisted even into the 21st century despite its devastating effects on marine ecosystems and fish stocks.

Determined attempts have been made to protect severely depleted marine species through quota systems, but in many cases these have had unfortunate unintended consequences. The European Union quota system was intended to conserve species, but it was so designed that it meant that excess catches, which are often unavoidable because the equipment is so efficient, could not be landed. Fish corpses were thus tossed back into the sea in obscene quantities, casualties of a human feeding frenzy of unprecedented proportions [5]. This "by-catch", as it is innocuously termed, consists of unwanted or forbidden species as well as quota surplus. The waste is heartbreaking, often equally so for the fishermen involved.

The result of such failed policy in European waters has been little short of catastrophic. Fishing fleets have destroyed about 95% of the species that used to live in the seas around Britain [6]. In 2008 the European Union (EU) fisheries commissioner [7] called this discard of by-catch and quota excess "immoral". Yet even he, who should be in a position to produce the answers, could not see what to do about it at the time.

A Typical Haul of Bycatch

Seven years on and I am glad to report that this appalling situation is at last changing in Europe. New rules are bringing in a system that has been known for years to work well elsewhere. This is to land all by-catch and replace quotas with "effort control", which restricts the days that fishermen can go to sea according to the state of fish stocks. Combined with limits on permissible equipment and the power to temporarily or permanently close off areas from fishing altogether if necessary, it is to the lasting benefit of fish stocks and fishermen alike.

Unfortunately, the problem doesn't end there. Too much has happened already. Unsated by diminishing fish stocks in home waters, the European, Far Eastern and US marine resource rush has been exported all over the world to places where poorer coastal nations are willing to lease their fishing grounds to richer ones in return for much-needed foreign currency. But by allowing technologically advanced fishing fleets to catch as much of their fish as they want for the lowest possible prices, the damage done to these countries' fish stocks and seabed environments has been incalculable. Such countries are forfeiting the future health of a resource worth billions of dollars, not to mention the future livelihoods of their own fishing communities, in return for poor, short-term financial gains [8]. They may just as well sell the soil from their fields. In financially struggling Argentina, for example, exports of fish leapt by almost 500% between 1985 and 1995 after it opened up its fisheries to EU boats, and as a result of the subsequent overfishing, catches soon dropped by a quarter [9]. Today, Argentina's hake population is on the brink of collapse.

The fishing industry and its regulators are learning environmental lessons the hard way and at great cost. They have learned that many target species (cod for a headline example) are subject to complex population dynamics, and recovery can be severely inhibited once numbers fall below critical levels [10] – so-called "tipping points". They discovered this not through scientific research but by participating in and presiding over the decimation of cod populations; and then it was too late. There has been some recovery, but cod numbers remain at a small percentage of their pre-1970s levels in the once teeming Grand Banks off Newfoundland, despite a complete ban on fishing there for more than two decades.

The cod problem is certainly serious, also destroying a 500-year human dependency with enormous socio-economic consequences. However, in reality it is only symptomatic of a very much greater but less high-profile malaise that is already at an advanced stage throughout the oceans. Worldwide at least a quarter of fish stocks are overharvested [11] and around 95% of the world's coral reefs have already been severely damaged. According to a global survey the culprit is overfishing, dynamiting, poisoning, pollution and ships' anchors.

Reef Check [12] was the first-ever such survey, and was carried out in the summer of 1997 in 300 sites in the Caribbean, Indo-Pacific region and the Red Sea. "…we now have evidence that coral reefs are being plundered on a global basis," reported Reef Check's coordinator, Gregor Hodgson [13], also commenting that "coral reefs on a global basis have been pretty well wiped out as far as the high-value edible species go. The results are very shocking" [14].

Others agree: the virtual elimination of the predator species such as reef sharks, grouper and snapper has taken place and is likely to cause a potentially irreversible ecological shift that would cause the collapse of the reef ecosystem, according to Charles Sheppard, a world expert on coral reefs [15]. And while an IUCN study of 2008 warns that more than 25% of sharks in the north-east Atlantic are at risk of extinction [16], the US National Marine Fisheries Service has been forced to recommend a reduction in the pollock catch by a further 18% because of falling numbers. It may need to be much greater to avoid a repeat of the cod fisheries disaster.

Another example is the Belize Barrier Reef Reserve System, the largest in the northern hemisphere and the country's top tourist destination. On the advice of the IUCN it was added to the "List of World Heritage in Danger" to help protect it. The islands and coastal lagoons that comprise the reef system are home to a number of threatened species, including marine turtles and the American crocodile. Yet a monitoring mission in March 2009 revealed alarming developments. Even in such an important environment, one that you might be forgiven for thinking would be sacrosanct, it was found that extensive mangrove cutting and the sale of mangrove islands had taken place. This was further confirmation, if it were needed, that nothing is safe.

These are but a few bitter tasters of the immense number of ecological problems in the seas caused by direct human interference. The true extent of direct and collateral damage to the world's marine ecosystems from pollution, ocean acidification, seabed destruction and overharvesting is far greater than I can do justice to here. Yet, as this book has been at pains to express, all have the same root cause – the resource-colonising imperative, resource hunger – so I believe them to be curable problems provided the urgent process of constructing a fully balanced, global economic ecosystem for the oceans as well as for the land is begun without delay.

So how can we ever hope to preserve the long-term health of our oceans and their natural inhabitants in the face of such determined and remorseless technohunting and gathering? If we consult Nature via *Junglenomics*, what does it tell us about what we are doing wrong and right, and what more could and should be done? First we need to understand the legal status of the seas and oceans, because without the rule of law to underpin economic measures, little is achievable.

Who owns the oceans?

The oceans differ from land in the important respect that so much of them – some 64% – aren't owned by any one nation. These "high seas" are therefore common property, and constraints on activities there can't be enforced without international treaties. Before the value of mineral and oil resources began to be realised in the 1930s, most countries claimed legal jurisdiction over territorial waters at only between three and twelve nautical miles from their shores. But the newly discovered undersea wealth soon resulted in nations expanding their claims. In 1945 President Truman laid claim to the entire North American continental shelf adjacent to the US, which stretches some 200 miles offshore. This was followed in kind a few years later by Chile, Peru and Ecuador.

Reacting to the realisation that such borders needed to be standardised the UN set up the first United Nations Conference on the Law of the Sea (UNCLOS I) in 1958. Two further conferences resulted in the beating out of a treaty in 1973 attempting to tackle the marine boundary issue. In the treaty all coastal countries would now control the economic exploitation of a 12-mile territorial sea and a further 200-mile "exclusive economic zone" (EEZ).

The 166 signatories to this agreement therefore now dictate over a 200-mile marine economic exploitation domain around their coastlines (where two countries lie less than 400 miles apart so that their EEZs overlap, the boundary is drawn at the midpoint). This means that in the case of an island, this 200-mile zone spreads out in all directions, and barring their being a territory within 200 miles owned by another nation, the owners of just one small lump of rock and sand in the middle of nowhere can control a marine area of $2 \times 200 = 400$ miles in diameter. All that is needed to qualify is that the island remains above water at high tide and is inhabitable. The result is that countries that control a scattering of many small islands, as France and the US do in the Pacific and Britain in the Indian Ocean, for example, have sovereignty over vast ocean areas, most of which contain rich marine habitats. The British Indian Ocean Territory (BIOT), a relic from the days of empire, adds up in this way to a vast 640,000 square miles, an area roughly the size of France.

Despite the UNCLOS treaty, territorial disagreements persist. After all, EEZs are not just about fishing; they are also about the control of valuable oil, gas and mineral reserves, as well as strategic military positions. Perhaps the most notorious involves China's claim to a large chunk of the South China Sea based on their claimed sovereignty over the Paracels and Spratlys. These two strategic island chains, along with dozens of rocky outcrops, atolls, sandbanks and reefs such as the Scarborough Shoal, all teeming with marine life, are hotly disputed variously with Vietnam, Malaysia and the Philippines, and are potential political and military flashpoints.

What marine conservation policy is there, and why is it not enough?

The accumulated area of all EEZs amounts to a third of all the oceans, and because they comprise shallower waters, including estuaries, reefs and mangroves, they make up the majority of the world's complex marine ecosystems. That makes it important to involve their sovereign owners in both designing and operating marine conservation programmes for them. But to do that, conservation policy needs to be got straight, which unfortunately at present it is not.

When it comes to marine conservation there are two main streams of thought broadly paralleling those on land – whether to exclude or include people in plans. Up until fairly recently the prevailing view of conservationists and politicians has been that because people lie at the root of the problem, the logical solution consists of keeping people away from depleted and sensitive marine ecosystems to allow them to recover. To this end, all over the world numerous "marine protected areas" (MPAs) have been designated.

For a while MPAs were widely regarded as a success, however in recent years they have come under scrutiny, and doubts have been cast as to their true effectiveness. Some scientists now believe that the entire MPA concept needs radical revision, and with good reason. The future recovery and health of the oceans depends on this, so these opinions should not be taken lightly, especially as *Junglenomics* supports their reasoning, as I will explain.

In some cases MPAs resemble an African-style national park in which all foraging economic activity is banned. This can make sense where land-based wildlife is concerned because there is little or no sustainable commercial harvest to be had. But in the oceans the situation is different because they do contain a potentially sustainable harvest. The optimum outcome would therefore be not to ban such harvesting but to maintain it at, or return it to, sustainable levels. The question is, what's the best way to achieve that?

Although MPAs that ban all fishing may be useful in some extreme situations as a temporary measure, for example to allow recovery or to protect fragile seabeds, excluding people long term is much too simplistic. Not only have such "no-take" MPAs been shown to be unconvincing for conservation purposes, as I'll explain in a moment, but they are anyway virtually ungovernable in vast and remote oceanic regions. Total human exclusion from MPAs without compensation can also create resentment and hence encourages poaching, exactly as it can on land; it also gives rise to "leakage", transferring the problem to neighbouring areas.

The problem is that, like their land-based counterparts, marine conservationists sometimes fail to appreciate the importance and desirability of economic inclusion from both social and environmental perspectives. The *Junglenomics* perspective is that it is better to build symbiosis between local people and the marine environment by involving them as guardians in conservation, just as it is in rainforests. Even where 100% "no-take" zones are deemed absolutely necessary, inclusive, symbiosis-promoting activities that incentivise local people to protect important marine reserves against marine poaching are important. These include benign tourism with leisure and sports activities including diving, snorkelling and catch-and-release angling. Permits and licences can be sold to compensate for the loss of fishing opportunities to benefit local communities.

Training local people as marine biologists living in the community can also help by educating adults and young people alike to the true, long-term value of the natural resources in their care and to enlist them as guardians and guides.

Furthermore, wherever it's possible to maintain a sustainable harvest in an MPA, a limited number of local, licensed fishermen with approved fishing methods and equipment should be allowed to catch quotas or spend limited time fishing as a *quid pro quo* for conserving them. To protect their legacy, indigenous peoples will naturally act as eyes and ears against poaching, especially by unscrupulous pirate fishing vessels that roam the oceans in search of unguarded fisheries to plunder.

People therefore need to be seen for what they can be (if properly educated and incentivised) – a force for good, an on-the-ground conservation force protecting resources in which they have a legitimate interest, rather than as problems as they have been.

Deficiencies of the marine protected areas concept

In addition to the issue of economic inclusion there also is a great deal of debate about the practical effectiveness of MPAs as they are currently designed. Many studies have shown that although they can help as a stopgap their beneficial effects are far from universal [17]. This is partly because there are so many variables in MPAs – the year they began, their size, the type of regulations and effectiveness of their implementation, the degree of previous damage, the type of threats involved (e.g. overharvesting, acidification or pollution), the species mix involved and so forth, that apparently it is virtually impossible to draw a firm conclusion as to their success.

In truth there is very little evidence that MPAs are effective at all. Evidence [18] shows that despite an enormous increase in the number of MPAs – there are now several thousand of them worldwide – they have had no discernable effect on species decline, which continues uninterrupted, the surest measure of their success or failure.

The enthusiasm for MPAs among many conservationists is based on analyses that seem to show that there is greater biodiversity and volume of species within them than without. However, a whole swathe of studies now demonstrates that this is far from universal [19]. There are factors that bias results, for example tendencies to report on success stories and ignore the indifferent or downright negative ones. In fact several recent studies appear to indicate that MPA failure may be more common than success [20].

There are several possible reasons for the failure of MPAs. For example, a major study [21] found that collapses in fish stocks are linked to depleted biodiversity in marine ecosystems, including non-fish species such as seagrasses, molluscs and corals. They concluded – and really this comes as no surprise – that every species in an ecosystem matters to the integrity of the whole. From this they extrapolated the horrifying prediction that at the current rate of marine ecosystem collapse there will be no commercial species left anywhere by the year 2048. A calamitous scenario indeed.

No one thinks that MPAs should be abandoned though, or that no more should be created. Where they are justified by results and can be enforced they are a valuable tool to protect severely depleted or threatened species and undersea habitats. It is also much easier to protect viable marine ecosystems than re-establish them. But the idea that simply cutting off all human presence is a panacea and a sure route back to good health just doesn't make sense any more. Marine conservation policy needs to get a lot more sophisticated. To effectively maintain biodiversity entire marine ecosystems need to be conserved over large areas, rather than small isolated patches. In other words it needs to become holistic.

One example of this holistic approach is to expand small MPAs. At the moment a high proportion of them are very small, often encompassing merely the area of a reef itself. Of the 4,500 or so MPAs in existence, some

30% are less than 2 km² and typically consist of coral reefs and seagrass beds. These tend to act as fish nurseries, leaving fish vulnerable to excessive exploitation if they leave the borders, which they frequently do. Small MPAs are also much more easily poached because getting in and out of them takes little time, greatly reducing the chance of being caught [22].

MPAs also need to be sited closer together. This is also an important factor as small isolated MPAs don't allow species to disperse, which enables free population exchange, maintains genetic diversity and avoids inbreeding [23].

Overall there is no evidence that, without other measures, simply creating even more no-take MPAs is going to do the vital business of stabilising, let alone reversing, the alarming fall in species numbers and biodiversity. Probably the worst outcome would be that they continue to be seen incorrectly as a universal remedy, allowing the decline of marine ecosystems to continue apace while providing a false sense of security.

Additionally, public disillusion and confusion with such failure will inevitably produce a lack of support for future, better thought-out solutions.

Geopolitical distortion

At a time when science needs more than ever to be at the forefront of conservation economics, it seems it still has to bear the burden of political posturing. Although a new, more sophisticated approach to marine conservation is reported to be gaining traction, some in authority seem either slow to learn or simply unwilling to take a broad, long-term view, preferring to press sweeping conservation buttons that grab headlines.

For example in 2010 the soon-to-be departing British foreign secretary, David Miliband, issued an order to create a vast MPA over the full 640,000 square miles of the British Indian Ocean Territory, conveniently excluding the Anglo-American military base island of Diego Garcia. This parting edict reportedly received the usual knee-jerk acclaim from some conservationists, but curiously Miliband issued it not only without establishing its scientific basis [24], but also in direct contradiction of well-informed advice from his staff [25].

British Indian Ocean Territory,
courtesy of www.theodora.commaps

Also curious is the fact that the Chagos Archipelago around which the BIOT is centred are actually one of the few marine areas that are *not* overfished, having had their local population removed some 40 years ago to suit the Americans on Diego Garcia. The fact that, to the discomfort of the American military, some 5,000 Chagossians had been lobbying to return to their homeland to set up fishing businesses could be seen by the cynical as more material to Miliband's decision than marine protection.

I relate this only to illustrate that geopolitics, as it did when George W Bush created a similar vast MPA in the Pacific on leaving office despite indigenous opposition and even a lack of full territorial integrity over the region, can easily displace good science. Before Miliband created the BIOT MPA, licence fees from a small, sustainable fishery had been paying for patrols in the region. Now there is reportedly just one patrol boat provided by a private foundation for this entire France-sized area, leaving it much more vulnerable to poaching and pirate fishing. This is hardly a sound basis for a long-term management policy of this important marine region.

Clearly much more effort is needed in marine conservation, and much of that effort needs to be internationally coordinated. Existing protected areas and the current rate of the creation of new ones will not on their own be able to overcome current trends of loss in either marine or land-based biodiversity, nor the increasing pressure from rising human populations [26].

This book does not pretend to have worked out all the answers – there is no one-size-fits-all for conservation because each situation demands its own combination of solutions. But as a foundation for policy and action in the oceans, as much as on land, the *Junglenomics* paradigm is the only viable, long-term basis for conserved, vibrant ecosystems surviving alongside human beings without conflict of interest. For this to be achieved (and I believe with determined action it can be), here as elsewhere, the economics ecosystem must be tailored to fit in with rigorous, results-based environmental science, rather than overzealous, incomplete science and political expediency.

The aquacultural revolution

The better conservation of important marine breeding grounds would be an important start, but lots more needs to be done to protect the seas and oceans against the onslaught of human colonisation and maintain its viability for the long term. There are a number of possibilities, not least the expansion of fish farming, aka aquaculture. In the last chapter I wrote about the "diversionary farming" of wild land species, and just as thousands of years ago farming took much of the pressure off diminishing stocks of wild game, so in principle marine aquaculture can do for the oceans.

The farming of fish is an ancient skill that goes back at least 5,500 years to the carp ponds of the ancient Chinese dynasties. However, even over all that time aquaculture never developed enough to contribute more than a fraction of the food that agriculture did. All that has changed though, and the scale of modern aquaculture is a new and, in most respects, very welcome development for marine conservation because it tends to reduce prices, in turn reducing the pressure on wild stocks [27]. There is no doubt that aquaculture is going to become ever more important as the pressure for food sources grows to feed the projected extra two billion people in the world expected by 2050 [28].

Marine Fishery in the Tropics

However, there's a big proviso to this welcome: aquacultural practices are still far from perfect in many respects, indeed in some cases it is highly destructive, and it needs to improve its act considerably. One of its chief problems stems from the fact that, while with few exceptions we do not rear meat-eating animals for food, many popular farmed fish species are predators – cod, salmon and bass for example. Because of this they need food that is high in fatty acids, which for the most part means they must be fed on other fish.

The problem arises because in order to feed huge, captive fish populations in modern aquaculture operations, sea fishing efforts have been diverted to harvesting ever greater quantities of small "pelagic" (middle sea-depth) fish to make fishmeal pellets. The wholesale plundering of the oceans that has resulted from this deprives captive species' wild counterparts of their prey, with severe effects on their populations and marine ecosystems. This is a large stain on the aquacultural revolution that needs to be addressed urgently.

Proponents of the farming of predatory fish argue that aquaculture "deserves" its place in food production because the energy conversion rate in captive stock fed with fishmeal pellets is twice as high as in wild fish. This means that it takes half the weight of prey fish to add one pound of weight to a farmed fish than it does to a wild relative, making it twice as efficient for providing food.

But true or not this observation entirely misses the point. One cannot sacrifice wild stocks for farmed ones on this basis because so much more is at stake. If the external cost of feeding farmed fish is the depletion of key ocean species, leading to oceanic ecological collapse, then it is too great a cost. And this is exactly what is happening. It's like saying that because domestic cattle grow at twice the speed of wild buffalo we should go and harvest the wild grasses on the African plains to feed them. It's a total nonsense.

Junglenomics for aquaculture

There are classic *Junglenomics* ways to address this problem. It is to subsidise the farming of plant-eating fish rather than predatory ones, for example carp, tilapia, catfish and basa (a relative of the catfish) with ring-fenced levies raised on the sale of fishmeal pellets. To this end the increasing sophistication of highly efficient "recirculating aquaculture systems" (RAS) probably represents the future of most, if not all, fish farming.

RAS can be used as hatcheries, nurseries or growth mediums for land-based freshwater or marine fish or shellfish and produce very large quantities of high-quality fish stock in quick time [29]. As their name suggests, whereas outdoor ponds are criticised by environmentalists because of their excessive water use and the pollution risks associated with untreated water, RAS filter and recycle water through large indoor tanks of fish using sophisticated, computer-controlled systems. A large RAS unit takes up merely 2.5 acres or so, so it can also be located in urban locations, using redundant buildings where possible.

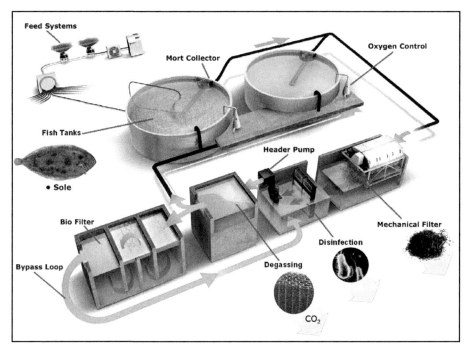

Feed Systems

Mort Collector

Oxygen Control

Fish Tanks

Header Pump

• Sole

Bio Filter

Mechanical Filter

Disinfection

Bypass Loop

Degassing

CO_2

Courtesy of AKVA GROUP Example of RAS Fish Farming System (Epic-aqua)

Few people have heard of RAS, probably because it is a developing technology and major units are still few and far between, though increasing around the world. But it looks like RAS could become the method of choice for aquaculture and deserves substantial public encouragement and investment. However this will not happen on the scale it needs to until RAS can gain substantial market advantage over less ecologically sound methods of aquaculture, which will probably only happen if the latter are made to pay for their external environmental costs.

When aquaculture is combined with vegetable growing in a process known as aquaponics the benefits are even greater because fish waste is a highly nutritious crop fertiliser. With aquaponics, fish reared in tanks exchange water with plants grown nearby. The system ensures that the plants clean the water of fish waste – especially ammonia – and the fish fertilise the plants in return. But though highly efficient and requiring only the poorest of land and minimal water usage after filling, such systems are expensive to set up. If they are to grow at the rate the world needs them to, these ecologically sound new "species" need fertile economic ground in which to flourish, and that means financial support.

So where will the money come from to enable the best forms of aquaculture to develop and grow at the rate it could and should? One answer is that it too could be brought within the scope of Environmental Services Investment Bonds (ESI bonds) discussed in a previous chapter. By enlisting vested financial interests from powerful economic actors, sustainable aquaculture could not only take the pressure off priceless wild fish stocks but also assure almost unlimited marine food supplies for the long term.

Symbiotic substitution

Another significant environmental problem in aquaculture is that large quantities of strong chemicals are used to try to protect against damaging parasitic sea lice infestations, to which salmon kept in sea cages are particularly vulnerable. This has caused significant pollution problems around shoreline-based salmon farms in Scotland for example (though in fact it is a significant problem for aquaculture worldwide), and there is a risk it may extend into the human food chain.

Yet this need not be so because there is a natural way to control sea lice numbers. It so happens that wrasse, a so-called "cleaner fish", are very fond of feeding on sea lice, and enterprising fish farms in Norway, Ireland and Scotland have been experimenting with their use in farmed salmon cages with encouraging results [30]. Experimentation has now moved the spotlight on to another cleaner fish, the lumpfish: not only is it hardier and, unlike wrasse, feeds all year round, but it is edible and grows to a harvestable size in less than half the time that wrasse take [31].

Lumpfish

The use of cleaner fish in this way is an exemplar of the *Junglenomics* approach to environmental problems because it sets up a natural, symbiotic relationship to replace a pollutive and environmentally destructive one.

Aquacultural vandalism

Unfortunately, there are also other problems associated with aquaculture elsewhere in the world, the environmental illiteracy of which is almost too extraordinary to be believed. Heading the list of acts is the entirely unnecessary destruction of hundreds of thousands of acres of mangroves, mainly in Malaysia and the Philippines, to create commercial shrimp and milkfish ponds.

Severe destruction of mangrove forests for shrimp farming

The loss of mangroves is an ecological tragedy for any region. Their benefits are immense and well documented: not only are they valuable fish nurseries, so that their destruction deprives local fishermen of a shared resource, but their removal releases trapped sediment that smothers off-lying coral reefs with resulting loss of valuable food chain ecosystems. Mangroves also have high economic value in protecting coasts from erosion, in flood control and in water treatment.

Other fish farming problems include the transmission of pathogens to wild species, the depletion of wild species through catch-and-rear farming (species caught in the wild and then reared to sell), and the genetic dilution of wild species from farmed escapees causing degeneration and loss of instincts [32], all of which could be eliminated by transferring to recirculating aquaculture systems.

The bottom line for fish farming is that the world must have marine food supplies that are sustainable for the long-term future, and the oceans simply cannot provide this alone. If the problems surrounding fish farm management are tackled with sufficient energy and urgency through a balanced combination of ecological, regulatory and market means there is no reason why sustainable fish farming should not become a major contributor to the rescue of the world's dying marine ecosystems. It all comes down to whether the will is there among governments to face this vital world issue, and to coordinate to implement a fully joined-up programme of measures to address its manifest problems and so enable aquaculture to realise its immense potential both for feeding people and protecting the oceans from further decline.

Fish suppers for animals

The use of fishmeal pellets is by no means restricted to aquaculture. In fact the greatest quantity of fish-based feed is used in producing high-energy food for livestock, especially pig and poultry rearing. Clearly there is a problem to be addressed here also. The combined, unsustainably high harvesting of pelagic species for aquaculture and livestock is creating an ecological nightmare in the oceans. Some 10% of the total marine harvest goes to making fish and animal feed, when it would be best left at the bottom of the ocean food chain where it belongs.

The result is that the true underlying cost of the fishmeal harvest – the depletion of key prey species – is far greater than is reflected by its market price, which only includes the cost of gathering it. The external cost to the overall marine environment is substantial and needs to be recognised and paid for if some balance is to be restored between the economic world and the oceans' ecosystems. This can only be done by taxing fishmeal and ring-fencing the proceeds to promote the market growth of sustainable alternatives. So what alternatives are there?

Caterpillar casserole anyone?

Trying to close such overexploiting markets purely by force isn't Nature's way, nor therefore is it that of *Junglenomics*. In Nature, when resources run low the organisms that rely on them begin to die off until the population balance between the eaters and the eaten is restored. Death is therefore Nature's simple, efficient answer to over-exploitation and its corollary, food deprivation. It is the terrible price that some of the poorest people in the world face every day, even here in the hubristic 21st century. The world now needs to adapt and find a shortcut to a state of economic-ecological balance before its food security is degraded even further, something its current unsustainable food production practices make a certainty.

Yet in our condemnation of such practices we shouldn't lose sight of the fact that, ecologically unsustainable though it is, feeding livestock and fish by trawling the oceans to make fishmeal performs a vital service – helping feed billions of people around the world. It cannot last, but for all the reasons explained earlier concerning the irresistible power of the resource-colonising imperative, efforts are better spent finding a market solution than attempting to "dam" the problem.

This means that, before its source populations plummet with catastrophic consequences for humans as well as marine ecology, fishmeal as a source of protein for agriculture and aquaculture urgently needs to be replaced with something else. And that doesn't mean simply swapping one set of problems for another by overexploiting some other hapless set of organisms into oblivion. To be a long-term solution this replacement needs to fulfil four primary criteria: to be ecologically harmless, plentiful, nutritious, and equally essentially – to be cheaper.

As it happens there is such a thing, one that could help solve the world's food problems and reduce the pressure not only on the oceans but also on the world's land-based wildernesses. We westerners may gag at the thought, certainly I do, but in many parts of the world insects are a popular addition to the dinner plate. More than two billion people like to boil beetles, marinate fly larvae (maggots) or cook caterpillars as part of their traditional diet. For example an estimated 9.5 *billion* fat, juicy mopane worms (caterpillars of a moth) are eaten every year in Southern Africa, while in Uganda grasshoppers are a prized delicacy, so much so that a pound of grasshoppers is more expensive than its like weight in beef. Now some scientists are convinced that, being high food-to-growth converters and rapid growers, insects could be the magic bullet to solve the world's looming food security problem.

A nourishing bowl of Mopane Worms

But because a maggot burger TV dinner may be hard to stomach for the rest of us and will take a while to catch on, the next best thing is to feed dried insect mash to livestock and farmed fish in place of fishmeal and soya. Since fish are naturally insectivorous, and we tend to regard "free range" chickens as superior because they are able to eat a few worms and beetles, this should not be such a hard sell.

That may be great for carnivorous fish, fowl and pigs, but cattle are herbivores, and although interest is growing in farming maggots as cattle feed to replace fishmeal and soya, necessary research is under way to ensure that no repeat of the infamous "mad cow disease" could happen. The results are promising.

The idea has attracted some serious money too, notably in South Africa where a pioneer company named AgriProtein Technologies, funded by private capital and an $11 million grant from the Bill & Melinda Gates Foundation, is looking to be the first to rear insects on a fully industrial scale. At full production capacity the factory aims to produce 24 tons of soldier fly maggots, consuming 110 tons of organic waste daily, to be ground up and sold to farmers as feed at a lower price than fishmeal.

This is a concept that needs to be closely watched. As soon as the technology and safety is proven, governments everywhere need to be prepared to back insect-growing enterprises with a lot more than enthusiastic hot air. This is going to be a world-saving technology that needs to accelerate through the often long and tortuous growing pains and bureaucratic mazes that so often stunt the growth of new business "species" in their early years. Even Bill and Melinda cannot afford to sub the entire world, so it will require public money – money raised and ring-fenced from the kind of unsustainable practices in the oceans and forests already described.

And if it makes some people into millionaires in the process, well good for them. It will only go to prove that being this environmentally friendly and helping solve one of the world's greatest problems can, and should be seen to, pay dividends.

Piracy on the high seas

The high seas have long been associated with remoteness, mystery, danger exploration and adventure. They are the realm of the Ancient Mariner, of Davy Jones's locker, of great battles and of the epic voyages of famous explorers like Magellan, Cook, Columbus and Raleigh. Protected by their vastness and inaccessibility, this immense region that covers more than 40% of the Earth's surface must then have seemed forever beyond the clutches of mankind's rapacious hand. They were the great highways to new worlds and belonged to no one.

Since those days science has taken much of the mystery out of the oceans. It has taught us not only about their complexity but also their importance for the stability of the biosphere. For example, we now know that they contain the world's largest single ecosystem and that this is the ecological nucleus that supports and nourishes the marine abundance of the coastal regions.

Unlike on land, man-made borders have no meaning for the marine ecosystem. Ecological diversity, including fish, sea mammals, coral reefs, or for that matter the pollution and plastics for which it has become a gargantuan dumping ground, do not recognise them. This means that when the health of the high seas declines, the health and viability of species-rich coastal regions will soon follow, whatever local measures we may take to try to conserve them.

Yet despite their vital role, the high seas are chronically undervalued and neglected by the economic world. These huge tracts of open sea far from land are the Wild West of the oceans, and today, as in the Wild West of old, there is a feverish, lawless resource rush going on for their newly accessible treasures.

The result is an oceanic crime wave, its tentacles reaching to all corners of the world. The nefarious practices of its ruthless gangs involve not only serious breaches of international law, but also the wilful ill treatment of people, including slavery. It has resulted in innumerable serious injuries and many deaths.

These crimes are different in that they are not directed against individuals, banks or businesses as with other criminal gangs. They involve the theft of something that, not only by right but also by law, belongs to all people in common wherever they may live. It dwells in the vaults of the high seas, and is infinitely more precious than anything to be found in the vaults of all the world's banks put together. The aim of these gangs is to rob the planet of as much of its fish as they can, callously overexploiting one of the world's most precious natural resources. It's very big business, involving billions of dollars annually.

This pillage is carried out by a minority using "illegal, unreported and unregulated" vessels, or IUUs, which still roam the high seas largely with impunity. As a result, like the coastal regions they serve, the great oceans and seas are in a state of dangerous decline. (A full overview of the problems the world faces as a result of weak and unenforceable international governance agreements in the face of a technologically sophisticated and determined resource rush on ocean species of catastrophic proportions can be found in the inspiring 2014 report of the Global Ocean Commission [33] (GOC) – *From Decline to Recovery – a Rescue Package for the Global Ocean*).

If this depletion of the world's oceans is allowed to continue much longer, it will have serious implications for the future prosperity of the entire world. As UNESCO has pointed out, *"there can be no long-term economic or social development on a depleted planet"*. Thus for economic reasons alone this is an issue demanding immediate attention and radical measures.

The failure of the UNCLOS agreement

One of the chief reasons that the world has been unable to stem the systematic emptying of the high seas is that while nation states may at least in theory be able to control what happens within the 200-mile limits of their offshore economics zones, beyond this, all sovereignty ceases. This means that no nation can lay territorial claim to any part of the high seas or their resources and take charge of their protection. In the vast wilderness of the oceans the only law that exists can therefore be that which nations collectively agree to and are both able and willing to enforce. To date such enforcement is in most cases weak, and in some non-existent.

In 1982, to try to bring order to the increasing exploitation of the high seas, a legally binding (UNCLOS) agreement was reached on laws to govern their use, subsequently ratified by the EU and 166 other states. At its heart was the concept of the "freedom of the high seas", by which they meant a responsible freedom to enjoy an equitable share of their then still copious bounty.

But it was a different world back then. In the intervening period a great deal has changed. For a start, enormous advances in vessel technology have been developed. These include more powerful engines with greater range, better refrigeration, sonar, and sophisticated fishing gear that permits longlines up to 60 km long, and deep-sea dredging equipment capable of ploughing the seabed more than two kilometres down.

So broad is the reach of these vessels that almost no region is inaccessible to them any more. With big capital investment topped up by subsidies, the exploitation of high seas resources has become an efficient and highly profitable business. It is no exaggeration to say that as a result, the high seas are being systematically pillaged of their marine life. The upshot is that the 1982 UNCLOS agreement is failing abjectly in its primary aims and is now no longer fit for purpose.

The tragedy of the high seas

The core of the problem lies in the unique legal status of the high seas that makes it a common resource to be enjoyed by all. It belongs to no one - and to everyone. In a highly territorial economic world that prizes ownership above almost anything, this status is a radical exception to the rule and it brings its own distinct set of problems concerning governance.

These problems arise out of a distinctly anthropological phenomenon that only affects commonly held resources like the high seas. It was identified by Garrett Hardin, an American ecologist chiefly known for his warnings on overpopulation. Hardin recognised that several individuals acting independently in their own self-interest will eventually run down a shared limited resource, even when they can see that doing so is not in anyone's long-term interest [34].

Hardin illustrated this theory, which he called the *Tragedy of the Commons*, with a simplified scenario [35] in which a medieval herder had rights of access to graze allocated parcels of land in common with a number of other herders. It is in each commoner's interest to add more and more cows to the common pasture because he benefits from each extra cow, yet only shares a fraction of the detriment from the resulting overgrazing. Although each extra cow steals a little bit from all the other cows, even if some of those cows belong to him he is still a net gainer.

In the high seas scenario the commoners are coastal nation states, and the cows are their fishing boats sent to "graze" the oceans. This situation is made more complicated than Hardin's example by the added presence of fishing IUUs. These are the equivalent to rapacious wild animals also entering the commons to graze by night.

The combination of the common ownership and ever easier exploitation of its resources makes the high seas an exceptional case in the economic world. Because the usual rules of ownership and responsibility don't apply, and those that have been agreed previously are out of date and inadequate, if the oceans are to continue to help feed the world an imaginative new way of governance that overrides the *Tragedy of the Commons* trap is urgently needed.

It isn't that UNCLOS have not made any attempt to update and improve high seas governance. A subsidiary agreement [36] provided for a network of regional fisheries management organisations (RFMOs) to oversee fishing efforts. But for a host of reasons, including the lack of an oversight body to monitor and enforce compliance, and of transparency and coordination between the signatories, the success of RFMOs at ensuring order, legality and sustainable legitimate harvesting in the high seas has been extremely patchy and in many cases a complete failure. Effective compliance even among those states who did sign up to the RFMO regime (which after 20 years is still less than half of the original UNCLOS signatories) is erratic, and in some cases virtually non-existent, largely because of perverse incentives in the system that still encourage selfish behaviour.

If they cannot guarantee their own compliance, is it any surprise that fleets of pirate fishing vessels roam the oceans hoovering up huge quantities of fish with sophisticated equipment largely unopposed?

Indeed such is the lack of fisheries protection against fish piracy in the high seas that volunteer Greenpeace ships feel obliged to try to fill the vacuum, shadowing IUU vessels in order to make life as difficult as possible for them. This is a valiant endeavour carried out at great risk to life and limb. Their efforts are not confined to the waves alone though, for they not only run patrols to keep tabs on pirate fishing but also maintain a database that includes a comprehensive blacklist of IUU vessels and the rogue countries that host them, among the most notorious being Korea, Taiwan and Indonesia.

In a civilised, properly managed maritime world Greenpeace would not need to do this; but it is a great credit to them that they do. However, relying on volunteer groups with no legal authority to intervene is no way to manage an invaluable world asset. Clearly a new international agreement is urgently needed. Many are calling for this, and there are a number of forthright actions that have been identified as needing to be incorporated into an agreement such as those put forward in the Global Ocean Commission's 2014 report alluded to above.

The GOC's declared ambition is not just to arrest ocean decline but to *"usher in a new cycle of regeneration and recovery"*. Their fully researched and carefully thought-out rescue package includes measures to put a healthy living ocean at the heart of development; to promote strong leadership and thus re-energise RFMOs; to reduce overcapacity including ending fuel subsidies to curtail long-distance fishing; to tag vessels and put a stop to IUU fishing; to keep plastics out of the sea; to ensure fully accountable oil and gas exploitation; to establish an independent "accountability board" to monitor progress; and to create a temporary ocean no-take recovery zone to help regenerate depleted coastal fisheries. This last call is in response to research that shows that the economic benefits to fish stocks in coastal zones would outweigh the cost of banning high seas fishing. But its success would depend on nations committing themselves wholeheartedly to measures to protect and regenerate their territorial coastal zones.

The inadequacy of policing alone

What is noticeable about the measures the GOC has put forward, intelligent as they are, is that they are mainly all about policing – a lot of stick with very little carrot. *Junglenomics* favours an element of policing because that happens successfully in Nature. For example, ants forcibly protect aphids from predators and parasites in order to enjoy the sugary honeydew that the aphids leave behind. However, ensuring the kind of long-term balance that Nature builds in an ecosystem demands something rather more sophisticated than policing alone. It requires the evolution of influential species that have a survival interest in reserving vital resources for themselves, and at the same time that they are unable to overstretch those resources without detriment to themselves.

Some might argue that those employed to police the protection of an environment are themselves just such a species, and at first glance that would appear plausible. Certainly if policing agencies were only paid by results the incentive would be there, but I suspect that is a complicated matter few would be willing to address. Policing on dry land is hard enough, which is why we still have a thriving trade in endangered species, let alone in drugs and stolen goods. It is also why we are afraid to walk in many city streets. Translate this struggle to the vast areas of the oceans and all that would be achieved would be a game of cat and mouse on an unprecedented scale, and an extremely expensive one at that.

Policing a no-take zone covering over 40% of the Earth's surface, including some of the remotest regions in the world, would thus be both impossible and impossibly expensive to administer. Because the high seas accommodate such a valuable and hence desirable resource, marine life, one way or the other the immense natural power of the colonising imperative would guarantee its continued illicit over-exploitation.

After all, the exploitation of natural resources recognises no limits; it is a no-holds-barred rush and everyone looks after their own interests, without regard for others. It ends only when the target resource runs out or diminishes to a point where it's not worth going after any more. As I have been at pains to explain, this is all natural and predictable because it is what would also happen in Nature were there no checks and balances in existence to counter it. Policing therefore cannot be a long-term solution on its own. It can only be part of a more comprehensive plan – one that creates a sustainable economic balance in the oceans.

The *Junglenomics* solution would be to enlist economic actors with a vested interest in protecting the high seas fisheries. The candidate that immediately presents itself is those who currently exploit the high seas legitimately and whose economic future relies wholly upon its future health – the fishing industry. As in the great forests, to be incentivised to protect their resources against fish piracy, these fishing companies would need to enjoy enforceable legal rights over fisheries, but with the proviso that quantities, species and regional accessibility may be varied according to prevailing ecological advice. This can only happen through an international agreement made between all nations who host high seas fishing fleets.

However, while legitimate fishing businesses should not be hard to enlist in this venture because they have good reason to resent the activities of IUUs, unarmed fishing boats and their civilian crews cannot be expected to take them on by force, especially in the lonely realms of the oceans. Some other economic entity, for which putting IUUs out of action is its absolute economic priority, is needed to work alongside the fishing industry and provide the muscle.

Bringing back privateers

Who could this be? Who could be vested with a mantle of benign economic power in the high seas that would enable them to dominate their vast domain and destroy or deter those who would exhaust its resources? Say hello to "Neo-Marine Privateers" (NMPs).

Back in the days of sail, a privateer – also sometimes known as a corsair or buccaneer – was a private person or company with a ship that carried "a letter of marque" – official authorisation by a state to attack and commandeer enemy vessels and their cargo during wartime. It was a useful way of harassing enemy merchant or fighting ships without cost. The letter of marque restricted privateers to attacking the ships of specific nations and in specific areas, and required the captain to post a "performance bond" to ensure compliance. This bond could be forfeited in cases of malpractice, and could be used to pay damages to a wrongly intercepted party.

The commissioning of privateers has many precedents in history, perhaps most famously during the English repulse of the Spanish Armada in 1588, when they became known as the "sea dogs", and during the American War of Independence of 1775-1783, when the American navy employed mixed squadrons of privateers and frigates against the British. Indeed there is a long history of such cooperation between national navies and privateers, who would buy retired naval vessels or armed merchant vessels for their purposes.

Private capital under the auspices of the green bond mechanism or similar could be put up to help capitalise neo-privateer companies, with shareholders receiving a share of the prize money.

To revive the privateer system, international agreement would be needed, allowing states to issue letters of marque to NMPs in designated areas of ocean over which they have been delegated rights and responsibilities. NMPs would be subject to strict protocols, regulations and oversight to enable them to peacefully arrest offending captains and crews and place their vessels, equipment and cargo under legal embargo. To ensure fair play, neo-privateers could carry a suitably qualified regional fishing management organisation (RFMO) representative as observer, and have to post "performance bonds" as assurance as of old.

Cases would then be heard in dedicated "prize courts" to assess the legality of arrest and, subject to proven guilt, to distribute the proceeds of seized vessels and their cargos to claimants, much as the British Admiralty and others used to do with captured enemy ships. To legally enable this, the NMP agreement could easily adapt a clause of the existing international law of salvage, which states that a person who recovers another person's ship and/or its cargo is entitled to a reward equivalent to the value of rescued marine property.

The 1989 International Convention on Salvage agreement already recognises that salvage can include the protection of the environment, including damage to species such as that caused by oil spillage for example. In preventing oil spillage, the salvor is recognised as performing a valuable service and will be rewarded with special compensation in the form of "liability salvage", as opposed to property salvage [37]. The adaptation could state that any IUU vessel would qualify as liability salvage due to its intention to cause damage to marine ecosystems through illegal fishing, and could thus be commandeered by a suitably licensed NMP.

Additionally, anyone reporting an IUU could also be entitled to a share of any consequent salvage, thus encouraging fishing boats, aeroplanes, private yachts, windsurfers, etc. – anyone whether on land or sea – to report sightings. This would incidentally reward Greenpeace for their efforts in tracking IUUs, funding more of the same. The rules could even be extended to cover "conspiracy to fish illegally" to allow the prosecution of gangs onshore as well.

To back this system up, ports of entry for fish catches from the high seas would need to be designated and exclusively licensed, so that landing high seas-caught fish elsewhere would become illegal and liable to seizure. Furthermore, devices enabling identification and satellite tracking should become mandatory on all fishing vessels over a certain size as a condition of certification for high seas fishing, making it much easier to spot IUUs and reduce time wasted checking legitimate vessels going about their business.

In addition to these measures, rogue states that issue licences excessively should face a withdrawal of international recognition of their certification status, meaning that all fishing vessels licensed by them would be open to legal salvage by NMPs. Port certification could also be withdrawn and appropriate sanctions imposed unless and until such countries came back into line.

I believe such measures could be highly effective. They would fulfil the aim to create a market in ocean protection and so bring private capital and energy into it. Naturally, any such arrangements would need close scrutiny for perverse incentives and legal traps; but the bottom line remains the same in all such scenarios: merely policing, or "damming" the colonising imperative where highly valuable resources are at stake will not work – it never has. Nature shows us that only by empowering powerful, self-interested economic actors to protect them can we change the economics of the oceans to create a balanced economic ecosystem and conserve their priceless resources far into the future.

1. By 1.5% – World Resources Institute (WRI)
2. International Union for the Conservation of Nature (2008)
3. Steve Palumbi et al, Stanford University in California, 2006: Science, vol. 314 p787
4. Http://www.wildlifeextra.com/go/news/lyme-bayprotection283.html
5. E.g.: http://www.telegraph.co.uk/earth/3776788/Jellyfish-on-the-menu-as-edible-fish-stocks-become-extinct.html
6. Callum Roberts, professor of marine conservation at York University and author of The Unnatural History of the Sea
7. Joe Borg
8. According to a UN report into the impact of free trade on the environment prepared for ongoing talks with the World Trade Organization
9. New Scientist 2325 12 January 2002
10. http://www.wwf.org.uk/filelibrary/pdf/hls_cod.pdf
11. Millennium Ecosystem Assessment 2005 UN FAO's report "Review of the State of World Marine Fisheries Resources", tables D1-D17.
12. Cambridge University Press: Coral Reef Conservation Series: Conservation Biology no. 13.marine biologist at the Institute for Environmental and Sustainable Development at the Hong Kong University of Science and Technology
13. New Scientist.2105

14. *New Scientist.2104*

15. *http://www.telegraph.co.uk/earth/earthnews/3418281/Atlantic-sharks-face-extinction-due-to-overfishing-and-shark-finning.html*

16. *New Scientist 2684. 2008*

17. *Newmark 1987, Rakitin & Kramer 1996, Thouless 1998, Epstein et al. 1999, Meijaard & Nijman 2000, Rivard et al. 2000, Brashares et al. 2001, Rogers & Beets 2001, Woinarski et al. 2001, Caro 2002, Parks & Harcourt 2002, Tupper & Rudd 2002, Edgar et al. 2004, Ashworth & Ormond 2005, McClanahan et al. 2006, Coelho & Manfrino 2007, Guidetti & Sala 2007, Whitfield et al. 2007, Graham et al. 2008, Mora 2008, Western et al. 2009, Mora et al. 2010 (as cited by Mora & Sale 2011)*

18. *E.g. Camilo Mora & Peter F Sale: "Ongoing global biodiversity loss and the need to move beyond protected areas: a review of the technical and practical shortcomings of protected areas on land and sea"*

19. *Newmark 1987, Rakitin & Kramer 1996, Thouless 1998, Epstein et al. 1999, Meijaard & Nijman 2000, Rivard et al. 2000, Brashares et al. 2001, Rogers & Beets 2001, Woinarski et al. 2001, Caro 2002, Parks & Harcourt 2002, Tupper & Rudd 2002, Edgar et al. 2004, Ashworth & Ormond 2005, McClanahan et al. 2006, Coelho & Manfrino 2007, Guidetti & Sala 2007, Whitfield et al. 2007, Graham et al. 2008, Mora 2008, Western et al. 2009 (as cited by Mora & Sale. 2011)*

20. *McClanahan et al. 2006, Mora et al. 2006, 2011, Guidetti & Sala 2007, Graham et al. 2008, Mora 2008, Western et al. 2009 (as cited by Mora & Sale. 2011)*

21. *Steve Palumbo et al, Stanford University 2006 – Science, vol 314, p 787*

22. *Kritzer 2004*

23. *Bell &Okamura 2005, Mora & Sale 2011*

24. *A Allen, Head of Southern Oceans, British Foreign Office*

25. *According to a subsequent judicial review by Richard Dunne, a barrister and coral reef scientist for Advances in Marine Biology vol.69*

26. *Mora & Sale 2011*

27. *Science 282. 88 3-884. Naylor, Goldberg, Primavera*

28. *United Nations 2014*

29. *See for example Llyn Aquaculture, North Wales, and Blue Ridge Aquaculture, Martinsville, Virginia*

30. *Scottish Aquaculture Research Forum SAR068*

31. *Hannah Chilvers, The Fish Site 2013*

32. *Thorstad et al., 2008*

33. *The GOC is an independent organisation hosted by Somerville College at the University of Oxford. England*

34. *Science, 1968*

35. *Provided in an 1833 pamphlet by William Forster Lloyd*

36. *the UN Fish Stocks Agreement, or UNFSA*

37. *(1997) Lloyd's Rep 323 (HL), pp 326–28*

PART 4
The Great Valuation Divide

Chapter 14
Reinventing the Developed World's Relationship with Nature

"Don't it always seem to go,
that you don't know what you've got 'til it's gone
They paved paradise, and put up a parking lot"
Joni Mitchell: "Big Yellow Taxi" (1967-8)

"O if we but knew what we do
When we delve or hew—
Hack and rack the growing green"
Gerard Manley Hopkins, from "Binsey Poplars" (1879)

The disappearing landscape

We in the developed world are pretty good at telling the rest of the world how important their natural environment is and how to go about saving it; however, all too often it turns out to be more "do as I say" than "do as I do". So in this chapter I want to look at what the developed world can do to protect its own environment and practise more of what it preaches. I don't want to advocate ever more tiers of rules and regulations so reviled by "nanny state" haters. I want it to make money – hard cash – because, as this book has been at pains to drive home, that is the only way to bring everyone on board for the long term and construct a fully balanced economic ecosystem. Doing the right thing must pay; and as we will see, it can, and to some degree already does.

Generating hard cash means realising the underlying value of, and profiting from our "natural capital", yes; but the sensible route is not to destroy the golden goose as you do so, but to exploit it sustainably. This is Nature's way. So because it is key to nearly all the world's environmental troubles, I am unapologetically going to return to the theme of value, this time in relation to the environments of developed countries. After all, recognising the true value of Nature and natural resources is essential to all conservation strategies in whatever part of the world they may happen to be. So the big question is, how can we get the world's most advanced economies to accommodate that value in economic policy in their own backyards as well as abroad?

I have argued in this book that market power harnesses one of the three great driving forces in Nature – to colonise resources. I have also argued that if the destructive side effects of this powerful drive are to be mitigated, a revaluation of natural resources in economics terms has to lie at the very heart of future conservation policies.

But don't get me wrong; that doesn't imply some straight trade-off such as, what's this rainforest tree worth in carbon sequestration, or as say, a living space for lemurs, against its value as lumber in the market. It means its value as an integral part of a life-sustaining ecosystem. If we try to put a value on Nature tree by tree, mangrove by mangrove, coral head by coral head, against its commoditised value in the marketplace we may as well wave goodbye to it all right now. Market forces will win every time. This is what is happening now, and is the main reason why the natural environment is disappearing so fast. I have also put forward market-oriented proposals to rectify this by attributing high value to the natural environment's survival rather than its consumption in the world marketplace.

Clearly, recognising the true value in natural assets is not just an issue for the world's developing nations. The degree to which we value our natural environments affects our lives in developed nations too, and because we are fast destroying them this issue also demands our urgent attention. After all, the degree to which we value our home environment characterises the health of our national parks, our cities, our rural areas and our wild places as much as it does in any developing or Third World state. It is also closely associated with our quality of life. It is not only hypocritical but also negligent to direct our energies to saving Nature in other countries while allowing it to wither in our own backyards. This is therefore something we have to address just as vigorously at home in America, China, Russia, Canada, Europe, Australia and Japan as we expect, encourage and help others to do so elsewhere.

The unfortunate truth is that the economic hypergrowth in the developed world that has resulted from the globalisation of markets has come at a high environmental cost. That cost is not only in headline things like air, sea and soil pollution: every year in developed nations vast areas of open land have been and continue to be lost to urban and industrial development. Land is a finite asset, as are the species that occupy it, and it is essential to conserve as much of it for Nature as we possibly can. What good is it to get rich only to live in an ecological wasteland?

Most land lost due to economic development in developed countries tends to happen in two stages – agriculturalisation then urbanisation or industrialisation. While agriculture tends to reduce and alter the flora and fauna of a region, agriculturalised regions all over the world demonstrate that a wide variety of species can still coexist with farming practices so long as those practices are carried out in a benign manner. Urbanisation and industrialisation are the last straw though; they are the ultimate nemesis of the natural world because they sound the death knell for all but a tiny proportion of indigenous species.

Some people argue that suburban (as opposed to city) development is relatively harmless, but our atavistic instincts know this to be untrue without recourse to the measurable factors that prove it so. And indeed, evidence of urbanisation's detrimental effects on biodiversity and species numbers is mounting. For example, there is the shortening of telomeres (DNA-protein structures found at both ends of each chromosome, protecting the genome from degradation, unnecessary recombination and repair, and fusion between chromosomes) in chicks exposed to urban noise, resulting in faster ageing and greater risk of associated disease [1]. The degrading effect of road noise on habitats is another [2].

A suburban garden with all its disturbance, pollution and artificiality can clearly never substitute for moorland, marshes, woodland and sympathetically managed agricultural land. Of course, much of what we in developed nations loosely call "countryside" and that we value for its wildlife and scenic qualities has already been drastically altered from its primal state. For example, much of England's reputation as a "green and pleasant land" is based not on pristine forests or heaths but on its rolling acres of cultivated fields and moors. Those acres may not be natural – they have been remodelled by mankind over thousands of years – but they nevertheless abound with wildlife.

Dartmoor for instance was created three or four thousand years ago by Stone Age and Bronze Age farmers who knew nothing of maintaining fertility in the land they farmed; yet the bleak, open landscape they created is now recognised as being of international importance for its many blanket bogs, upland heaths and oak woods, each supporting a broad array of creatures, wild flowers and other plants. Here one can find rare ferns, lichens, mosses and fungi, such as the orange-fruited elm lichen and the curious luminous moss, *Schistostega pennata*, also known as "goblin's gold". The moor is also host to endangered species such as the blue ground beetle, the horseshoe bat, the flax-leaved St John's wort, and the delicate southern damselfly.

The British people are profoundly attached to their countryside with its familiar roll call of species – rabbits, badgers, foxes, robins, blackbirds, thrushes, kingfishers, skylarks and so forth; yet despite this, and despite also being among the most vehement protesters against the destruction of natural environments abroad, they continue to allow their own countryside to be eroded year-on-year. They lose it to the grasping and greedy tentacles of insatiable urbanisation. And for every acre of land that is lost to this process, several more acres of adjoining countryside are also degraded – with noise, disturbance, artificial light and pollution. Consequently degraded, such areas then fail to qualify for protected status; they become low priority and as such more vulnerable to yet further development. So the downward spiral of land loss is kept in perpetual motion.

It is the same story the developed world over. In the US, for example, as cities and industries spread outward so farms disappear. Between 1982 and 2010 over 24 *million* acres of prime US farmland was lost to development. To put it in perspective this adds up to an area the size of Indiana and Rhode Island combined [3]. It's a shocking statistic. In the 1990s the annual rate of rural land lost to development rose to about 2.2 million acres. This means that in the US alone there are 2.2 million acres fewer each year for wildlife to live in.

These are disturbing figures and have naturally rung alarms bells, yet there is still no respite: rampant urban invasion continues undiminished; areas where the soil is rich and plentiful continue to be paved over to make way for single family homes. Some may think this is a necessary evil because people need somewhere to live; but much of it isn't. According to the associate chief of the US Forest Service, open land, much of it forest, is being lost at the rate of 6,000 acres every day mainly for parking lots and second homes. North Carolina alone lost more than 6,000 farms and 300,000 acres of farmland between 2002 and 2010, more than any other state.

Europe is not much better: each year between 2003 and 2006 on average 100,000 acres of land were lost under tarmac and concrete in Germany alone. The reason for this leaching of agricultural land to urban development is very simple: on a yard-for-yard basis urban development is vastly more profitable than agriculture.

It isn't that people don't care about this. They are aware that if commercial forces are given their head they will lose a great deal that they value and that is valuable in its own right, and considerable efforts are made to protect valued landscapes. For instance, national parks are established and green belts or green spaces are demarcated around great conurbations as bulwarks against urban sprawl.

To a limited degree this has worked: national parks systems in particular have been successful. But these are inevitably only set up in obvious regions of outstanding value and beauty that one would be utterly crazy to allow anyone to build over – moors, mountains, undisturbed forests, places of exceptional beauty and recreational value. Yellowstone is a classic example, as is the Snowdonia national park in Wales. The downside is that less highly valued landscapes are much more vulnerable to development; but that doesn't mean they are ecologically sterile or scenically unimportant – far from it.

However, while national parks have proved fairly resilient to incursion from development, unfortunately the same cannot be said for green belts. Despite government after government confirming their commitment to them, even these bastions of conservation are not safe. Critics, unsurprisingly supported by the development lobby, put up arguments against them as obstructions to the natural expansion of cities, which according to them should be allowed to grow organically *ad infinitum*. Their future is one where town and country merge into a vast amorphous mass of suburban sprawl, with Nature fleeing before it. Such critics only see the small, parochial view; they are utterly oblivious to the greater worldwide context in which we all must play our part if we are to change our habitual, destructive behaviour and rescue our children's inexorably diminishing heritage of natural capital.

Developers as economic predators

The parlous state of the green belt circumventing London is a depressing example of the impermanent nature of legislative protection against economic forces. It was created in 1934 to provide London with a "lung" and to prevent it sprawling into the surrounding countryside. Yet under remorseless pressure from developers the cracks in the legal shield are starting to appear. "Modernisation" of green belts has become the newspeak euphemism for eating steadily into them [4].

Courtesy of www.saltfordenvironmentgroup.org.uk.

So why is it that even jealously guarded laws are effective for little more than a few decades to protect something as supposedly sacrosanct as the surroundings of Britain's capital city? The answer is simple: where development land is in short supply, land prices inexorably rise; pressure builds to irresistible levels; money begins to speak louder than conservation.

I suspect that in the real world, legislation alone will rarely provide more than a temporary respite from overdevelopment where there is development pressure, even in sensitive cases. What chance then for remote rainforests and marshes far out of the public gaze? All the while market pressure intensifies against the regulatory dam, until eventually it starts to crack, for as an economic species, property developers are naturally pushy: they risk large amounts of capital on land speculation and as a result they don't easily accept no for an answer; to them it represents an acceptance of failure. Patience, perseverance and a Machiavellian manipulation of rules and regulations are the name of their game, and overall this is a winning strategy for them. Little wonder then that property developers make up such a large proportion of the world's rich lists.

Of course, developers' perseverance doesn't materialise out of thin air; it is created by an irresistible lure – that of substantial profit, and the resource that makes it for them is land. The larger that profit, the more tempting the target, and the more they persevere. It is a natural instinct – the same instinct that drives a fox to keep revisiting a chicken coop, only for them the draw is the smell of fresh poultry. Sooner or later they hope to find a weak spot; or if they are really lucky someone will forget to shut the henhouse door properly (the priceless legal loophole).

The euphemisms here are obvious: you cannot train developers to resist the urge to seize the chance of profit any more than you can train the fox to resist chickens – they just cannot help themselves. Their argument goes – if they don't do it someone else will; besides they aren't really the villains, they are public benefactors solely dedicated to the good of the nation, aren't they? The same goes for innumerable other businesses tempted into circumventing clear policy intentions. Even governments themselves, under political pressure to improve their housing figures, may surreptitiously loosen the reins.

Two prime examples come from South America: Brazil's supreme court has recently loosened its laws on the protection of the Amazon rainforest by reducing penalties for illegal deforestation and reducing the amount of deforested land that must be restored. According to Brazil's attorney general these revisions are constitutional and aim to create a balance between environmental protection and economic development. One doesn't need to be a cynic to draw different conclusions. Now Mr Bolsanaro has arrived in power, the leashes are really off.

Meanwhile Peru has likewise approved a new law to cut down trees in the Ucayali region of the Amazon in order to build new roads. Peru's official daily newspaper claims that the plan is in line with Peru's "priorities and national interest". The Peruvian government regards this project as a positive step forward, as the road will grant access to untouched parts of the forest. This is a well-travelled road that leads to ever more forest destruction. Would either of these moves have happened if those forests were worth more standing than felled?

As we saw earlier in the context of wildlife conservation, such attempted "damming" of environmentally destructive economic pressure is expensive and in the long run inevitably doomed to failure. As such it can rarely be more than a holding measure. Because you cannot guard every gate forever, securing long-term protection requires a more sophisticated approach. Because profitability is ever the lure, it is on the removal of that profitability that the focus needs to fall. It is the only way that businesses which prey on the environment for a living can be made to lose interest. Chicken needs to be made indigestible to the fox.

Everything I have ever read, seen and heard has convinced me of this inescapable fact of economic life: that no amount of rule-making can divert the unrelenting colonising power of the marketplace for long. Only economic revaluation can.

The opportunity costs dilemma

The big challenge that governments in the developed world face is in deciding, not whether to protect rural and wild environments from development, but how much of it to protect. They have to take the costs of such protection into account: not only management costs, which are relatively small, but another, much larger kind of cost – that of the economic opportunities that are foregone when any particular choice is made – known as the "opportunity cost". For example, when a green belt is established around a city an opportunity cost would be the profits and ongoing financial and social benefits of industrial development or housing.

Clearly, ways need to be found to continue economic growth in developed counties without turning vast tracts of green land into impoverished agricultural factories and sterile urban deserts. On the face of it this implies we in the developed world must also make a tough stand at home against the apparently unstoppable – the full force of the colonisation imperative as practised by one of the most efficient and destructive colonisers the world has ever known.

But does it really? Nature shows us that manipulation rather than confrontation of the colonising imperative is the best way to curb its undesirable outcomes.

Anyone in business should be aware of the need to keep their businesses developing to remain competitive in changing market conditions and to stay in the race for survival. Though a few *coelacanth*-like outfits may defy the odds and survive relatively unchanged for decades or even centuries, the thatching industry for example, most need to continually adapt to cater for new competitors, technological advances and evolving markets.

We know that one of the greatest threats to wildlife is the introduction of invasive species that outcompete indigenous ones: cogon grass, European green crabs, European earthworms and water hyacinth in the US for instance, and the same goes for businesses. However, while it has shaken out some businesses, the globalisation of trade has also enormously increased opportunities. It has expanded markets, improved efficiency and widened consumer choice.

For these reasons governments are often loathe to draw lines in the dirt over the development of rural land. They tend to leave the development door slightly ajar, exposing such regions to the spectre of blight and overdevelopment. Give developers the smallest sniff of weakness in administrative resolve to protect rural environments and they will exploit it – that is their job after all.

It's all a question of *value*. Because most mainstream economists tend to view opportunity costs only in commercial terms, when advising on change of land use they assess land value in terms of what immediate financial gain over loss can be made from it. A development that eats into countryside is thus compared only in terms of say, a loss of food-growing capacity or of amenity, against commercial or residential development value. Aesthetics - Nature for Nature's sake, and ecosystem services, do not enter the value reckoning because they have no quantifiable economic value.

In a way, this is understandable: when making planning decisions it is extremely difficult to attach a monetary value to "one more field lost" to contrast it against easily quantifiable commercial benefits. An economist may anyway regard it as "one more field better utilised". This is what one might call the "nibble effect". Although, with respect to Nature, the whole may be recognised as providing valuable services such as supplying nitrogen, locking up carbon or precipitating rainfall, these are cumulative on the grand scale; they are not measurable in pocket-sized bites. Yet put together they add up to shocking overall amounts.

How does one then assess the contribution of just a single field or an acre of woodland to the natural world? Nibbling at farmland, primal forests or wetlands always looks cheap because its value is virtually unquantifiable; it can only be properly assessed as part of a whole. This is why countryside goes on disappearing one more field at a time, why forests and wetlands get eaten into acre by acre, and hence why many species native to them are in steep decline [5].

There is another important yet often overlooked factor involved in cost-benefit calculations for land development: the time factor. The commercial valuation of countryside is always immediate, yet land that in one decade carries little agricultural value may suddenly become highly prized in another. During the 2001 foot-and-mouth epidemic in Britain for example, agricultural land values fell to levels not seen for decades; yet just twelve years later they had soared by some eight times to unprecedented heights. One result of personal interest to me was that a beautiful golf course near my Dorset home, built on what had then been cheap agricultural land, was ploughed back into farmland after less than a couple of decades.

Another major factor affecting land valuation is food security: uncertain political times unfailingly bring this vital issue back to the fore, and the political volte-face in Russia is beginning to make Europeans nervous about their dependence on imported food.

Markets are fickle and land valuations therefore time dependent and unreliable. Land valuations therefore need to discount immediate market conditions and take a broad, long-term view. There is a frequently voiced and undeniably true maxim about land in Britain that "they aren't making it any more"; one could add to this that "when it's gone, it's gone for good".

So what is the answer? It must be to make the opportunity costs equation work the other way. For example, the degrading of environments caused by a decision to develop may only result in a tiny measurable reduction in the environmental services they provide such as carbon sequestration and water supply; or perhaps a loss of profit from tourism or amenity for local residents; but that's when viewed in isolation. When all such developments in a region or state are taken together the accumulated effect is substantial, so each must be seen as a part of a syndrome, just as notified and medicated cases of a contagious disease are. After all, doctors wouldn't say – *"there's only half a dozen cases of 'X' notifiable disease around here so we won't bother to take it seriously"*. At least you hope they wouldn't.

Taken as a whole, therefore, the future benefits of maintaining a long-term, healthy environment are a clear and reckonable factor for the opportunity costs calculation and need to be recognised as such in any cost-benefit calculation. Just like forests in Sumatra, healthy, biodiverse environments in developed nations have to be recognised economically as well as aesthetically and as being worth a lot more alive than dead in the overall scheme of things.

The development conundrum

To put the economics-ecology valuation dilemma in developed countries into perspective and look for practical market solutions I'm going to illustrate it using a classic scenario – one that time and again puts Nature in the balance. The scene is a proposed road bypass for a substantial rural conurbation – I'll call it "Shiretown" (it sounds English, but it could be anywhere in the world).

For decades people have flocked to Shiretown for the jobs, architecturally interesting antiquity of its town centre, diverse shops, open-air market and the labyrinth of smart new-build housing estates in leafy suburbs. However, this growth has come at a price: that of hundreds of acres of fields and woodland, and hence of their natural services, wildlife and tranquillity.

It has become apparent that Shiretown has now outgrown its infrastructure. It is suffering from traffic congestion, air and noise pollution, and increasing road accidents. So-called "through" traffic, once the town's lifeblood, has now become the bane of its existence. A national road-building company has been indulging its customary practice of trying to cajole the town council into financing a new road to bypass the town. Powerful arguments finally persuade a majority on the council, and a proposal for a new two-lane highway is passed in principle. The main drawback is money; with limited finance available there is a strict budget limit.

It is soon apparent to the town council that the shortage of funds creates another sticky problem: the cheapest route for the road would take it through a substantial tract of hallowed ancient woodland and agricultural land with historic and scenic value. A vocal minority is soon expressing opposition. The council therefore appoints an economist to assess other routes for the bypass. He comes up with the following:

1. Route A, the original one that cuts through the ancient woodland and the scenic farmland.
2. Route B, which cuts through just a corner of the woodland, and still spoils the farmland.
3. Route C, which takes a wide berth around the woodland, but still cuts through scenic farmland.

Routes A, B and C are progressively more expensive.

The economist begins with a classic cost-benefit analysis. Route A, being the shortest, is the cheapest of the bypass alternatives in cash terms. But the valued ancient woodland would be carved in half, its integrity and amenity value lost forever.

The question now arises, what is the *worth* of the ancient woodland? Is it worth the extra £5 million ($8m) that Route B, which only cuts through a corner of it, would cost? Is the loss of amenity, productive farmland and wildlife that valuable?

To a certain extend the answer to this depends on what kind of economist you use. A regular one would tend only to take into account the impact on the local economy such as any potential loss of tourism. On the other hand an environmental economist might factor considerably more criteria into his valuation equation: amenity, historical associations, scenic value, noise pollution, carbon sequestration and so forth. Indeed he might go even further: he might for example assess the value that woodland-loving people all over the nation – indeed the world – place on the survival of such ancient woodlands. Simply knowing that they are safe, and feeling free from the stress of hearing about their destruction is now a recognised factor in environmental economics.

A survey finds that public opposition diminishes slightly for Route B, but remains significant, while Route C, costing £5 million more again (£10 million more than Route A) causes least opposition among those who believe a bypass of some sort is necessary and inevitable. But where will the extra cash come from? It is an extremely difficult choice, and whichever way it goes a lot of people are going to be unhappy. But a decision has to be made, and because this is fundamentally a matter of affordability, cost is to be the major consideration.

The questions therefore arise – should the government step in and pay the extra to protect the woodland fully using Route C? Or should it outlaw the bypass altogether to protect the countryside? Could it justify that decision to a mother whose child suffered from asthma as a result of car fumes, or worse, was knocked down by a car racing through residential areas to avoid a snarled up town centre? On the other hand what about the loss and degradation of precious and diminishing countryside? Does anyone have the right to erode it even if they are in a majority locally? Does local democracy confer the right to enforce development blight in the name of progress? The economist knows it's a controversial issue if ever there was one.

Everyone wants their say. The tree-huggers say, "the trees are sacred" and chain themselves to them.

The townsfolk say, "we don't care which route, just give us a bypass".

The farmer says, "I'm an important food producer and my family have been here for generations – over my dead body".

The Treasury says, "make it the cheapest".

The politicians say, "make sure the decision doesn't rebound on us".

The economist thinks (but may not dare say), "a plague on all your houses; this is all about economic efficiency. Just leave me to get on with my job".

The contractors say, "There has to be a road; and we'd like the contract".

So the economist gets out his calculator and counts up the costs and values of all the factors he recognises and feeds them into his equations. The temptation is to look for the "route of least unhappiness", the one that will generate the least flack for him. But the complaints he may fear most is that from his employers, and he knows what they want – the cheapest bypass with reams of impenetrable equations to justify it.

Then there's a bizarre twist in the story. One day a letter arrives from the Indonesian Embassy. It reminds us how vociferously we condemn the felling of rainforest and asks us how we can lecture them, a poor country many of whose citizens are desperate for ways to earn a living, while we, a rich country who has already destroyed the majority of its natural wildernesses, can even contemplate destroying what little we have left? Our hypocrisy is blatant. No one wants to pen the reply.

So what do you, the reader, think? The economist can quantify the economic benefits, but in addition to building costs, what is the environmental cost? And which is the route of least political or financial resistance? In the end it all comes down to valuation. Some would say, "in a land with millions of acres of woods and farmland what's a hundred or two more under tarmac? It's plentiful and relatively cheap, and people matter most".

Yet that kind of argument has not stood up well when it comes to, for example, cosmetic product testing on animals. Here the moral argument has largely won the day over the financial one; there may be millions of lab rats in the world but that is not an argument for treating any of them cruelly. The cost of public displeasure at animal suffering merely to test shampoos and beauty creams has been adjudged to be greater than the benefits of the testing, and so it has been banned. Not so when it comes to animal testing to protect human health, though. People sue when medicines fail, and that is a powerful economic incentive to check drug safety very carefully indeed. Although concessions have been made, due to the high economic value attached to human life, the cost-benefit analysis still comes down in favour of continuing the laboratory testing of medicines on animals.

Another moral question now presents itself, stimulated by the Indonesian interjection. In all the commotion of their parochial affairs how much world perspective is passing through the minds of the pro bypass Shiretown folk? When it comes to passing judgement on the felling of millions of acres of tropical forest, or on wildlife reserve encroachment in faraway places affecting the lives of people they do not know, where do most of their sympathies lie? After viewing a David Attenborough wildlife programme would they side with the "greedy" loggers, or with the trees and animals? (Are they greedy or just people trying to feed their families like everyone else?)

These are also equations involving economics, ecology and morality, and it's fair to say the people of Shiretown would, along with most of the people of the Western world, favour conservation over forest loss – until it comes to their own backyard. Then the costs and opportunities lost are up front, not thousands of miles away in another land, affecting other people.

The chief lesson from a relatively minor yet typical controversy such as this is equally relevant to much greater ones anywhere in the world. It is that the outcome of economists' cost calculations where human economic development runs up against the natural world hangs on one thing – the monetary value that is ascribed to Nature. In the Shiretown scenario it is ancient woodland and rural landscape. Elsewhere it might be the drowning of valleys, the extending of airports or the concreting over of green fields for industrial estates and car parks. We are at a point in our worldwide economic development where we first need to take stock of, and then entirely re-evaluate, the natural world; not just in Africa, Asia and South America, but also in our own backyards.

We need to ask, what are natural environments *really* worth?

Most ecologists might say we should not even be entering into the realm of deciding the fate of the environment at all; that it should be sacrosanct and inviolable. Would that it could be so, but I suspect such an extreme would be unachievable in the foreseeable future. Nevertheless, the current rate of species diminutions and extinctions means that the sliding scale needs to slide a great deal more in favour of the environment than at present. That means attaching a far higher price on ecology, environments and landscape than we have. This is to reflect two things: firstly, the invaluable services they provide, and secondly today's unprecedented public awareness of and empathy with Nature and its immense value for our survival.

Back to Shiretown, and the bypass controversy begins to really hot up as it goes national/statewide. Groups of protesters begin to turn up, swelling into a large crowd. Some are middle-class folk deeply resentful of the creeping loss of landscape to development. Others represent Friends of the Earth, the Green Party and rural protection organisations. A couple of B-list film stars put in an appearance, casting trite, *clichéd* sound bites to the gathering media circus. An online petition finds a hundred thousand signatories in a few days. Suddenly it's big. A lot of people really care. The value equation is shifting. If one unit of value were attributed to every supporter and objector *nationally*, and then extrapolated internationally, which group would benefit in the end? I suspect we know the answer.

The Shiretown folk put on a brave face and claim it's all a fuss about nothing. But the truth is this has turned into a power struggle – a test case. Here are two possible outcomes:

Outcome A. Realising that their bypass has caused a national furore, and inspired by the Gerard Manley Hopkins poem at the head of this chapter, the Shiretown folk and their councillors undergo a Damascene conversion. They now see that the new road will forever destroy part of a precious national treasure. They also realise the country cannot build its way out of one set of problems without building themselves into another – more houses, more traffic, more overstretched infrastructure. They withdraw their plans, dismiss the economist and send the contractors off empty-handed. They opt instead for a raft of remedial measures: traffic calming, extra public transport, variable routing, pedestrianisation, congestion charging and low emission zoning.

Outcome B. Option 2 (the route through the corner of the woodland) is chosen as the compromise solution.

The tragedy of environmental loss continues; challenged, mitigated a little, but still unabated. Much of the wildlife living in the remainder of the wood retreat or flee from the new noise and disturbance. For those that remain their telomeres grow shorter and their populations decline.

Of course Outcome B is by far the most likely. In fact, historically it is almost inevitable. The reason is simple: Shiretown has become a battleground. On the surface that battle is between two sets of people with starkly opposed interests. But in reality the conflict runs far deeper than that. For the real protagonists are, on the one side, the raw power that is the juggernaut of the colonising imperative in its financial guise, and on the other, moral conviction, aesthetics and ecology: money versus morality and natural science. The way economic valuations are currently calculated there can never be much doubt who will win because monetary economic valuations favour development almost every time.

The compensation game

So how to assess Nature's value – not just in general but in real time situations?

A typical economist's means of assessing economic value between parties with conflicting interests uses the twin concepts of "willingness to pay" (WTP) and "willingness to accept compensation" (WTAC). For example, in the Shiretown bypass scenario, how much is the government willing to pay (WTP) for the land to build the bypass on? The other side of the deal is how much would the landowners be prepared to accept (WTAC) to overcome their reluctance to sell their land and to compensate for loss of income? Both sides have to agree a price for a deal to take place. Often compulsory purchase is imposed, arbitrarily setting a deal at commercial market rates. Either way this is currently a classic two-party deal that takes no account of the third party involved – the natural environment and its wildlife.

Here's another common scenario in which an agreed valuation resolves a private dispute but again ignores the ecological dimension. The river on your ranch runs dry because someone is extracting most of the water upstream for irrigation. Your cattle now have little to drink. You demand your neighbour stops, but his agriculture is valuable too and he wants to negotiate, giving you compensation instead. What will you accept? The cost of drilling boreholes to water your cattle, just for starters. Then there is the value of the fishing you've enjoyed in the river since you were a kid. And then perhaps something for the hassle factor and the lost beauty of the river landscape that means tourists might not stay in your holiday cabin any more. For these perhaps you would accept a large lump sum in cash and the cost of an annual vacation in Miami.

The upstream neighbour will have a limit on his willingness to pay (WTP) based on the economic value of the water to his new operations. After lengthy negotiations, his WTP and your WTAC meet up and you have a deal that you are both happy with. But where in all these strictly human compensation calculations are the fish, the insects, the amphibians, the waterfowl, the microorganisms, the wild mammals that drink in the river? There is no compensation great enough for the loss of their very means of survival. Economics is all about *human* affairs, *human* value, *human* compensation, not Nature's. Surely Nature should be included in all such WTP and WTAC equations where they involve the environment, even if it turns out to be at a price the economic negotiators do not find viable? In which case, human ingenuity being boundless, people will find other, less destructive ways to achieve their ends.

But in the Shiretown scenario there is another dimension not present in this last one – the objectors. They have strong feelings against environmental encroachment, and as such, do they not represent the interests of the environment? Are they a nuisance that needs to be contained or should they be somehow included in the calculations? And if they were included, would they feel strongly enough about the threatened woodland to pay enough money to compensate the Shiretown folk for *not* having a bypass? If so how much compensation would the latter be willing to accept from the protesters for the bypass to be cancelled? A new school? A state-of-the-art hospital perhaps?

Or would the protesters say, "Hell, why should *we* have to pay to save the environment? It should be sacrosanct anyway. And besides, if we did that it would only encourage people to hold the environment to ransom for the pay-off". You can see the problem. Any which way you look at it, in this kind of scenario protecting the environment comes down to levels of compensation and who is willing to pay it.

So how does Nature get a look-in? The answer is that, unless some rare plant or animal can be found on the doomed land, it doesn't. And that is why all over the world development remorselessly continues to bury millions of acres of countryside under concrete and tarmac every year, just saying "no" doesn't work. Adding substantial taxes to land development on a sliding scale depending on perceived environmental value may sound good in theory but would be unwieldy and controversial and open to endless legal challenge.

Yet there is a way. Given that it is not desirable to prevent all development – after all where are growing populations to live without new housing for example? – but only to neutralise its effects on the natural world as a whole, we can involve Nature in the WTP/WTAC equation. But to do so developers need to pay Nature's price – the price environmentalists

What are Biodiversity Offsets?

BIODIVERSITY OFFSETS ARE CONSERVATION ACTIONS DESIGNED TO COMPENSATE FOR UNAVOIDABLE HARM DONE TO LOCAL ENVIRONMENTS FROM ECONOMICALLY ESSENTIAL DEVELOPMENT PROJECTS

OPERATES WHEN FOR PRACTICAL OR ECONOMIC REASONS AVOIDANCE OR SUFFICIENT MITIGATION OF HARMFUL ENVIRONMENTAL EFFECTS IS NOT POSSIBLE

Features and Benefits

THEY CREATE A MARKET IN ECOLOGICALLY RESTORED OR ENHANCED LAND THAT CAN BE USED TO "OFFSET" AGAINST THE NEGATIVE ENVIRONMENTAL IMPACTS OF DEVELOPMENT.

THEY CAN INVOLVE ANY NATURAL ENVIRONMENT, SUCH AS FOREST, WETLAND, SHORELINE OR HEATH

THEY CAN BE ONE-OFF, AND INVOLVE A LEGALLY ENFORCEABLE OR VOLUNTARY TIE-UP

THEY CAN BE NOW OR IN THE FUTURE, PROVIDING OFFSETS IN ADVANCE OF DEVELOPMENT

THEY CAN BE USED TO BALANCE ECONOMIC WITH CONSERVATION NEEDS, AND ENSURE NO FURTHER NET LOSS OF BIODIVERSITY have been demanding on its behalf for decades. That price is no net loss of environment and biodiversity, as the following section explores.

Biodiversity banks: how they can protect Nature in developed economies without stifling them

Blamed as they largely are for the great credit crunch of 2007-8 and the economic woes that followed, bankers may not be the most well-liked people in the world right now. But there is an interesting new species of banker that is creating reactions that are making them extremely popular – at least with those who care about conserving Nature. These are "biodiversity bankers", and as their name suggests they run "biodiversity banks".

What is a biodiversity bank? Unlike a regular bank they don't store money, but carefully restored natural environments instead. It is an innovative idea that sprang from the need for developers to find "offsets" for environmental damage caused by their developments, which they were obliged to do under new environmental regulations in parts of the US.

It means that, just as carbon emitters buy carbon credits to offset their carbon footprint, so increasingly in the US and elsewhere developers are required by law to mitigate their environmental impact by purchasing "biodiversity credits". These credits represent improvements in an environment elsewhere to the development that are at least equivalent to the anticipated environmental loss their development will create, in order to try to ensure an overall "no net loss" of biodiversity in a region without stifling all economic development. Exactly how many and what kind of credits are needed to compensate for any given new development follows the verdict of an Environmental Impact Assessment (EIA) carried out by specialist surveyors.

However, before being allowed to apply to buy offset credits the developer must first satisfy three important criteria. The first is that, where possible, any environmental impact must be avoided completely; secondly, where complete avoidance is not possible any residual impact must be minimised; and finally, any unavoidable impact must be offset against environmental improvements made elsewhere, preferably nearby. "Avoid, minimise, offset" is thus the mantra, and it is a good one. Although the minimum ratio of such offsets is expected to be one-to-one (equivalence), many planning authorities insist on it being greater than this so that a net environmental gain is made.

In the US three main types of biodiversity offsets have emerged.

Two of them are retrospective in that they attempt to compensate only *after* some environmental impact has taken place. The first of these two is self-managed by the developer, who is then held responsible for the maintenance of the offset in perpetuity. The second is externally managed through specialist trust funds into which the developer pays cash and which then manage the designated biodiversity offset on their behalf. Both of them are therefore reactive to development, meaning that the offsets don't need to exist beforehand, can start from scratch and don't involve a biodiversity bank.

Achieving net positive impacts for biodiversity through the mitigation hierarchy. Courtesy of BBOP

The third type of offset is particularly attractive, however, because it is the instant front runner as a *Junglenomics* candidate. It involves private sector entrepreneurs creating offset "credits" in advance by establishing or restoring environments and biodiversity on private land up front, thus creating the aforementioned "bank" of new biodiversity, for which they can then sell credits to developers in appropriate chunks on demand.

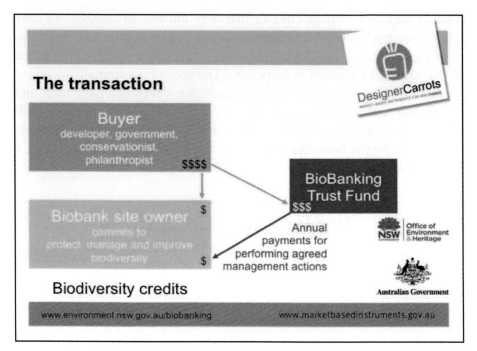

NSW Gov. Biobanking principles

The credits here are rather like banknotes that, technically at least, represent gold held in vaults, only the offset "gold" is real and tangible in the form of chunks of restored natural environments and biodiversity. The banks can continue to sell their offset credits in a particular location until all of them are sold out, at which point that particular biodiversity bank becomes closed for further business, and the location is protected in perpetuity.

Here's a possible example: let's say as a biodiversity banker I buy up 500 acres of low-grade upland farmland and moor in, say, Scotland, UK. I then create a lake and marsh, plant native trees, introduce a wide variety of appropriate insects and wild plants along with frogs, newts, fish and small mammals under the expert advice of ecologists. I then sell the credits this creates as offsets in blocks of say, five acres at a time, to developers. Their money compensates my biodiversity bank for my investment and pays for the maintenance of the offset, creating a new wildlife reserve that should last in perpetuity.

The biodiversity bank is particularly appealing because it avoids the main difficulties of the self-managed and trust-funded offset schemes. For example, the self-managed offset creates problems with monitoring and enforcement, as well as with guarantees of quality and continuity. After all, what happens when a firm goes bust or neglects its obligations – who do you sue if the offset fails and its rich collection of new species die off? The locked-in funding and arm's-length management that biodiversity banking brings is essential to avoid these problems.

Then there is the question of scale: small impacts that impinge on, say, just an acre of marshland, cannot easily be recreated with its full panoply of biodiversity in isolation elsewhere. Ecosystems are often multifaceted and require a variety of adjacent environments to function properly. Where singular offsets may easily fail on small parcels of land equivalent to the area to be developed, a biodiversity bank allows substantial ecosystems to be recreated.

Furthermore, while the trust fund option avoids the pitfall of poor diligence by companies because it is run at a distance with locked in funds, it has particular drawbacks of its own. Firstly, because there is no formal linkage between the environmental impact and its mitigation under this scheme, there can be no guarantees of offset equivalence. In other words, environmental damage caused by a development may not be met like-for-like when the money is spent in another region, perhaps in an entirely different type of ecosystem, high, open heath rather than lowland forest for example. Even if an equivalent ecosystem were to be found it is uncertain whether the offset payments would be sufficient to support it in perpetuity under different challenges. In addition to this there is often no built-in time frame for compensatory investment, only a general ongoing programme of conservation. This means that a trust fund's policies and investments are potentially vulnerable to political influence that could undo its original purpose.

In contrast to this, a biodiversity bank has already done all the hard work and the newly restored or enhanced ecosystem is already up and running ready for commercial takers. A wide variety of offsets will then be available so that equivalence can be almost guaranteed. The Australians seem to have solved this particular problem rather well.

Biodiversity Banking - The Australian Option

EITHER A: BIODEVERSITY BANKER BUYS SUBSTANTIAL AREA OF DEGRADED OR NATURALLY LOW-GRADE LAND
OR B: PRIVATE LANDOWNER OFFERS HIS LAND FOR RESTORATION OR ENHANCEMENT

EITHER A: RESTORES LAND AND INCREASES ITS BIODERSITY AT OWN COST, OVERSEEN BY ENVIRONMENT AGENCIES
OR B: ADVERTISES LAND AS CANDIDATE FOR OFFSET RESTORATION, SUBJECT TO CONTRACT

A DEVELOPER UNABLE TO PREVENT OR MITIGATE BIODIVERSITY LOSS ON IMPORTANT DEVELOPMENT SITE, BUYS CREDITS THAT REPRESENT BIODIVERSITY OR ECOSYSTEM RESTORATONS EXCEEDING THAT TO BE LOST

PROCEEDS OF SALE HELD IN TRUST IN PERPETUITY FOR THE MAINTENANCE OF OFFSETS UNDER PUBLIC SCRUTINY

Biodiversity markets have caught on well in parts of Australia; indeed some of the most advanced research and design in market-based mechanisms have taken place there. For example in 2008 the Department of Environment and Climate Change and Water (DECCW) of New South Wales introduced a biodiversity banking scheme that uses a public trust fund as a stakeholder. The DECCW maintains public registers and referees the issue of credits and distribution of income to private biodiversity banks.

They also allow private landholders to sell credits in two classes – ecosystem and species [6]. Credits can be bought and sold freely so that brokers and dealers can make a market in them. But they do not have to remain on the open market. Philanthropic organisations – environmental charities for example – can buy credits from a landowner and then "retire" those credits so that the land is managed in perpetuity according to its offset-designated criteria, which means that the charity say, is funding increased biodiversity in designated sites with no development strings attached.

The combination of public scrutiny and uniform licensing standards in a discrete government organisation in Australia is a big improvement over the non-specific ecosystem trusts seen elsewhere, whose deficiencies I have already outlined. Under the Australian system landowners need not go to the expense of fully setting up their bank either. They can merely register their interest in doing so, and if interest is subsequently expressed via the central register they can enter into direct negotiations with the potential buyer to create a new tailor-made offset site.

In Australia the nature of the development impact has to be closely matched with that of its biodiversity credit offset site. For example, a particular type of marshland must be matched with a newly created one with the same conditions in which the same species will thrive. This means that supply and demand pressures will tend to value rarer ecosystems more highly, creating healthy market price disparities according to rarity. It will also attract investment to recreate the more unique environments and hence make more homes for rare species. All this creates true and enduring market value for Nature, probably the surest long-term protection plan yet devised.

The wider implications of the Australian model are extremely interesting too because it paves the way for all landowners to be paid to improve the biodiversity of their land as opposed to neglecting it or reducing it through ecologically unfriendly agricultural practices. Making good ecological husbandry financially worthwhile would benignly influence the management of forestry, scrub, field margins, wetlands, waterways and soils alike – not just year by year according to the ever-changing winds of, for example, European Union agricultural policy, but in perpetuity; and all funded by business rather than the state. This could mean that instead of a green field being developed and its "natural" role ending, another edge nibbled from Nature, in the future it could be that many other fields would be co-opted to become managed in an environmentally beneficial way in perpetuity.

Biodiversity offsetting in the Shiretown context

So could biodiversity offsetting bring solutions to awkward situations like the Shiretown bypass? To recap, the three headline biodiversity offsetting principles are: *avoid, minimise* and *offset*. Under a biodiversity offsetting regime the value of the threatened land on each route would be recognised and the planned bypass would come at a significant additional cost – that of paying for the replacement and permanent upkeep of a greater area of ecosystem nearby. As we saw in the Australian model, the rarer and more complex the ecosystem, the more expensive its biodiversity banking credits will be if free-market supply and demand are allowed to rule. So because in the biodiversity banking world ecosystems are valued at the cost of recreating them nearby, the most ecologically complex are going to cost the most; in which case the lowest impact option may well turn out to be the cheapest despite its increased construction costs.

However, the biodiversity offset ticket doesn't address local amenity issues such as the loss of landscape, leisure pursuits, nor the distress at their loss, which have to be assessed separately and added to the "natural cost benefit" (the reverse of the economic one, where the cost to the environment of lost land is calculated). After all, even if ancient woodland replication were possible – which of course it isn't within many lifetimes – what good is it to Shiretown nature lovers if their beloved ancient woodland is replanted 30 miles away?

The answer is that it is no good – not for people or for Nature, so it *must* be conserved. Yet that is not to say that new woodland areas cannot be created to offset measures that *are* carried out. In a little village in Essex, England called Wendens Ambo, a millennium donation of bare farmland by a prominent local landowner is now growing woodland glades and is already prized by local residents and has become a new home for wildlife for the first time for perhaps a thousand years. That is progress. The price? Around six much-needed new houses on a small area of long-abandoned, ground adjacent to other houses. I leave you to decide whether that is a good deal both for Nature and for people.

Overall, economic valuing gives the natural world a powerful weapon with which to fight back – a market-oriented weapon. It allows number-crunching planners to put figures on Nature's side of the financial equation, rather than the nebulous, hard-to-value factors they have to work with now.

In the UK, the economic valuation of Nature is attracting attention as a potential defence against overdevelopment. To this end a "Natural Ecosystem Assessment" (NEA) was carried out and published in 2014, granting valuable guidelines to planners that bring ecosystem services and amenity value more fully into the equation. "Value transfer" is central to the NEA paradigm, allowing it to apply previously established values of ecosystem services to a specific case.

However, the NEA's report was not phrased in a biodiversity banking context, and natural systems are very complex things to attach monetary values to cold. Assessing the economic value of an ecosystem using a menu of values based on the ecological services they provide – the preferred methodology – is only possible where they are clearly quantifiable: think of the mangroves, reed beds or coastal marshlands discussed at the Bonn Climate Change Conference for example. But it would struggle to attach value to all biodiversity, as it needs to. It would only protect biodiversity that is economically useful at the time of valuation, which falls well short of what is required – which is a no net loss, better still a net *gain*, paradigm. I found the most troubling aspect of the NEA approach to be that attaching high values only to financially quantifiable ecosystems may render economically insignificant biodiversity even more vulnerable to destruction as a lesser or even zero-economic sacrifice. All over England green fields are falling daily to developers because they cannot put up a sufficient defence under this system. England's rural idyll is on the retreat before an advancing urban invasion, and some 30% of habitats in the UK are in decline, while many others are in a reduced or degraded state.

The *Junglenomics* position bears out this judgement. By requiring enhanced replacements, biodiversity banking avoids much of the necessity of valuing the minutiae of ecosystems and the services they provide; instead it focuses on the survival of whole ecosystems. The song of the thrush is unpriceable; and I don't want to have to pay to hear it, or for that matter some sterile recording of it. That song is not something to be considered in isolation: it is just one element of an ecological matrix. It is those matrices that need protecting, or where absolutely unavoidable due to powerful economic need, transferring to a previously degraded area, not just the thrush and its song.

The very concept of the biodiversity banking system also ticks *Junglenomics* boxes because it creates a new network of classic economic species, comprised of biodiversity bank investors and managers operating in a market and subject to normal market disciplines. Their efforts are driven, as is natural, by the profit motive, to which end they are focused on the survival and welfare of all biodiversity for the indefinite future. Biodiversity banking does not aim to stifle economic development – in fact far from it: its primary objective is to ensure firstly that developments take account of the cost of their impacts on diversity into their equations; and secondly that where the cost of impact still renders their development viable (and it is acceptable for planning reasons) there is no resulting net loss of biodiversity.

With respected NEA valuations and Environmental Impact Assessments supporting them, offset biodiversity banking businesses can provide a solid platform for the defence of all undeveloped environments.

Instead of scratching our heads interminably over the economic value of no-brainer, must-keep regions of our nations, we should be exploring how an unloved agricultural field or degraded wasteland long deprived of its natural quota of wildlife can be sacrificed to much-needed housing, yet can at the same time translate into a greater area nearby devoted in perpetuity to the enhancement of Nature. This is a win-win for people, for Nature, and even for developers, whose "planning gain" would be forever partnered with "Nature gain".

Biodiversity business for all

Of course, the success of all biodiversity markets depends heavily on the structure of the regulatory regime that moulds them. This has to be carefully put together to be fully conducive to biodiversity-friendly business. It involves a strong and enforceable combination of laws, taxes and subsidies within a setting of social approval and support. Given a well-prepared foundation, creative and wealth-producing new economic species will inevitably colonise to adopt classic roles in biodiversity-friendly marketplaces, just as biological species do in natural ecosystems. This involves not just biodiversity bankers and their staff, but brokers, ecologists, agents, accountants, consultants, lawyers, field workers and very many others. The self-interested, symbiotic involvement of such actors will help counterbalance the destructive externalities of business and industry without stifling economies, just as species do for each other in natural ecosystems.

There is also a wider range of potential for biodiversity offset programmes to do more good than its immediate purpose. Instead of taking state handouts to manage their land in a biodiversity-friendly manner as happens in Europe for example, landowners can be encouraged by a new legislative framework to become "mini bankers". They can improve the biodiversity of their land, for example by creating new wildlife-friendly habitats such as lakes, marshes and native woodlands, and thereby earn credits to sell on to industry through offset brokers.

This means that, where at present funds have to come from state reserves at enormous cost, landowners could now, for example, receive income from entrusted capital deposited in regional trust funds by developers of bare land, paying these landowners to maintain their holdings in good ecological health in perpetuity. That way, biodiversity-rich but agriculturally poor land can move from being cheap, unproductive wasteland, ever vulnerable to lucrative but biologically destructive development, to an income-earning asset of significant value. So not just high-value ecosystems but every green field taken for development will contribute to trust funds dedicated to increasing biodiversity. Biodiversity can at last begin to compete with intensive agriculture and the persistent attentions of property developers. Nature will finally begin to be properly valued, and in ruthless market economies that will surely be its most effective protection.

There is little doubt that properly constituted, biodiversity markets are an exciting development that could help once and for all turn the tide on centuries of environmental destruction and degradation. Harnessing market forces is the only practical, immediate means available for saving most of what remains of the natural world. Biodiversity markets could thus become a device for stemming the loss of declining biodiversity.

All now set up and ready to go then? Is offset biodiversity banking the big thing everywhere that it deserves to be? Unfortunately, this is far from the case. In addition to Australia, which is perhaps the world leader, the UK, US, Canada, Brazil and Switzerland have nascent biodiversity banking programmes under way, and some other countries are following, but elsewhere it appears sporadic, inadequate or non-existent.

The European Union is distinctly unimpressive, for example. Its "Environmental Liability Directive" of 2004 should have led to Europe-wide schemes, yet fourteen years later little of substance has happened and biodiversity is still declining at an alarming rate. For instance, a German study [7] found that 38% of all animal species in the country are threatened, a situation not helped by the fact that German nature reserves comprise a mere 3.3% of the country's land area.

Time is running out for ever more irreplaceable species and habitats in the world's advanced economies. Although models are being developed through experience gained by the many organisations that have become involved, offset markets still show little sign of igniting on the scale that is so urgently needed. Given the necessary impetus, biodiversity banking schemes would have a very good chance of becoming something very big indeed.

Predicting unintended consequences

So why is there such reticence? Biodiversity banking looks to be a win-win, market-based answer to development blight; so you might easily think, "that's it then, there's the answer. Now get on with it".

But in human affairs there's always a drawback. Inevitably there are reservations about biodiversity banking, notably in the planning process. For example, some commentators say, with some justification, that a major potential pitfall for biodiversity offsets is that otherwise unacceptable developments will be harder to resist under the pressure of potential biodiversity "planning gain". In other words, that getting a net biodiversity increase out of the deal could tempt planners to pass development plans they otherwise would not, thus lowering the protective shield on biodiverse environments rather than increasing it as intended. But there is no reason these should not be overcome through intelligent design.

In the same vein, it is feared that ecological objections to a proposed development might be weakened by the very availability of the offsetting scheme, allowing planners to be pressurised to make a deal where they might not have previously. This applies to all offset programmes, public or private, and it makes it all the more important that Environmental Impact Assessments, offset management and the planning process are kept strictly separate from each other in terms of decision-making. The selection of ecologists also needs to be independent and their reports peer reviewed to minimise the chance of distortion from political pressure or corruption. The planning process in relation to environmentally sensitive sites needs to start from a presumption of refusal, placing the onus on applicants to provide an overwhelming case for exception.

In the public sector, where government agencies are holding large funds for spending on offsets, there is also the potential for a leakage of those funds for other purposes. So where the state is involved, trust funds and their managers need to be ring-fenced and inaccessible to other agencies who might try to purloin or borrow their capital sums. The solution to this lies in oversight by an independent body.

Oversight shouldn't be used as a prop though. It is also essential that from the very beginning the new array of economic species created by the biodiversity banking industry be vested with the right incentives and deterrents to ensure their colonising "heart" is in the right place and not diverted by perverse incentives. This takes careful planning as well as close monitoring, and a capacity for rapid adjustment of the rules. Without that, irregular outcomes cannot be ruled out.

There will be many such challenges – the setting of robust standards for the assessment of true equivalence between impacts and offsets being a major one – but that is no reason to be faint-hearted. The offset biodiversity banking concept is pure *Junglenomics*; it is the natural way to replace the stale, failed, existing paradigm with one that at last recognises and accommodates the true value of Nature within an economic world that will otherwise continue to obliterate it.

Opponents of biodiversity offsetting

Despite its obvious attractions not everyone welcomes even the concept of biodiversity banking. Some ecologists and greens for example look on it with suspicion if not open hostility. Friends of the Earth (FOE) has been running a campaign against it, for example, claiming that offsetting carries unacceptably high risks (the more cogent of which I have just addressed).

However, perhaps the biggest problem for most objectors is that offsetting goes against their closely held tenet that Nature cannot be valued in classic economic terms because this turns it into a market commodity with a price on it, and they fear the consequences of this. (This is the same "commodification" argument that I touched on earlier in context of countering the trade in rare plants and animals.)

The segregational approach to Nature that greens tend to prefer is easy to empathise with: ideally, we all surely would want the natural world simply to be left alone; but it is naïve, wishful thinking to imagine that policies that attempt to segregate the economic world from the natural world can ever rescue our diminishing environment. It is a failed policy that is self-evidently incapable of getting the desired results in an economics dominated world that is every bit as irrepressible as the natural one. Opponents of offsetting, and indeed all market instruments aimed at protecting Nature, consistently fail to grasp this bigger picture.

In fact, it is surprising how many intelligent people believe that a broadening worldwide "consciousness" will soon attain an impetus that will somehow rescue the world from its present environmental dilemmas. Welcome though such an event would be it is far too nebulous to count on.

Like it or not we inhabit an economic world that can only be changed by mechanical means. It's time to get real and make change happen now rather than wait for some vague nirvanic ideal to somehow rescue us.

Besides, there is a particular aspect to biodiversity bank offsetting that may not be fully appreciated by some ecologists, conservationists and eco-warriors alike. In fact they should welcome biodiversity offsetting, not least because it provides a golden opportunity for them to take action to support their opinions. They can take advantage of a biodiversity bank system by buying up and retiring private biodiversity bank offsets, thereby increasing biodiversity in perpetuity through direct, real time action.

Caveats noted and accommodated, therefore, the financial upvaluing of Nature is something that this book strongly promotes because economic revaluing is the only way – the scientific way – to protect Nature against the immense, destructive and all too real power of the marketplace – the irresistible colonising imperative incarnate in economics.

Diligence, transparency and accountability in biodiversity markets

I suspect many of the objections of greens and others arise from a lack of understanding of the principles of natural capital accounting, which is something I have tried hard to address in this book. Despite all the attractions of offsetting we need to keep in mind that even the best-laid schemes can easily be undone by poor public relations and lack of access to information. These only exacerbate the kind of suspicion and hostility alluded to. With such precious and irreplaceable assets at stake – the planet's biodiverse wealth – above all, biodiversity markets need to earn and maintain credibility.

According to observers, credibility depends upon three fundamental things: quality assurance, accounting and transparency. Yet critics say that in many places the US biodiversity markets are shrouded in impermeable, administrative fog, and that detailed information is still hard to come by. This is short-sighted and disappointing. It appears as if those involved don't really comprehend the importance of the model they have created, nor of the example they are setting the rest of the world. To address this problem, efforts are reportedly now under way to create a national database in the US. Let us hope that a great plan is not hampered or undone by bureaucratic incompetence.

To attract private capital, biodiversity market projects need to above all instil confidence, and this requires injections of top-level investment expertise. They need to be run by well-paid senior managers recruited from the private sector – successful fund managers for example. Their remit would be to produce substantial biodiversity benefits through profitable market instruments. But to function successfully these investment managers would need a number of essential conditions to be established. Among these are a stable, credible market structure; a high-tech international trading platform; consistent certification and accreditation meeting agreed international standards; credits as solidly underwritten and freely tradable as currency; and regulation and monitoring of the system by an international FSA-type body backed up by enforceable international law.

Finally, biodiversity markets will need to incorporate guaranteed social benefit: a fair share of wealth needs to reach local communities as a qualifying requirement.

Once their reputation is established these new and by then secure markets will inevitably begin to evolve as all markets do, and in time new financial instruments will begin to appear. It could all become as accepted and commonplace as the trading of commodities is today.

Mistakes of the past

Yet however many guarantees, checks and safeguards are put in place, the bottom line is that if substantial amounts of essential capital are to be attracted into conservation markets of all kinds, above all they need to be profitable, which is more than one can say for some previous attempts at biodiversity markets. Among those who have launched biodiversity-market investment vehicles in the past are governments and NGOs who focused on enlisting philanthropic, cause-driven investors rather than opportunity-seeking entrepreneurs [8]. Their schemes were hampered by onerous attached conditions, or were risky and low yielding, combinations that are not at all conducive to corporate institutional investors, for whom the higher the risk, the higher the expected yield.

But perhaps their chief downfall was quite simply that they were not commercially viable. They were suited mostly to the environmentally committed, not to big, international investors with cash to devote and investors to keep happy. As a result private equity failed to materialise on the scale hoped for and grant funding had to be relied upon.

I have gone into some detail on this subject in order to show that with sufficient science-based planning, legitimate concerns about biodiversity offsetting can be met, allowing it to achieve its enormous potential. There are always going to be possible pitfalls in any system – certainly current, mainly segregationist environmental regimes all over the world are riddled with them. But where biodiversity offsetting is organised, not just as a convenient tool to help development run smoothly, but as a revolutionary economic mechanism intended to create symbiosis between economic development and natural ecosystems, it is considerably easier to anticipate and forestall potential systemic glitches before they arise. This is one of the beauties of the *Junglenomics* paradigm – we have Nature's template to guide us.

While there are few certainties in life, one of them is that land on which wildlife depends for its existence and we depend for ecosystem services and peace of spirit is going to go on being swallowed up because growing populations need houses to live in and places to work. Something must yield, and we must make sure it isn't Nature. Properly set up and managed, biodiversity offsetting puts a true value on ecosystems and at the same time gives the world a practical way to turn the tide on destructive development and make sure we humans at last begin to give back to Nature more than we take.

A whole environment approach

Opinions on what is the chief cause of the world's environmental ills are numerous: Western consumerism, bureaucratic corruption, communist unaccountability, capitalist greed, cultural dumbing-down, even loss of spirituality – all have attracted accusations. Yet despite all this opined insight we still seem no closer than ever to a working long-term solution. Caught in the crossfire between economics and ecology, democratic governments tend to avoid making decisions. While they draw attention to the tackling of less controversial environmental problems in an attempt to accumulate green credentials, the great environmental problems are seen as potential vote-losers, and "brave" decisions concerning them tend to be postponed.

One can sympathise a little with such procrastination, for while it is all very well to argue in terms of principle, in real-life, situations are not always so definite, and some compromises can be difficult to avoid. Perhaps the greatest dilemmas arise where a stark choice must be made between the fate of individual species or groups, against some clearly defined and highly desirable economic benefit. Some economic protagonists will ask whether the loss of the odd butterfly here or plant there out of so many really matters. After all, did the demise of the fabulously numerous passenger pigeon or of the dodo really compromise the integrity of the biosphere? There isn't any apparent evidence that either did. Extinctions have been taking place for billions of years, and will continue to do so for as long as life survives, with or without human interference.

So is it not then arguable that, if mankind needs to take over a few new niches here and there in order to help secure the health and prosperity of its kind, and it is to the detriment of a few other species, then so be it? Perhaps some species could be viewed as little more than minor irritations to man's progress – once dealt with life goes on.

Such fatalism derives from a profound fallacy, though – that economic growth necessarily displaces ecosystems because they are incompatible and mutually exclusive. True, it often has been so in the past, but a central message of this book is that it need not be. Compromising the viability of eco-destructive economic niches while simultaneously boosting that of less or non-destructive, sustainable ones that satisfy the same markets is a workable alternative that has yet to be systematically exploited on a national, let alone an international scale (with perhaps the exception of Costa Rica). This is a sad indictment.

True also that economic species, fundamentally parallel as they are to ecosystemic ones, will naturally tend to colonise wherever they can. To date they have been restrained mostly by more enlightened governments and agencies; but this has proved an entirely inadequate counterbalance to the excesses of a largely unconstrained economic-colonising imperative.

The world population continues to grow at a compound rate, and with it destructive economic activity. This means we can no longer afford to postpone devising and implementing macroeconomic strategies to manage this fundamental force. Because there will always be some pressing economic, social or political argument as to why this forest should be cut, this wilderness be cultivated, that reef be denuded of fish, environmental and species conservation has to become a universal discipline, not merely an occasional thematic luxury to appease the more vociferous expressions of public dissent. Ultimately it is a matter of good planetary housekeeping, one of adopting environmental conservation, not just as a legislative, but as a cultural theme.

Here in essence lies the great conflict between the environment and development. The old economic paradigm may have lost our trust so far as the conservation of Nature is concerned, but that does not mean we should reject economics as a solution to environmental problems. We need instead to thoroughly reappraise the value of the natural environment *within the economic equation* so that it comes out on top. This is what I meant when I said that valuation lies at the heart of the ecology-economics divide.

Does that mean that real human issues from traffic nuisance to child poverty should be set aside in favour of conserving ecology, subjugated to a perceived greater environmental good? Of course not. By no stretch of imagination could that be described as a compromise – it is amoral and would be a sure route to resentment and social division.

The bottom line is that conservation has to be holistic. To conserve the natural world we cannot pick and choose; only a whole environment approach will work. You can't value and thus protect individual species for their tourist income for example, other than in the kind of mundane ways so rightly despised by ecologists. We cannot hold environmental barricades acre by acre, species by species. Many species go unprotected because they have no commercial value, yet many of them are known to hold key positions in food webs, which means that their demise can have far-reaching effects on ecosystems [9]. Likewise, commercial and ecological health go together in the oceans; so says a major report on ocean biodiversity [10], which concluded that "every species matters" in marine ecosystems. The survival of whole ecosystems is therefore essential for maintaining the supporting environment for those species to which we *do* assign market value. Almost nothing in the natural world should be regarded as expendable.

If environmental policy is to be joined up and supported by ecologists and economists alike, it needs to enshrine an inviolable principle: that the conservation of entire environments, rather than individual species that happen to hold present-day economic value, is of paramount importance.

Equally essential is that the poorest peoples of the world, who so often live in or border on important and sensitive ecological territories, are able to participate in and materially benefit from the sustainable exploitation of natural resources to a degree that comfortably betters any erstwhile gain from its destructive exploitation. Whether you are from Birmingham,

Boston, Bangalore or Beijing, a powerful economic incentive to do the right thing, the environmentally friendly thing, is now urgently needed. The market has caused these problems, and only the market can put it right and keep it safe. It's up to us to devise ways to make markets work for Nature instead of against it.

Achieving that goal will take carefully researched, organised and coordinated economic management on an international scale.

1. *National Centre for Scientific Research, France, 2015*

2. *Ware, McClure, Carlisle & Barber, Proceedings of the National Academy of Sciences, USA 2015*

3. *American Farmland Institute*

4. *E.g. see http://www.buildinglanduk.co.uk/greenbelt-land-uk.htm , for this and other ongoing breaches of UK green belts*

5. *E.g. Aronson et al, Proceedings of the Royal Society 2015, McKinney 2002, etc.*

6. *Guide to Biodiversity Credit Broking Register, Australia*

7. *German Federal Agency for Nature Conservation (BfN)*

8. *State of Biodiversity Markets Offset and Compensation Programs Worldwide*

9. *See: "Signs of Life" by Richard Sole, and "Simple Rules Yield Complex Food Webs" by Richard Williams and Neo Martinez, Nature vol.404. p.180*

10. *Steve Palumbi et al, Stanford University in California, 2006: Science, vol. 314 p787*

Chapter 15
Aligning the Interests of Farming and Nature

Forgiving past sins

Farmers have a relationship with the natural world that is very different from the rest of us. They stand at the interface between nature and markets, and they are constantly torn between what is good for the long term and profitable for the short term. There is a simple reason for this inner conflict and that is an all too frequent misalignment between market incentives and environmental good. So in this chapter I want to look at how, with the help of market forces, the relationship of farming with the natural world can be revolutionised to the great benefit of both. Firstly I am going to argue that to make real progress we need to wipe the slate clean and start again.

When it comes to agricultural land and wilderness our feelings tend to run pretty high. Perhaps our deep attachment to the natural environment is inbuilt; and maybe it has been reawakened by its accelerated degradation and loss. Those that manage land have now come under the spotlight, and everywhere moves are afoot to stop the decline and set things right again.

Because farming is such a major source of pollution there have been many attempts to try to control it through economic measures as well as regulation, which have been found not to work very well on their own. The economic approach is laudable in principle, but among these schemes are those that for many people stretch credulity: for example, those that involve farmers being paid to restore natural systems that they themselves have previously degraded for profit. Another is for loggers and farmers to be paid *not* to destroy ancient forest (a subject discussed earlier in relation to REDD schemes).

Most farmers have long argued they are a unique case: that the special importance of what they do sets them outside the conventions that govern other industries, most of which, unlike them, are essentially expendable. For a long time, their special pleading has stood them in good stead; but in this age of environmental awareness the regulatory omissions they have enjoyed for so long have come to an end. Accelerated by various notorious public scandals, DDT for a prime example, their less salubrious practices have come under close public scrutiny. To be fair, most such practices have been induced by a chemical industry that has capitalised on the demand for more and cheaper food in an era where they were not subjected to the rigorous level of oversight that has now become the norm. In those days the need for food production overrode that for environmental security, so for decades the environmental costs of this alliance were ignored or glossed over. Consequently, like so many other industries, with no requirement to internalise their environmental costs, farming built up its productivity and profitability on the back of some highly pollutive and environmentally destructive practices.

In some parts of the world, farmers' organisations are now (somewhat shamelessly some might say) campaigning for financial help to clear up the dreadful problem they themselves have made. To reinstate environments costs money, and what they claim to be their merely marginal profits will not stand that burden, these farmers say. They reject regulation without compensation as unfair. They want the taxpayer to settle the clean-up bill, or at least to share in it. For example, in Canada the Ontario-based Alternative Land Use Services (ALUS) Alliance [1], formed in 2009, advocates that farmers should be paid for providing environmental services. Being paid to maintain or improve the natural environment for its natural services is one thing, but should land managers receive public funds to put right damage they themselves have done? Some opponents [2] see their pleas as a thinly veiled attempt to obtain more from the long-suffering taxpayer; that it contravenes the Polluter Pays Principle; and that it flies in the face of all notions of natural justice going back centuries.

My initial reaction to the idea of paying land degraders both to restore land and then not to degrade it further was that it does indeed go against the fundamental principle that environmental costs should be internalised. It rewards those that have polluted in the course of their industrial process. It is therefore a form of protectionism [3]: pay us or we will have no option but to go on ruining the environment. Surely the very last people who should receive payments are those who cause pollution and habitat destruction in the first place?

ALUS argues that farmers need not only farm food, trees and fuel: they can also provide ecosystem services, filtering water, storing carbon, preventing flooding, creating habitat and protecting rural landscapes. But they cannot provide such vital services free, they insist. If the public benefits, the public should pay for such services at fair market value. On consideration, I cannot find much to quarrel with in this argument. It is based on an enlightened principle, admirably demonstrated in Costa Rica, that the only way to get good land stewardship is to reward it. But only so long as it remains in positive territory – farmers need to be held strictly liable for further damage or pollution they subsequently cause, as breaches of contract. They need to internalise future clean-up costs like anyone else or there is no incentive to improve their practices. Propping up uneconomic, polluting farming methods is in no one's best, long-term interests.

Although in principle polluters should pay, there is a lot to be said for an amnesty in this instance to get things moving in the right direction. After all, farmers were to a large degree led to their present activities by powerful economic incentives and lack of oversight that characterised the economics of the past. It is surely reasonable, if past environmental damage is to be rectified, that temporary support in the form of loans, grants and expert advice is made available to all land managers. Farmers presiding over diminished landscapes with marginal means, whether Canadian, American, Guatemalan or Kenyan, need the chance to make a fresh start in a clean and fully functioning natural environment. For this to happen, farming interests need to be aided and motivated to restore designated land and locked into its ongoing management plan. Biodiversity banking provides one good vehicle for this, providing not only capital but also ongoing income for maintenance. After that there need be no second chances; further environmental degradation should attract fines or taxes as a stick to reinforce the carrot.

Inevitably there are caveats: although an amnesty in aid of land restoration might appear sound policy, it can have pitfalls if not carefully carried out. For example, if landowners get wind of an amnesty and the advent of lucrative grants to restore degraded land, what is to stop them rushing to strip every harvestable asset from their land in the sure knowledge that they will soon be paid to reinstate them? That after all is where the natural economic imperative would direct them, simply because potentially it is the most profitable course. For example, I recall a time in 80s Britain when in East Anglia, subsidies from one government department were encouraging farmers to drain wetlands, while those from another were simultaneously paying to restore them. Clearly such contrary and perverse incentives have to be anticipated and safeguards built in to prevent them. New high-tech satellite imagery could prove indispensable for this, establishing a comprehensive and incontrovertible state-of-the-land database.

Farming in conflict with wildlife – the wolf wars

Environment and wildlife may be two sides of the same coin, but that doesn't mean looking after one side automatically enhances the other. For instance, consider a scenario in which the "complainant" for unfair treatment is an animal. There is a real-life case where ecologists and activists successfully joined forces on behalf of a threatened mammal, the American grey, or timber wolf [4].

American grey wolf

Blasted out of existence in the West by the 1930s and declared endangered in the lower 48 states in 1974, there appeared to be clear signs that the end was near for this rapacious top predator. But while livestock ranchers and hunters had for centuries viewed the timber wolf as a serious competitive nuisance, conservationists had come to recognise the creature's ecological contribution. They discovered that the wolf had had two important immediate effects: it kept elk numbers in check, and even more importantly, kept the elk herds from lingering around water margins.

The reason this is ecologically beneficial is that, when patrolled by predators ever-ready to surprise the unwary, watering places are risky places for prey species like elk, so they tend not to linger there longer than necessary. Once the wolf packs had been all but eliminated the elk were freed from this "ecology of fear" and were able to linger safely around the water's edge for as long as they liked. Ever larger herds began to decimate the once dense waterside stands of aspen, willow and cottonwood causing a radical upset in the local ecology. Songbirds lost protective cover and nesting sites, while the loss of shade killed off species living either in the water or on the river margins. Fish also lost the insects that used to fall from the leafy overhanging canopies. Fish were further compromised as banks were eroded, making streams wider and shallower. Beavers too were deprived of nutritious twigs and leaves, and of trees for their dams. This in turn deprived numerous other organisms of the rich ecology of pools and marshland created by them. Furthermore, in the absence of wolves, coyote numbers also burgeoned, depriving other mammals such as badgers, foxes and raptors of their prey. Ecologists have coined the phrase, "trophic cascade" to describe this top-down effect, where whole ecosystems are radically altered by the presence or absence of one species at the top of the food chain.

The case for the timber wolf as a pivotal species in the local ecology was thus overwhelming.

However, being the persistent coloniser it is, the timber wolf's time was not altogether over. In the 1980s a handful made their way down from Canada to Glacier National Park in Montana, and as their numbers grew they began to disperse into the national forests. Meanwhile their supporters pressed for and, despite strong opposition from farmers and hunters, succeeded in the mid 90s in getting some new Canadian packs reintroduced into the 2.2 million acre Yellowstone National Park as well as central Idaho's wilderness areas. The result was thriving wolf populations that inevitably spilled over on to private lands.

That meant war – range war. For while wildlife enthusiasts and tourists were ecstatic, many livestock farmers and hunters were, literally, up in arms.

The wolf was once again treated as vermin.

To soften the economic losses, compensation became payable on wolf-kill carcasses; however these had to be confirmed as wolf kills, which is often impossible; besides, the problem wasn't just the killing of livestock but also wounding and worrying. It is therefore perhaps not surprising that, despite some licensed culling of wolves, many farmers have taken matters into their own hands.

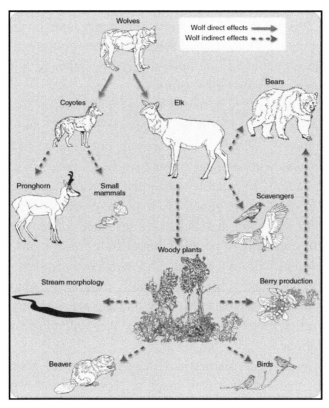

Courtesy of William J Ripple -Schematic of the trophic cascades enacted upon the reintroduction of the wolf to Yellowstone National Park in the late 20th Century

A coalition of fourteen environmental and wildlife groups led by Earthjustice subsequently created a formidable lobby in favour of timber wolves so that some farmers have had to accept the inevitable – that the will of the courts and the American public at large means that wolves are back for keeps. So it is not only that elk are changing their behaviour to the renewed presence of wolves, humans are having to adapt too. It is after all what we do best.

The E factor

I have related this particular example because it demonstrates what happens when the "E" (environment) factor is introduced forcibly into a commercial equation rather than through gentle, incentivised elision. Americans want farmed meat, but they want wolves too, particularly those involved in the tourist industry, which makes tens of millions of dollars a year out of their reintroduction. So how does such an impasse get solved? For *Junglenomics*, compulsion and policing is not a sustainable long-term option. It is a stopgap while something better is set up that renders it obsolete. For a solution to work for the long term it must actively benefit all those whose livelihoods are intrinsically in conflict with one another; that means an economics-based solution.

So as expected, although timber wolves may have recovered to some extent the issues surrounding them are not resolved and they are still far from safe in the US. Whatever insincere support farmers and hunters may give in public they will continue to shoot wolves discreetly simply because the cost of a bullet is so much less than that of a dead calf, and the ranges covered are so vast they are impossible to police properly. Besides, policing it an expensive operation that cannot be sustained for hundreds of years ahead: the cost, not only of policing, but also of prosecutions, inspections and compensation will only mount. The *Junglenomics* view is that only where farmers and hunters benefit financially from the presence of wolves and other "nuisance" animals will they and the ecosystems they help to maintain be safe for the long term. Until then they will remain at war, albeit an undercover one.

This is a lesson being learned in Africa where conflicts between farmers and elephants that devastate their crops are common, and it goes equally for the US and anywhere else where humans are in economic opposition to wildlife. Where farmers benefit from wildlife you can be reasonably sure that it will flourish.

Today there is a powerful lobby to remove timber wolves from endangered species protection. In many places it has succeeded, only to be reversed again under pressure – a policy swing that shows little sign of achieving consistency and a stable long-term relationship between land managers and wildlife. Why? Not because the wolves' numbers have recovered to a point of never being endangered again: the true reason is the lack of policy to alleviate the concerns of opposed interests – mainly farmers. Bring them into the benefit equation and the calls for the removal of protection will largely melt away. If that means permitting licensed, limited hunting where appropriate along the same lines as Scottish deer stalking for example, so be it. Landowners will see a benefit in healthy wolf populations where at present they see only loss. In addition, the demand for hunting is assuaged and kept in plain sight where it can be regulated – a win-win scenario if ever there was one.

This is not meant to be special pleading on behalf of the American timber wolf in particular. It is, for example, this same absence of vested interest that has caused Asian herders to be responsible for the deaths of more than half of the 450 rare snow leopards killed every year since 2008 in revenge for livestock losses [5]. The timber wolf's case is a generic one that illustrates how markets not just can, but *should* be used to create a balance of interests between those who manage the land and its ecology.

Costa Rica learned this lesson years ago, when it began to pay farmers for the natural services their land produced. Examples like the timber wolf reinforce the position that only a rebalanced economic ecosystem based on a revaluation of Nature and natural systems can establish and sustain a stable natural environment for the long term.

And there's new evidence that an economics-based approach can pay dividends for conservation in the U.S. too: American Prairie Reserve (APR) aspires to build a version of the Serengeti on some 3 million acres of Montana prairie. If APR's motion-sensing cameras prove that bears, prairie dogs, cougars and a list of other animals are present on their land, ranchers get paid. These rewards are raised by "Wild Sky", which receives premium prices for its wildlife-friendly beef. It means for example that ranchers can earn an extra $12,000 a year just for having a pack of wolves on their land. Making wildlife worth more to them alive than dead has ranchers now seeing it as an asset rather than a liability. The project is even overcoming entrenched suspicion and hostility towards conservation among independent-minded ranchers because it avoids the need for petty regulations and much-resented outside interference from sometimes hostile and antagonistic conservation ideologues. Thanks to a market approach, a profound change is thus taking place in many corners of the American West, to the lasting benefit of its wildlife.

The case of the American timber wolf forms the perfect cue for the final part of this book because it illustrates the gap – sometimes the gulf – between the two main tribes of would-be conservationists – ecologists and economists. Both may feel equally passionate about conservation, but each usually wants to go about it in different ways, ways that often reflect their world view rather than practical considerations.

This is an important subject because this economist-ecologist divide continues to hamper progress in achieving the one thing everyone wants, a well-managed, sustainable planet for the long-term future.

There is also division between developing and developed nations over who should carry the greatest burden in addressing the world's environmental problems, and this has perhaps been the single greatest stumbling block in international negotiations, as the next chapter explores.

1. *For summary of ALUS see: http://www.deltawaterfowl.org/alus/index.php, and http://www.gov.mb.ca/ agriculture/soilwater/ecological/feg01s00.html*

2. *E.g. Elizabeth Brubaker: Financial Post 5th May 2009 http://www.environment.probeinternational.org/ news/agriculture/polluter-pays-polluter-gets*

3. *An illegal activity whereby people are forced to pay people not to maliciously damage or disrupt their homes or businesses*

4. *D H Chadwick: Nat. Geographic May 2010*

5. *Rishi Sharma, WWF 2016*

PART 5
Delivering Change

Chapter 16
What Stands in the
Way of Change?

*"Some people don't like change, but you need
to embrace change if the alternative is disaster"*

Elon Musk, founder of SpaceX

World summititis

Working out what is needed to get us out of the huge environmental hole
we humans have dug for ourselves is a difficult enough proposition; getting
substantial, effective and enduring policy changes to actually happen on the
ground even more so. At the beginning of this book I asked the question –
why despite the enormous support it enjoys has the environmental movement
failed so miserably to stop the slide? I answered it by saying that it was
because we have been going about it in all the wrong ways, and up to this
point I have been explaining how we could do it a lot better if we looked
to Nature for our inspiration. But resistance to revolutionising economic
policy is by no means the only obstacle to overcome; there are others that
also need to be resolved if real progress is to be made soon enough to save
what's left of our precious natural heritage.

This final part of *Junglenomics* therefore looks at three big obstacles to
progress and describes how we might rise above them and get good things
happening much more quickly. The first of these obstacles can be found in
those much vaunted but ultimately disappointing meetings of the great and
the good – world summits.

You may well be familiar with the procession of major world summits on
the environment and climate change – Stockholm (1972), Rio (1992), New
York (1997), Geneva (1990 and 2009), Johannesburg (2002), Copenhagen

(2009), Durban (2011), and completing the circle – Rio de Janeiro again for Rio+20 (2012) and so forth to the present day. These names are etched into the memories of anyone even half interested in the survival of our planet as we know it. However they are not the only ones: ever since 1995, Conferences of the Parties (COP) have actually been convened every year to review the Rio Convention's implementation. All were heralded with optimism and publicity and carried through with enthusiasm, most turning out targets and promises to deliver profound change for the better.

However, although it is more than 45 years since the first of them, their chief legacy has been, not the visionary triumphs they aspired to, but the bitter disappointment of failure. So what went wrong, and can such conferences ever bring about the necessary degree of change?

The chief problem has been that, if bringing the disparate concerned parties together is rather like herding cats, when you finally manage to assemble them in one place, getting them to agree is like persuading those cats to consent to being neutered. Everyone knows that something must be done or they wouldn't be there; but only so long as others bear the brunt of the necessary sacrifices.

Take for example the seminal 1992 conference in Rio de Janeiro – the "Earth Summit". There the United Nations brought the world together for the first time to discuss ways to address the decline in environments and biodiversity. The conference was generally acknowledged as a triumph for conservation. It was expected to begin the process of guiding the world towards a sustainable future enacted in three major documents: the "Rio Declaration on Environment and Development", "Agenda 21" (concerned with sustainable development), and "Forest Principles". It also opened two legally binding agreements for signature: the "Convention on Biological Diversity" and the "Framework Convention on Climate Change" (UNFCCC).

Since then world leaders, conservationists and economists have continued to try to maintain momentum by colluding in a large number of major biodiversity-conservation initiatives independent of carbon control schemes. The setting up of national "Biodiversity Action Plans" (BAPs), for example, came in response to the Convention on Biological Diversity. Through BAPs, countries were expected to formulate and implement strict regimes to protect their biodiversity. The first target was simply to stop the deterioration – to arrest the shocking worldwide decline in biodiversity. The deadline for this was to be 2010, nominated to be the International Year of Biodiversity.

The Johannesburg disappointment

A decade after the 1992 Rio Earth Summit the UN convened a new gathering of national leaders and interested groups in Johannesburg. This was considered a landmark opportunity, but its failures came to epitomise the malaise seemingly endemic to nearly all world summits on the environment, so it makes a convenient case in point.

Johannesburg's declared aim was to review the progress made and to convert Rio's aspirations into a more concrete process and timetable of action. Curiously though, this time the organisers of this "World Summit on Sustainable Development" set the reduction of world poverty at the head of its agenda. Its secretary-general, Maurice Strong, confidently declared, *"No place on the planet could remain an island of affluence in a sea of misery... One part of the world cannot live in an orgy of unrestrained consumption while the rest destroys its environment just to survive"*.

Despite this altered focus, however, the Johannesburg Summit was also a real test of whether and how far Rio's ideas and aspirations had taken root. As it turned out, delegates were disappointed to find that on the whole progress had been dismal. Environments and biodiversity had continued to decline alarmingly and greenhouse gas release had risen sharply. Poverty also remained stubbornly high, with half the world's population still living on under $2 a day. Furthermore, the increase in carbon emissions remained unchecked. Not much to cheer about then.

Whether or not it contributed to this lack of progress in the intervening years since Rio, it soon became apparent at Johannesburg that despite a profusion of good intentions, old divisions between conservationists and economists were still raw. The chagrin felt by some conservationists from the outset about the summit's declared central focus on the relief of poverty rather than environmental issues characterised this rift (this is an important issue in itself that I will return to shortly). Many participants also felt that the summit's anger had anyway been provoked by the dismissive absence of the American president at the time, George W Bush. His spokesman had gloomily warned that a workable world plan for sustainable development "may not be found" at Johannesburg, a damning prognostication.

Bush, with the Australian government close behind, had also taken a jaundiced view on the ambitions of the Kyoto Protocol (Rio's climate change dedicated offshoot) to cut emissions. He regarded the protocol as dangerous to American industry and the economy. To his way of thinking, only free-market activity would bring the wealth that poor nations need and therefore world trade must be unfettered. But the major problem with this, it is claimed, has been that attempts at free trade have exposed poor nations not so much to investment in infrastructure and internal development, but rather to a swindle of their natural resources, including the destructive exploitation of natural wildernesses.

Although overshadowed by Bush's absence and negative attitude, from the outset there was a general atmosphere of hope and anticipation at Johannesburg. These sentiments, it turned out, were not entirely misplaced, for after much wrangling the conference did eventually agree to a number of important targets. They resolved to restore depleted fish stocks by 2005; to set up networks of marine protected areas; to halve the number of people without connected water supplies by 2015; to substantially increase the use of renewable energy; to minimise health and environmental impacts of chemicals by 2020; to significantly reduce the rate of loss of species by 2010; to tackle overconsumption in rich countries; and to promote corporate responsibility and accountability.

These were admirable intentions, without doubt; however setting targets was the easy bit. The critical point lay in how such an ambitious wish list was going to be implemented, especially in the light of previous failures and the lack of commitment from recalcitrant major nations like the US. The main proposal was that they should mostly take place by way of "business partnerships" in which industry, local governments and community groups would be enlisted to help meet the summit's targets.

Despite the obvious good intentions there was little realism about these aims. While the recognition of the need to involve business in the ecology-development equation was certainly not before time, the planning was over-optimistic, ill-defined and in some cases arguably naïve. Take for example the commonly expressed hope that rich nations would thenceforth replace greed with altruism, apparently simply because they were asked to.

It therefore came as no surprise that Johannesburg's new "partnership plans" were soon exposed as being largely rhetoric, according to *New Scientist* magazine's post-summit investigations [1]. These revealed that the UN's aims to build "bottom-up" partnerships, in which local populations are in the driving seat of economic renewal, was just not happening either in plan or practice. There was also confusion as to how the partnerships would be made to work, and suspicions that public owners of resources would be coerced into surrendering their assets to private interests, the report said.

Nevertheless, enthusiasts hailed partnerships as representing recognition that governments cannot do everything, and that communities need to be empowered to take charge of their own destinies. But although enterprise does indeed often spring from local roots, in general this view may be too simplistic. Most governments would have seen the partnerships scheme as yet another bottomless pit into which they were expected to pour cash, propping up and distorting local economies with non-viable enterprises, rather than nursing them towards independence within a vibrant and competitive economic framework as advocated in this book. Once any such cash flow dries up, as they unavoidably do, how long will such abundance last if it is not built on sound market principles? Without appropriate incentivised market regimes at national and international levels and continued monitoring and adjustment, most such flash flood economies will inevitably return to drought.

Thus Johannesburg's business partnerships were an idealistic compromise between socialism and capitalism. They attempted to walk the jungle in dressing gown and slippers - well meaning, certainly, but entirely inadequate. Judging by past performance, the availability of that community cash in the first place was always in serious doubt, as it indeed transpired.

Yolanda Kakabadse, president of the International Union for Conservation of Nature (IUCN), was one who had seen it all before. She pointed out that the IUCN had been doing partnerships like this since 1948, and that for them to mean anything different there must be new funding.

An old, failed plan demanding new money then? There are no prizes for guessing how that revelation was received by those governments expected to provide most of the funding.

Agenda 21 – the failure of direct
aid as a long-term solution to poverty

There were some depressing statistics revealed at Johannesburg: the 40-chapter Rio blueprint known as Agenda 21 had specified the principles that should guide governments. It also required $625bn a year to implement, and participating governments had pledged to increase their financial contributions accordingly. But despite an increase in global output of some 30% between 1992 and 2002, governments had failed even to maintain preexisting aid budgets, let alone the new ones. In fact they were slashed, in some cases by as much as half. So instead of reducing the already massive debt burden of poor nations as Agenda 21 intended, it had increased it by a third to a phenomenal US$2.5 trillion.

Even the targets set by Agenda 21 involving the most basic human needs – safe drinking water and sanitation – had been decimated by the twin perils of rising debt and falling aid. More than 1.1 billion people rely on unsafe drinking water, and about half the world's population, almost 3 billion people, do not have adequate sanitation. The result is that around 2 million children under five die of water-related diseases each year.

I will not enter here into a statistical litany of impoverishment and destitution from which so much of the world continues to suffer. They may inflame passions, but in themselves such figures are meaningless other than as a gauge of past and present failure. The past can never be changed but the future can be, so it is surely right to focus there. All right-thinking people abhor such terrible deprivation and very many contribute to the plethora of worthy organisations that fight to alleviate it. Some heroically dedicate their entire lives to easing the burden of the very poor. But I think it is true to say that many of the rest of us ordinary mortals feel impotent in the face of such monumental and never-ending problems. Perhaps this is because we believe in our hearts that they really need monumental resources to resolve.

The Third World begging bowl sometimes seems more like a sieve to those under whose noses it is continually waved. The call to send ploughshares rather than food seemed to make good sense in the 80s and 90s, but despite such ostensibly pragmatic approaches good results have not flowed on anything like the scale that was hoped for and that is so desperately needed. A part of the reason for this must be that other factors have interfered, the worst being war, ethnic cleansing and drought.

But the underlying malaise has been the lack of a powerhouse to drive economic development in poor regions. Subsistence farming is too tenuous an existence to support growing populations in uncertain times and unreliable climates. The ancient tribal model has broken down in many places but is not yet replaced with something more dynamic to cope with life in the 21st century.

Although very many people will continue to rely on direct aid for a long time to come, ultimately aid is not a solution; it is a sticking plaster, albeit a vital one. It has, or at least should have, no significant place in the long-term scheme of things other than to cover emergencies. For the hungry billions with whom we share this still bountiful planet the future lies in the world community adopting policies that identify and harness natural economic forces; policies that create and nourish viable and ecologically sustainable economic environments for them to participate in. If they do not, then the world's poorest will surely be condemned to go on lurching from crisis to crisis indefinitely. And as the effects of climate change deepen, so they will be forced to seek sanctuary elsewhere, with potentially catastrophic results.

This means that, however much it may turn the stomachs of the dedicated greens among us, the only effective long-term solutions to economic inequality and destructive natural resource exploitation will be those that light up the eyes of industry and commerce. I fear that policy results will continue to disappoint far into the future, just as greatly as Rio and Johannesburg's, until the reality that is the power and beauty of natural forces working equally within both biological and economic realms is faced.

Spawn of the Devil syndrome

The overall picture that emerges from most COP summits is one of good ambitions undermined by unscientific economic policy. Indeed it is an ongoing source of wonder to me that so many conservation-minded people still hold such uniform and polarised views of business motivation. They either seem to believe that all corporations are evil and need their greedy capitalist noses ground into the dust, or that businesses can be converted to the conservation cause merely by having the inappropriateness of their ways politely pointed out to them.

Certainly some conscientiously led businesses do invest in conservation for philanthropic reasons. A few more do so where it rewards them with at least some measurable bonus – say, good publicity, political credit, tax concessions, or perhaps a market toehold for future exploitation. But the vast majority will only respond to the solid promise of investment return. This is their *raison d'être* after all, and there is nothing evil or sinister about it – it's just Nature.

Any plan that fails to recognise and accommodate this unchanging, unchangeable and entirely natural state of affairs is doomed at best to inadequacy, at worst to failure. From the outset, Rio's inability to recognise the absolute need to construct a more realistic model through which to realise its worthy aspirations disappointed many. As the UN Secretary-General himself remarked dryly at the time, "*Unsustainable approaches to economic development remain pervasive*". Intentions were undoubtedly good, but the proverb, "the road to hell is paved with good intentions" leaps to mind.

The sparseness of joined-up policy so evident at world summits of the past highlights the need for a much broader input and consensus on policy, and this requires a coming together of minds intent on a single purpose and equipped with the tools to carry it out.

The great biologist and thinker Edward O Wilson famously underlined the need for cross-disciplinary collusion in his seminal book, *Consilience*, and this brings us from failed world conferences to the next great obstacle to progress – the polarity between the impassioned, Nature-oriented world view as articulated by ecologists, and the humanist orientation and objectives of capitalist economics. Bringing these broadly disparate disciplines together in partnership is an urgent priority if human needs are to be balanced with those of the natural world to the lasting benefit of both. I will argue that *Junglenomics* provides a sound working platform for this to take place.

The economist-ecologist divide

Introducing changes that affect the behaviour of large populations and the operations of big and influential businesses is undoubtedly a challenging task, and represents the second great obstacle to positive change. Resistance to change can be formidable. This means that the case for change after world summit failures has to be overwhelming. To stand much chance of being adopted, therefore, new environmental policies need to be underpinned by a united economics and ecological policy front.

Unfortunately there is still a deep ideological gulf between these two key disciplines. Despite the fact that most ecologists are no more equipped with know-how in finance than most economists are in biodiversity management, it is no secret that there is often a lack of mutual understanding and even respect between them. Integrating the two agendas is a long-standing problem that has yet to be resolved [2] and, as the failure of world summits have shown, this is one of the main reasons why successful environmental policy has proved so elusive.

The division is perhaps no surprise. Each discipline has been learned in very different schools and comes at environmental matters from very different standpoints and with different priorities, timescales and jargon. For their part, economists are generally oriented towards public welfare. For example, it is often the case that the people bordering ecologically valuable regions live in poverty, the relief of which is a priority for economists. They tend to take the view that if a tract of land will support more humans under the plough than not, then that is how it should be used. Overall biodiversity should not necessarily be preserved, they argue, where hungry people need its territory to survive.

Most also believe that to automatically protect organisms and their environments from human incursion irrespective of whether or not there is an exploitable economic value in them, is presumptuous. This means that they are inclined to assign economic value to natural resources according to what they assess the potential economic usefulness is to people rather than to the viability of ecosystems for their own sake.

In contrast, most ecologists take the view that there simply is no contest. They hold the health of natural systems and species diversity as paramount and argue that it therefore must be protected by direct means at any cost against human incursion. They point to a host of problems caused by human intrusion into natural habitats, among them the loss of diversity, of ecosystem stability, of potentially valuable plants, of nitrogen and carbon-absorbing biomass. They observe that economic exploitation causes the expulsion and abuse of remote tribal Indians and the impoverishment of their culture and lifestyle, as well as the erosion of the world's biodiversity, natural beauty and wilderness. They also argue, often vehemently, that economists' favourite solution – to allocate economic value to environments – is not a solution but the very opposite; a recipe for ecological disaster. They claim that in practice it tends to protect only those few plants, animals and environments with already established economic value while other, non-valuable species do not receive protection and by implication are expendable. Indeed they tend to attack economics-based solutions to environmental issues on principle, including biodiversity banking.

Despite such stinging criticisms the economics camp remains undeterred and continues to enthusiastically promote economic valuing as a sound way to manage wildlife and reduce poverty simultaneously. It dismisses the ecology first argument as mere academicism from scientists removed from the everyday plight of humanity.

Although I too am a harsh critic of much environment-related economic policy, I would say in economists' defence that just because they have thriving economies rather than Nature at the forefront of their agendas that is not to suggest they are entirely mercenary and don't care about Nature; it is just that their disciplinary priorities are geared that way. They strive to find routes to the most efficient use of resources and to greater well-being and prosperity for people. In the case of the very poor, that may mean any prosperity at all.

This is not to suggest that economists are essentially philanthropic. It is that their discipline *requires* them to find ways to make economies more prosperous. It is simply what they do. So to them poverty is not only a blot on the economic landscape but also a mark of failure.

Economists, therefore, should not be left out of environmental policy; they should be brought on board through argument and persuasion to embrace a new economic paradigm that puts Nature and people in the same equation (which indeed they are), rather than one being subservient to the needs of the other. When it comes to saving threatened species, history shows that in the long run neither political ideology nor simple love for Nature does the trick; hard economic policy does. In reality it is poverty, not greed, that is mostly to be found at the core of the world's worst environmental woes, and conservation in isolation from human need is the prerogative of the well fed. Yet prolonged poverty can never be overcome at the expense of the natural environment because, as the world is finding out, it only replaces one set of problems with another.

Because I have a philosophical interest in both camps I can not only understand but also sympathise with each. I recognise the sources of the mutual antipathy to be fear of unhumanitarian and costly, economically inefficient agendas on the one side, and on the other as mistrust and cynicism over the profit motive. Unfortunately, while the great and urgent need is for environmental far-sightedness backed by sophisticated economic instruments, this too often translates as economic naïvety versus environmental myopia.

Yet the stark realities of Nature brought home by knowledge of the all-powerful resource-colonising imperative now allows these protagonists to step away from these parochial battle lines and look at the bigger picture. That picture shows that an intellectual and practical collusion of talents between ecologists and economists, without compromise of principle, is not only highly desirable, it is also perfectly possible.

So how can this happen? To find out we first need to dig into the deeper reasons for the ecologist-economist divide.

When we look beneath the rhetoric, the chief differences between ecologists and economists are more extensive than a mere academic diversity of approach. Ecologists' Nature-oriented stance is much more than just a scientific discipline; it is a matter of philosophy – even morality. This is perfectly understandable. When you spend your life immersed in the staggering variety and complexities of Nature it comes to hold far more than just aesthetic value for you; it verges on the spiritual. As such the concept of economic valuing can appear, not merely unwise, but positively philistine. How do you measure the value of an acre of rainforest, the bluebird of paradise or the orangutan? What is the true worth of an elephant, a whale or a rare orchid? Is it its potential dollar earnings from tourists or from their rendered carcasses, or as cogs in vital ecosystems are they actually beyond a price being set on them – indeed are they price*less*? Those of an ecological inclination would passionately make that assertion. For them, classical economists fit snugly into Oscar Wilde's definition of a cynic – knowing the price of everything and the value of nothing.

From the strength of emotion with which these arguments are often advanced it is evident that the ecologist-economist divide is therefore essentially a disagreement between conflicting sociopolitical cultures, each devoted to a fundamentally different belief system. On the one side stand the champions of economic growth and development and of homocentric environments; on the other, those of uncompromised biodiversity and untouched, pristine wilderness. It is a conflict that seems to mirror the real-life struggle between economic development and the natural environment, and each side is utterly convinced it is the good guy.

Yet for all their emotional attachment, strong views and sophisticated knowledge of biology and ecosystems, ecologists have so far failed spectacularly to stop the decline in the world's environment. Theirs is a world full of yearning and aspiration backed up by very little on-the-ground success, even where they have been given free rein – in many East African national parks for example.

And for theirs, while economists have significantly reduced, though far from eradicated, the blight of world poverty, they have presided over policies that have been catastrophic to biodiversity and the environment alike.

Despite such abject and ongoing failures, many in both factions have still so far refused to look beyond the narrow confines of their belief systems. They have remained polarised, clinging tightly to flimsy, increasingly irrelevant ideological tenets in the face of destruction and devastation at a time when the need for a concerted effort to halt the world's decline has never been greater.

Bridging the gap

Recognising the true value of Nature in order to conserve it now demands a team effort – a collusion of expertise. For this a working partnership between the key players – ecologists and economists – is essential. Such an alliance will of course demand compromises on both sides. For their part, ecologists will need to become more pragmatic and less anti-capitalist. Their solution to the economics/ecology conflict is currently enshrined in what they call *ecological economics*. Ecological economists argue for economic restraint and an end to economic growth. Unfortunately, this translates as an end to increasing per capita wealth, something that could only happen by imposition because the natural inclination of people is to grow their wealth. Like setting a score limit in a football match it would result in much the same stifling of ambition and enterprise as Joseph Stalin's Russia or Mao Tse-tung's China.

Besides, the economic engine could not be so easily set to idle. The resource hunger it embodies is far too powerful and unrelenting. As history bears out, sooner or later markets always have their way. If ecologists really want to see Nature rescued it is time for them to address the possible rather than stubbornly cling to an ideology that, however well-meaning, is unachievable. That course can only result in continuing failure and ongoing decline.

There are glimmers of hope that suggest a much wider collaboration between ecologists and economists may indeed at last be possible. For their part, however much it may offend their colleagues' sensibilities, some ecologists' hearts are at last being overruled by their heads. These pragmatists, such as those advising bio-offsetting schemes for example, are finally recognising that the old strategies are just not working, and that to stand any real chance of success environmental conservation needs to acknowledge and accommodate the power of market forces.

And on the economics side, although there has been ample cause for mistrust in the past, ecologists need no longer suspect all economists of pro-business bias and collusion at the expense of the environment. Whereas before, economists would rarely enter industrial environmental costs (externalities) into their equations because they were considered free, now a new enlightened breed of "environmental economist" has fully acknowledged the immense value of healthy, natural systems. For such "natural resource economists" environmental decline is now a mark, not just of environmental, but of *economic* failure because it demonstrates the inability of certain markets to control and correct the bad outcomes of industrial processes. An overly polluting industrial process, for example, is an inefficient one, and that to economists is bad. They therefore label such events as "market failures", a term previously reserved for imbalances between supply and demand.

In recent times economics has also arguably become less remote and more in tune with people's wants and needs. Refreshingly, wildlife, landscape, sense of place, spirituality, even beautiful views – all these are beginning to be included as being of real economic value (and have been recognised as such in Britain's recent Natural Ecosystem Assessment, previously mentioned), if only because they bring happiness and well-being to people. Conversely public distress at environmental degradation and demand for conservation are also now significant economic criteria to be factored into environmental economics policy [3].

So economics isn't always just about money and profit any more; it is gradually becoming about human welfare of mind too; and that brings the sensibilities of ecologists firmly onto their radar. This is a significant development that marks a sea change in economic thinking. It also could and should help bridge the gap with ecologists.

Am I saying that environmental economists are now getting it right and hence advocating a neo-economist hegemony? Emphatically not. There are still considerable dangers in leaving even these more enlightened economists in sole charge of environmental issues. After all, how are they to know what is "overly" polluting or damaging to an environment? How does an economist decide when an industrial process needs reining in and when its behaviour is acceptable? And when, if ever, is a piece of environment or a species expendable for some perceived greater good? For them the answers to such questions are to be found in value equations, the results of which are dependent on the subjectively selected and entered coefficients. It is said that if you put ten economists in a room you will get ten different opinions, so where will consistency be found? To quote Laurence J Peter: *"An economist is an expert who will know tomorrow why the things he predicted yesterday didn't happen today."* Harsh, but not altogether untrue.

The thing is that economics is not a science, nor is it always accurate in its analyses or predictions. It is a sophisticated and continually evolving discipline – a toolbox for manipulating economic functioning at any and all levels from a household, to a village, to a nation, to the entire world economy.

Besides, randomly devised economic strategies are too deeply affected by the varying winds of politics to trust the world's natural crown jewels to them. New governments often appoint economists with diametrically different views to their predecessors in order to fulfil electoral promises and endorse political dogma. There is no empirical, universal wisdom. Some believe in top-down control, others in grass-roots efficiency; others again in deregulation and free markets. Economic policy is also often enveloped together with issues such as social engineering, national culture, even birth control.

The bottom line is that economists and ecologists need each other; they are two legs of the tripod (the third being government) on which the future of the world environment rests. To turn the page on this embarrassing era of rampant environmental destruction, a disciplined, ecology-inclusive, science-based economic plan is needed. Such a plan would not only provide the tools and information to protect valuable environments, but also allow us to play business at its own game. That is the only effective way to stop destructive business in its tracks for the long term. The vast majority of marketplace predators are hard-headed, single-minded, profit junkies who are generally deaf to conservation issues; they respect only products and services made of dollars, not lectures on ecology and morality. That is the stark reality that must be accepted if we are to progress.

For their part, rather than advocating economic repression, ecologists need to accept and acknowledge two fundamental realities: firstly the unstoppable and inescapable dynamism of the marketplace, and secondly the potential for economists, with their help, to achieve good ends by harnessing that dynamism in the right ways. By focusing on their own area of expertise – identifying environmental problems and their causes – ecologists can and should cooperate with environmental economists to tailor effective market strategies to protect and enhance them. *Junglenomics* cannot happen without major ecologist input; that much is certain. Their understanding of how ecosystems interact and self-balance is essential information for the creation of the newly balanced economic ecosystem that this book advocates.

Such collaboration is not without precedent. Ecologists, climatologists and others fought and won the argument for action to mitigate climate change. They did so only because they managed to convince economists that there would be a substantial *economic* cost to a warming planet. Had they not carried this argument it would have been almost impossible to get economists and the governments they advise to support the huge financial burden that emissions reduction is placing on economies worldwide. The effect is that economic value has been assigned to an environmental factor previously ignored – steady state global average temperatures. Only the ignorant and perverse now deny these realities.

The same argument now needs to be won over environment and biodiversity and the vital services they provide to maintain those temperatures. Unfortunately, while it is difficult to overestimate the significance of the climate change coalition in terms of closing the ecologist-economist gap, it may have a detrimental side effect on Nature conservation. This is because, by focusing so many policies and resources on what is seen as the foremost environmental issue, the other great issues discussed in this book – pollution, wilderness destruction, marine loss, land loss and poaching – are being relegated to inferior positions in the world's attention. These issues are closely interlinked, and the effects of ongoing resource colonisation and population growth are likely to be at least as severe on wildlife as those of global warming, perhaps more so. Never before have they had to survive the attentions of a species with the destructive ability to mow down its forests, plough up its sea floors, pollute and dry up its seas and rivers, knock down its mountains, and even blow the entire planet apart if they get their political calculations wrong.

The tragedy of the world commons

If we do finally manage to replace subjective with science-based economic policy by combining the talents of ecologists and economists, the third formidable obstacle to then overcome is how to get enough governments worldwide to participate given the dismal success record of world summits in this respect. It is all very well to achieve results in small, reasonably well-run countries like Britain for example; but it is the emerging and developing economies, especially in equatorial zones, that the conservation problem is most acutely felt because that is where the vast majority of biodiversity lives.

We might hope and believe that our arguments are persuasive and our plans watertight, but despite all the best intentions and carefully constructed plans there are times in international negotiations when no amount of logic will do, whichever nation is involved, most notably the US. You can argue for evermore about pollution, greenhouse gasses, the decline of biodiversity and the rest; but when you are up against national governments, then however persuasive your case, however widely shared your opinion, however alarming the apparent consequences of inaction, you are still unlikely to gain much advantage unless you can clearly demonstrate national economic interest.

Markets can often be manipulated to modify their own behaviour, yes, but governments are another matter because it is their primary duty to look after what they see as the interests of their citizens. Although those interests may seem narrow and short term when viewed from a world perspective, national leaders follow irresistible cues like any business, or for that matter any species. Even where their national strategy proves highly detrimental to the world as a whole, getting it to change it is a daunting task. This is especially so if that nation happens to be a leviathan like China, India, Russia or the USA.

It isn't that they haven't tried though. At the 2009 Copenhagen Summit many nations came together to try to settle on a common strategy for tackling climate change, but failed conspicuously to do so. Many different reasons were given, and blamemongers enjoyed a field day; however the chief reason for this failure could be ascribed to a global version of Garrett Hardin's *Tragedy of the Commons*, described earlier in relation to the high seas. For the common global environment is no different: it is a vast commons in which Hardin's "commoner" is a nation rather than a herder.

Here the commons apply not just to air quality, but also to biodiversity, for I do not believe that wild organisms "belong", as domesticated plants and animals do, to the nations on whose territory they happen to live. I regard them as belonging to no one but Nature. As such they are a common asset and hence a responsibility to all nations, which is why all nations should play their part in protecting and conserving them even within other nations' borders. It is a privilege and a delight to do so, not a burden.

The blame game

The problem is that developing nations take a very different view to developed ones regarding who should be doing something about excessive carbon emissions, pollution and loss of natural environment and biodiversity. It is as though (in Hardin's analogy) they are late-joining herders, claiming their share of grazing and blaming the incumbent herders on the degraded pasture; only in this case Hardin's metaphor equates to global carbon and pollution emissions and wilderness destruction rather than to overgrazed land.

The justification developing countries put forward for their stance is ostensibly persuasive. They state that they are not responsible for most of the mess the world is in, developed nations are. And as developed nations remain far greater polluters and carbon emitters on a per capita basis, why should their efforts to escape poverty through industrialisation be restricted? It is for wealthy, well-fed nations to rein back, not them, they argue. In this way they justify continuing to increase pollution and GHG emissions in pursuit of their long-awaited economic growth and prosperity. They deploy the same argument concerning forest destruction: the West has cut down most of its forests for agriculture and is being hypocritical to expect them to refrain solely for the good of the planet rather than for much-needed hard cash, they say.

As was found at Copenhagen, it is difficult to argue against the logic of this. There is no getting away from it – developed nations *have* caused most of the problem. They also continue to be by far the greatest per capita polluters and carbon emitters.

Unsurprisingly, First World countries are not at all enthusiastic about a one-sided rein back. They see it as a major threat to their long-held tenure at the top of the economic food chain. And given a backdrop of weakening competitiveness against rapidly growing "Asian tiger" and BRIC economies (Brazil, Russia, India and China), along with contractions caused by post-crisis recession and more recently China's slowdown, many developed world businesses and their governments are understandably sceptical and reluctant. The main objection is that the high Polluter Pays taxation and carbon offset costs that developing nations want to see them bear would reduce their competitiveness even further. Only a level world playing field would maintain the balance of international trade for them.

This is why some [4] think that carbon offset trading will not work without the compliance of all major economies. They therefore believe that the better option is to focus on technological solutions to carbon emissions. That would be fine except for one thing: the necessary technology will not be developed nearly quickly enough if there aren't economic incentives to do so. That involves making carbon emissions expensive and rewarding reduction, and that's exactly what carbon trading markets are designed to do. The alternative is a carbon tax, which attracts the same criticisms: it is anticompetitive unless international. The situation cries out for even-handed incentives and penalties – that is, subsidies and taxes – on all carbon and pollution-emitting businesses internationally, but that will probably require an international body to oversee.

There is another important factor to reckon with: if a two-tier system were to be allowed in which some countries were excused part or all of their environmental obligations, the natural business response would be to relocate pollutive manufacturing processes from high-cost to low-cost regimes. Clearly this "carbon leakage" would defeat the object. And if special rules were to be applied to businesses originating from developed countries to counter this flight from tax, it is argued this would again be anticompetitive and unfair.

It was clear from Copenhagen and Durban that emerging and developing nations were simply not prepared to impose constraints and costs on their economies. They persisted with their justifiable but unrealistic view that, having caused the damage developed economies should bear the full brunt of sacrifice. Thus we were back to square one so far as international competitiveness and cooperation are concerned, and at an impasse. The only other available level playing field would be to return to a pollution free-for-all, which is something no one wants to see.

Yet we are already using up over 1.5 planets' worth of the Earth's resources and that figure is climbing. Since 1961 our demand for natural resources has risen 2.5 times; at that rate of increase, by 2030 we will need 2 planets' worth to maintain consumption [5]. In 2018 "Earth Overshoot Day", the date when demand overtakes the supply of ecological resources and services, was marked on August 2nd; a date that is getting earlier every year.

So there you have it – the global commons impasse. Everyone wants their piece of the commons cake that is the world environment and its resources, and to eat it as well; but it just isn't big enough to go around. Yet a remarkable change of heart appears to have taken place.

COP21 and the Paris Accord

Climate summits have been likened to a globetrotting carnival run for the benefit of diplomats, environmentalists, journalists and others. Each one goes off in a fanfare of expectant and high-minded aspirations, and ends with postponement and disappointment. Copenhagen was a classic example; Durban not much better because in effect nations merely agreed to start again in 2020 and do what they could in the meantime. There was one small victory however, in that the Kyoto Protocol was extended by a handful of nations, though just 15% of global emissions would now be affected. And it was considered a breakthrough by some that all participating nations, including previously reticent ones, had at last agreed to set legally binding carbon emission targets beginning in 2020 (2020 – hadn't they been listening?). They had until 2015 to agree a formula and create the required instruments if they could – there were no guarantees.

The problem is that under "business as usual", by 2020 emissions will probably have risen above the levels necessary to keep global warming below the all-important (though still excessive) 2 degrees; so if it was a victory it was a slim one. It also left deep uncertainties. What would happen at the 2015 deadline? Was there any chance at all of getting a legally binding universal agreement after so much bickering and infighting?

As it turned out the 21st Conference of Parties (COP21) held in Paris in December 2015 turned out to be unexpectedly different from everything that had come before. Its remarkable success seems to have turned on one particular modification to the Durban Accord: there would be no legally binding targets to mitigate climate change; instead there would be commitments by countries to carry out specific, self-nominated pledges. In place of the legally binding targets that had caused such problems before, the new agreement created a mechanism to "facilitate implementation" and "promote compliance". This mechanism was to comprise a committee of experts whose services were to be "facilitative" in nature and operate in a "non-adversarial and non-punitive" manner and report annual progress to future COP meetings.

This new softly-softly approach was a stroke of genius: instead of arriving at COP21 on the defensive and prepared to fight each item every step of the way as in the past, delegates were more likely to vie with each other for what they could be seen to be doing to contribute. The result was an atmosphere of cooperation and goodwill rarely, if ever, seen before. It had taken 20 summits, but finally some basic psychology had won the day. All 195 countries signed up to do their bit. By any measure it was an extraordinary success.

Missed opportunities at COP21

Yet even the most enthusiastic of supporters agree the COP21 agreement is undemanding. The initial agreed agenda is not going to be nearly enough to reach the required goal of less than a 2 degree rise in global temperatures as it stands either; so much more is needed, which is why the agreement included a clause that requires steadily improved GHG emission targets over succeeding years. Nations, especially small and emerging ones, will have to think long and hard as to how they are to adjust their economies to meet their declared aspirations.

Despite all the euphoria, there was a big defect in the COP agenda. Notably absent from any first-line mention was the future of the world's most precious resource – its rapidly disappearing biodiversity. Where were the clauses about forest, marine and land degradation? Where were the undertakings to aim for no net loss of biodiversity?

I referred earlier to America's proposed "Energy Innovation and Carbon Dividend Act" (p. 140). This could form an ideal foundation for an international treaty binding the trading block, enlarged and expanded with appropriate agreements relating to sustainability, conservation and pollution. This block could thus become a "Green Union" of nations dedicated to low carbon, environmentally benign economic activity.

While it was recognised in earlier summits that wilderness and biodiversity have an important role in climate regulation, not one of the 195 nations acceding to the COP21 agreement made specific commitments regarding its biodiversity. Once again Nature had been afforded second place to climate change. Brazil, for example, did not commit to saving one single tree, let alone the entirety of its forests that it and others need to. The acquiescence by Indonesia to the destruction of nearly all its rainforests within 20 years had not been affected one iota. Unfortunately the politics and economics of global warming mitigation relegated these vital matters to a mere coefficient of climate change, not stand-alone aspirations as they most certainly should have been.

Don't misunderstand me, the COP21 agreement is a remarkable achievement and enormous credit needs to be given to the negotiators and organisers for achieving the apparently unachievable – the greatest gathering of world leaders on one day in history, and their unanimous agreement to act concertedly on climate change. But as I remarked at the start of this book, it is only a beginning. Although it solicited important and substantial commitments on reducing GHG emissions, its promises were still in effect only "firefighting" strategies largely driven by popular demand within their own electorates. The necessary profound economic reforms advocated in this book to defend Nature, not just in the atmosphere but in all its facets, were nowhere to be seen at COP21. This surely implies that, while the urgent economic necessity of tackling climate change is almost universally recognised, that of conserving biodiversity is as yet still not so. This needs to change.

In order to turn words into reality nations now need to build on COP21 by cooperating more closely with each other in order to create fertile conditions within their borders not only to reduce GHG, but also to begin a comprehensive economic-environmental revolution. This can only be achieved via a whole economy policy that balances the needs of humans and the planet alike in every sphere for the long term.

The politics of self-interest

So how do you get nations to rise above the natural self-interest characterised by Hardin's *Tragedy of the Commons* and put the planet first?

The answer is simple: you can't, and you won't. And this is why.

National decision-making processes of such great consequence can rarely be enforced from outside, as the negotiators at COP21 so astutely recognised. It is not only impractical, but even if it were possible it would only elicit retaliation, resentment, cartels and trade wars. A way round the constraints of national self-interest has to be found, and for this we can again fall back on Nature for guidance.

In Nature, resources similarly get overstretched, particularly so in times of drought. Travelling through Botswana some years back I witnessed the pitiful results of a long period without rains: a hippo stranded in a nearly dry mudhole; emaciated antelope, zebra and wildebeest standing around listlessly; innumerable white-bleached bones scattered in the dust. Only the predators looked contented; though without imminent rain their turn to suffer would inevitably follow.

This decimation of populations in times of hardship is the natural but hard way back to ecosystemic balance, the way we desperately need to avoid. In Nature each is for itself – nothing deliberately leaves so much as a blade of grass for another, regardless of whether that other is of the same species. Each species inhabits an essentially selfish and anarchical world in which it competes for its own corner in which to survive.

Yet that isolation is the key. Those who govern nations are occupying niches that do not and could not exist in the wild – they have no equivalents. The intense influence that governments exert over their markets makes them almost godlike, for they can alter business motivations, priorities and environments simply by pulling their financial strings. In a natural analogy, they can in effect create grasslands, trees, lakes, marshes and mountains for economic species to colonise; or conversely they may destroy them and create sterility, all at the stroke of a pen. Thus they distort the natural international ebb and flow of goods, services, money and people as they see fit (notwithstanding black markets). In so doing, governments may do temporary good service for their own citizens in terms of quick cash returns, but also accumulate long-term damage to their economic, social and natural environments.

The internationalisation of business – a leverage opportunity

However, as markets become ever more international, national influence over business weakens. Businesses that trade only within the borders of their own country may be vulnerable to the whims of their national governments, but that is not really the case for international traders because they have to comply with the regulations of the foreign countries they want to trade with.

All exporters are prized by their host nations, but especially so among emerging and developing countries for the much-needed foreign currency they bring in. This presents an ideal opportunity for leverage in order to marginalise the selfish influence of national governments and bring in much higher environmental standards. Developed and major developing nations could, if they wished, form a trading block underwritten by treaty that sets high environmental standards for trade between them. Within this block, taxes – for example carbon tax, GHG offset markets and pollution penalties

– and on the other side of the coin, subsidies, could be applied evenly.

One of the main objections to conservation measures is that they hamper business unfairly if not universally applied. Such a treaty would provide the opportunity for a level international playing field in environmental protection. No longer could it be argued that such taxes and subsidies are anticompetitive. The result would be a committed environmental elite that could trade with each other on equal terms. The idea would be that to avoid paying substantial tariffs, any company wishing to trade with other treaty countries would have to produce certified assessments of their net carbon, pollution and biodiversity footprints.

However, in addition – and this is the key to also bringing emerging and developing nations themselves into the fold – this trading block would require that imports to them from anywhere outside the treaty block would also have to meet the same certified standards. These exporters would also likewise have, for example, to buy carbon offsets for products with a carbon footprint and other pollutive emissions, and to certify no net loss of biodiversity.

By ensuring that any business wishing to trade with the trading block adhered to them, environmental trading standards on world markets could achieve levels never seen before. Whether it be farmed or wild fish, timber, minerals, electronics, plastics or machinery, all would need to comply with the standards at levels that will address the tragedy of the world commons once and for all. In this way, all exporters' unremitted external environmental costs – their true costs – would be included in the price of their exported goods and services. Nations are already familiar with fair play rules pertaining to international trade (as overseen by the World Trade Organization), and this arrangement would simply add environmental fair play to its rule book. (This is essentially an extension of the proposed US "Energy Innovation and Carbon Dividend Act", mentioned earlier, but covering all human-, ecology- and environment-endangering activities.)

It would mean that companies such as Daewoo International Corp and its parent company, POSCO, along with Genting Berhad, IJM Corp Berhad, First Pacific and Kulim Malaysia, which were formally divested by Norwegian megafund, GPFG, after investigations by the fund's Council on Ethics revealed their palm oil plantations and other activities cause severe environmental damage, would be forced to price in their damaging externalities to their products. It is hard to think of any better way to force them to re-evaluate their alleged deeply damaging biodiversity and carbon footprints.

Whether or not emerging and developing nations' governments themselves chose to sign up to this treaty would be irrelevant because an ever-growing proportion of their businesses would be obliged to do so in order to participate fully in world markets. Likewise, these businesses would in turn need to demand higher standards from suppliers within their home country in order to avoid tariffs.

Furthermore, donor countries would then be in a good position to provide and fund the necessary technology and expertise to poorer nations to enable their exporting businesses to comply. In this way ever more exporting nations *de facto* could be cajoled into achieving the standards of the treaty throughout their economies even without their becoming co-signatories, creating a new culture of environmental awareness and respect for biodiversity securely based in economic fundamentals.

Changing culture

Culture is the key word in all this. Integrating environmental externalities, not just into law but into the culture of all international trading, may be the only sure way to protect the world commons for the long term.

Culture is thankfully not a rigid, immutable thing. Historically it can be seen to be flexible and pragmatic, evolving in response to prevailing social, environmental and economic necessities. Culture represents a statement of belief, of priority, of intent, of direction, all reflecting the perception of common good. Rarely can such a direction have ever been as distinctly signposted as it is today. Fifty years from now this sea change may be seen as having been a perfectly natural evolution, and people may wonder how it didn't happen a lot sooner.

I believe that the cultural change in economics that this book calls for is already in our hearts and minds: all right-minded people want to conserve our planet in a fit state for our descendants. The time of the great resource rush is past. To enable each to survive, the new era must bring the unification of economics with ecology. Leaders must now respond to this cultural yearning and step up to shepherd the world economy into this new post-destructive age.

This demands international cooperation and coordination to a level that cannot happen efficiently or fairly on the *ad hoc* basis of annual summits. It needs a dedicated central body that acts as a reservoir of information, technology and policy development, and as a facilitator of international, environmentally sensitive trade programmes.

In the next and penultimate chapter, I explore how such an organisation could be made up.

1. *New Scientist 2359 p.8*
2. *Shell/IUCN combined report 2008*
3. *E.g.: Hanley, Shogren & White*
4. *E.g. members of the American think tank, the Property and Environment Research Center (PERC)*
5. *Global Footprints Report 2010*

Chapter 17
A World Environment Organisation

Leading potential WEO constituents

Who, then, are the powerful manipulators of international economic development and environment policy that need to bring an Ecosystem Economics paradigm into the heart of their philosophy and guidance?

There is a substantial number of organisations dedicated variously to the protection of wildlife, the conservation of ecosystems, sustainable economic development, the alleviation of poverty, climate change mitigation and the maintenance of fair and free international trade. Their missions encompass the entire spectrum of emphases, ranging from humanist at one end to environmentalist at the other. The array of scientific, economic and organisational talent, as well as political and financial influence represented by their combined membership is truly formidable. If that talent could be channelled into a common cause I believe it could wreak real, rapid and highly beneficial change that would help secure the long-term future of Planet Earth.

The United Nations

Perhaps the greatest of these organisations is the UN, which runs a multitude of vital aid and development programmes throughout the developing world. It also underwrites the annual COP meetings.

The agenda of the United Nations Development Programme (UNDP) includes political and economic development, public health, crime and environment. All of these, they claim, can no longer be managed within the boundaries of any single government. They pride themselves in bringing together governments, civil society, multinational corporations and multilateral organisations to look for innovative ways to address particular issues of concern [1]. The UNDP's goals include reducing poverty, hunger, illiteracy, environmental degradation and discrimination against women, and in connecting countries to the knowledge and resources to achieve these objectives. They produce reports on all these areas and, according to its own literature, the independent team of experts who write such reports *"draw on a worldwide network of leaders from academia, government and civil society who contribute data, ideas, and best practices. Developing countries and their international partners use the Report to gauge results and shape new policies"*. Clearly this puts the UNDP in an ideal position to promote and support a new international economic programme.

In addition the United Nations Environment Programme (UNEP) is the leading global environmental authority. It sets the global environmental agenda, promotes and advises on sustainable development within the United Nations system, and speaks out authoritatively for the global environment.

The World Trade Organization

Next, in its role as the ultimate arbiter of international trade, the WTO is another agency with powerful influence over international economic policy. Its advisers show countries how they can benefit from international trade without compromising the welfare of their people and their environments. Through agreements negotiated between the large majority of participating nations, the WTO tries to ensure that trade flows freely and fairly under legal strictures. It is hard to imagine any agency better placed to influence the pattern of international trade for the good.

The World Bank

While the World Bank is *de facto* an arm of the UN, its status and influence stand it apart. The word "bank" is a bit of a misnomer; in fact it is an agency – a combination of five organisations, including the International Bank for Reconstruction and Development, and the International Development Association. It is made up of 184 member countries responsible for how it is financed and how its money is spent to alleviate poverty, hunger and disease throughout the world. The bank's staff is huge – it claims to employ around 10,000 people, including economists, educators, environmentalists, financial analysts, anthropologists, engineers, and many others. Such a wealth of diverse talent under one roof presents an extraordinary opportunity. With some $8.1 billion at its disposal in 2002 for projects in low-income countries, the World Bank has not only the brain but also the brawn to become a prime mover in an enviro-economic renaissance.

The World Resources Institute

Then there is the WRI, an independent, non-profit organisation with a staff of more than a hundred scientists, economists, policy experts, business analysts, statistical analysts, map-makers and communicators. Their remit is simple and admirable: to work to "protect the Earth and improve people's lives". Its inherent expertise, ambition and global perspective make the WRI a significant potential player in any reform programme.

The International Union for Conservation of Nature

The IUCN is the world's largest species conservation network. Issues such as habitat protection, wildlife trade, illegal logging and the promotion of environmental awareness, lie at the core of their agenda. They work in particular at identifying and gathering detailed information on species in danger of extinction, adding them to a "Red List" to emphasise their plight. Significantly for an organisation primarily in the conservation camp, they now recognise that social, economic and environmental issues are interrelated and appreciate the importance that environmentalists and development agencies begin, at last, to work together. Along with this refreshingly enlightened outlook, the IUCN's wide experience in conservation matters and their ever-growing bank of data also make them worthy potential participants.

The International Monetary Fund

No economic reform programme could work without the prominent involvement of the IMF. It was conceived at a United Nations conference convened in Bretton Woods, New Hampshire in July 1944 to reassess international economic policy and avoid a repeat of the disastrous policies that had contributed to the Great Depression of the 1930s. Its remit was to help promote the health of the world economy. Headquartered in Washington DC, the IMF is governed by and accountable to the governments of the 184 countries that make up its near-global membership.

Article I of the Articles of Agreement sets out the IMF's main responsibilities: promoting international monetary cooperation, facilitating the expansion and balanced growth of international trade, promoting exchange stability, assisting in the establishment of a multilateral system of payments, and making its resources available (under adequate safeguards) to members experiencing balance of payments difficulties. At the time of writing the IMF has $97 billion in loans outstanding to 84 countries. Thus it is in a uniquely powerful position, not just to advise on national economic policy but to influence it directly. This is particularly so among Third World emerging economies, which tend to have the greatest biodiversity as well as the fastest growing populations.

The stability of the international monetary and financial system is the IMF's chief responsibility – it aims to prevent crises by supervising sensible national economic policy. However, this is coming under pressure from several directions, potentially the most dangerous of which are burgeoning populations, the degradation of environments, and climate change. Its other declared aim, to help reduce poverty, cannot be sustainably achieved without first achieving two goals: tackling AIDS effectively and encouraging the poor towards stewardship management of species-rich environments through market economics.

The World Wildlife Fund

The WWF is another household name that could make a significant contribution to a WEO. Its statutory purpose is "to conserve the natural environment and ecological processes worldwide". This is taken to include fauna and flora, the landscape, water, soils, air and other natural resources, with particular emphasis on the maintenance of essential ecological processes and life support systems. Further WWF aims are the preservation of species and ecosystem diversity, and ensuring that the utilisation of wild plant and animal species and natural ecosystems is sustainable.

The WWF's stated mission reflects these ambitions – to "stop the degradation of the planet's natural environment and to build a future in which humans live in harmony with Nature". True to its adopted role as an independent, global conservation outfit, the WWF has already recognised the link between poverty, migration and macroeconomic policy and biodiversity loss, and hence the need to involve local communities in the protection of their environment.

Furthermore, its new-found recognition of the critical part the private sector has to play as a partner in conservation matters is a welcome development. With their vast experience in the field of conservation together with this new flowering of imaginative, open-minded and constructive pragmatism, the WWF's input could be invaluable.

The UN Convention on International Trade in Endangered Species

Finally, having been discussed in an earlier chapter, the UN associated CITES needs no further introduction. Its role at the centre of matters concerning the trade in endangered species is its own qualification for full participation at the centre stage of international policy debate and design.

Coordination and cooperation

With the existence of so many benign organisations of such stature and influence and with such high and worthy declared ambitions and such exalted manpower, one could be forgiven for asking, so what's the problem? Why despite the intense activities of these highly qualified, experienced, dedicated and influential organisations does environmental decline continue on such an immense scale?

Unfortunately, while there is no shortage of expertise and good intentions, much of the good practice, coordination and international political backing necessary to fulfil their ambitions is lacking. Because we live in an increasingly global economy [2] many of the economic and environmental problems we face now require coordinated global solutions. This increasing globalisation has created new economic and political paradigms which cannot be challenged from the bottom up.

Some environmentalists argue that the world has failed to control the excesses of multinational corporate power in recent decades. They are right of course, but as we have seen, they themselves do not have workable solutions to the problem. Their talk tends to be peppered with words like "greed", "restrict", "penalise" and "prevent", notions that find few sympathisers where it really matters – among multinational corporations and financial institutions, and only serve to raise suspicions and discourage constructive dialogue.

To address major environmental problems for the long term it is essential that influential international agencies begin to throw off the restraints of unilateralist and politicised policy; that they move towards harmonising their activities under a common umbrella of policy based on science and scientific economic analysis, rather than whichever prevailing political canon currently characterises the ethos of their organisation.

The best way to achieve such unity is to bring them all under one roof. At present there are more than 40 different agencies with environmental programmes in the UN alone, yet environmental governance is still failing. A single body could respond to the needs of individual nations directly by tailoring proposals relevant to their environmental problems with greater authority. It could prioritise and concentrate effort and finance in the most efficient and effective ways.

This is no lone voice in the wilderness. Not only did senior economists at the Copenhagen Consensus in 2004 call for a WEO, but since then German Chancellor Angela Merkel, ex-president of France Nicolas Sarkozy and Pope Francis are among those who have also called for it.

The WEO I envisage would not be legislative because nations would be unlikely to accept another WTO-style organisation imposing itself on their sovereignty with rigid rules. Instead its chief role would be as a centre for excellence in understanding and combating environmental issues through economic policy. It could become a focal point for channelling ideas and showcasing innovative technology – the go-to place for all environmental issues, protection, mitigation and renewal alike. In place of the periodic "medical" check-ups of sporadic summits, it would keep a finger permanently on the pulse of the entire world environment and its biota, able both to anticipate and respond to the challenges of a changing world climate far more quickly, comprehensively and effectively with the best and most up-to-date ecosystemic economic "medicine".

A WEO could also act as a hub for new environmentally benign business by hosting trade fairs in which companies, inventors and entrepreneurs could present their strategies, products, and inventions either to make sales or seek investors and partnerships. Such fairs could help to disseminate ideas and technology far faster than otherwise. Some such fairs are already ongoing, such as China's 2018 Environmental Protection Expo in Beijing, and Brazil's ECOMONDO in São Paulo, but the centralisation of new ideas and innovations in rotating WEO destinations every three or four years could make it the World Cup or even the Olympics of environmentally friendly technological advance.

The fact is that in the brief span of human history we are at the eleventh hour. The world cannot afford to continue to act in the semi-chaotic, piecemeal, sectarian way that it does at present. The crossing of the Rubicon represented by the formation of a World Environment Organisation could set the stage for a new era of international cooperation and coordination in economic-ecosystemic affairs. A meeting and melding of some of the leading minds in science, sociology and economics, presently scattered and disconnected in diverse organisations, cannot but produce huge benefits.

1. *Mark Malloch Brown, Administrator of the UNDP*
2. *Between 1970 and 2006 the number of multinational companies jumped from 7,258 to nearly 79,000 (UNCTAD World Investment Report 2008)*

Chapter 18
Conclusion: Taken at the Flood

"There is a tide the affairs of men,
Which, taken at the flood, leads on to fortune;
Omitted, all the voyage of their life
Is bound in shallows and in miseries.
On such a full sea are we now afloat,
And we must take the current when it serves,
Or lose our ventures."
William Shakespeare: *Julius Caesar*

A time of opportunity

These well-known lines of Shakespeare have been much overused; however, they are supremely expressive of the momentousness of the point in our human story at which we now find ourselves. This book is far from the first warning that we will "lose our ventures" if we do not act decisively to rescue our declining planet. Yet it is significantly different from others because it founds its conclusions and solutions in science – on an understanding of the genetic and developmental roots of our predicament. As a result, broadly speaking it comes down in favour of market-led policies. Although this in itself is not new because the market approach is already widely supported, the very fact of justifying its virtuousness through an understanding of its place in the natural order should place it at the forefront of new environmental economic thinking. By recognising economics as a natural rather than a man-made phenomenon we can transform its management from a much-disputed discipline into a full-blown natural science.

Is this "scientising" of economics really necessary though? With so much theoretical and practical evidence and such widespread support in favour of market-led environmental strategies, much of it surely looks like plain common sense. Yet if that were indeed the case one could be forgiven for wondering why these strategies haven't already become front-line policy around the world. The reality is that although the principles have been thoroughly argued in erudite quarters, and examples of their success in pilot form are plentiful, the expected rush of market-led reforms never actually gets going. Everyday things like bubble wrap, expanded plastic foam, even shotgun cartridges are all perfectly recyclable by specialist companies; yet they are consigned to landfill for the want of a small subsidy from those who manufacture them to make their collection viable.

I consider it a scandal that governments have been so complacent, not to say idle, that they cannot manage this simple task. We, the public, need to let them know we are extremely unhappy with all this waste. There is much talk about the "circular economy", for example, but where's the substance? For people and organisations this failure is highly frustrating. It suggests its logic and value has not been fully absorbed or sufficiently accepted by those in the driving seat of governments all over the world. This has to change, and it is up to us to build the pressure to persuade them to "make it so", as Jean-Luc Picard of the starship *Enterprise* would say. It really could be as simple as that.

However, such landmark policy reforms are slow to catch on for good reason. To begin with they require something of a leap of faith: you don't step willingly from a familiar platform to a strange new one without being very sure its foundations are rock steady (or at least until the old one gets too perilous to cling to any longer, which may soon become the case). But perhaps the main reason it is still so difficult to achieve the much-needed paradigm shift in policy prescribed here is because market economics have for so long been steeped in political, cultural, psychological, not to mention hard-nosed, business prejudices based on an almost unlimited supply of disposable natural resources. With such a conservative and entrenched economic status quo, the challenge of achieving consensus and action on a fundamentally new policy agenda might appear nigh on impossible – a distant dream. Although arguments in favour of progressive change may appear overwhelming to those like me who put them forward, in economics as much as in any other intellectual arena, what is common sense to one man can seem to be naïve, or just misguided dogma to another.

Without the credentials that only the objectivity of empirical science can lend, therefore, such policies would seem to need proselytising to an unfeasibly extreme degree to stand even the remotest chance of gaining a foothold among those who shape world economic strategies – the sort of strategies that are discussed at G20 summits for example. Purely idea-driven, market-led environmental policies will also come up against vociferous opposition from those who fundamentally mistrust market solutions to ecological problems because they believe sooner or later they always lead to greed, exploitation and inequality.

The focus of this book has therefore been on trying to plug this gap in confidence in appropriate market-led strategies. I have tried to show that what I have called *Junglenomics* is not just another protocapitalist solution to environmental and poverty problems – good on paper but destructive in practice – because it can be securely underpinned by evidence and rationale. A wide acceptance that market economics is driven primarily by resource hunger in precisely the same way and by the same mechanisms as is Nature, is in my view essential to help energise a new era of environmentally compatible and socially responsible capitalist economic activity.

But such studies cannot remain marooned in the realms of dry academic discourse enervated only by pilot projects. The current crises of poverty and environmental degradation, let alone the dire predicted outcomes from climate change of droughts, floods, mass migrations and social unrest, demand that they come alive and become widespread both in policy and practice, not in some distant future decade but in this one.

No one could be more aware than I of the ambitiousness of the propositions put forward in these pages. Such changes would first require understanding, acceptance, consent and action at the highest levels if they were to move leaders of world communities towards the broad unity of purpose and policy advocated here. So why should they listen now when they have remained so deaf to previous arguments and pleadings?

The answer is that *Junglenomics* is very different from what has come before. Nearly all previous messages and recommendations to those that govern us concerning the world environment have come cloaked with strong political undertones. Most economists and governments remain deeply suspicious of the green agenda, for example, because though well-meaning, it is often utterly unrealistic; it demands major sacrifices, including an end to all economic growth in advanced economies. This is unfeasible to attempt, and it undermines interest in a far more realistic and pragmatic green agenda. Governments, business and industry are right to be suspicious of the motives of those who advocate unattainable economic restraints and strictures that translate as enforced economic stagnation. They want to find solutions to our environmental conundrums that are neither anti-capital nor anti-growth, yet that plot a sound and safe route to managing the planet's resources so that they last for the foreseeable future.

I believe this book provides just such a route. Its message could not be clearer – that there is only one correct answer to this great conundrum of our times, and that is a new kind of economic development and a new phase of economic growth driven by a thorough reappraisal of environmental value. In spirit, such a revaluation has already begun; certainly the will is there. But so far it is amorphous, disorganised, and lacks cohesion, leadership and focus, something that I have argued a World Environment Organisation could provide.

I sense that everywhere the aware and concerned members of the public are deeply frustrated; they know what they want to happen but they do not how to achieve it in the face of seemingly unstoppable, opposing market and political forces. We know from history that we humans have in recent centuries developed a strong tendency to mistreat the environment in the pursuit of our own interests, but we expect our leaders to work this out for us and make it right. Yet while many of those leaders sometimes make the right noises so that at times it appears as if we may have at last reached bottom and are set to rise again, the truth is we still haven't, and the decline continues apace.

We also know what choices we want others to make when the natural environment is at stake, but can be reluctant to step away from destructive practices when it is our turn for the spotlight. Some might see this so-called "Nimbyism" as hypocritical, but if we and our families are going to lose out this is only natural. We aren't angels after all. We need concrete incentive – carrot rather than stick – to participate wholeheartedly, because that is what, from coal miner to pulp mill owner to fisherman to farmer to house builder, our genes tell us to do – that which immediately benefits us and our families either in business or in our everyday lives in the universal, eternal and unchanging pursuit of resources.

In the meantime, we watch as the planet continues to deteriorate and those of us with our heads out of the sand feel a growing sense of desperation that with time running out, so much is said and yet so little achieved. Some join pressure groups, others to go on protest marches. I have chosen to write a book in which to argue that to rescue the world from this untimely fate we urgently need – not just *ad hoc* quick fixes, but genuine long-term synchrony between the natural world and the economic one.

Exploring and understanding the common principles at work within these two systems is the key to this. The natural system that I would have imitated in economics is one that has performed spectacularly well for billions of years, and the human mind arguably represents its crowning glory. I have demonstrated that species – latterly economic ones – have in reality not been drivers of, but slaves to its excesses, arising from Nature's inherent and essential drive to colonise resources blindly, almost regardless of consequence. The looming crisis in the natural world does not therefore stem from a Man-Nature conflict as is commonly supposed, but from an economic-ecosystemic one. We humans are only the vehicles for the economic phenomenon, and it rules our actions *en masse* as surely and compulsively as does Nature.

The inevitable conclusion must be that, whatever conscience-inspired plasters we may stick on a few of the world's bleeding wounds today, no strategies will work over the long term that cannot fully reconcile the interests of resource-driven economic colonisation with those of ecology.

However, we cannot solve our problems simply by shutting ourselves off from that ecology. The economic dimension cannot exist in isolation from the world's ecosystems because it is interlinked in innumerable ways both obvious and subtle.

Nor can we leave it to future generations to realise these facts and act decisively upon them. We have reached a watershed in our economic development and cannot afford to postpone concerted action any further. If we are to prevent the blessing of technology becoming instead a curse, it is vital that we begin to turn the tables on our natural economic impulses where they threaten the viability of the planetary ecosystem that supports us. Only when the planet is viewed and managed as a single corporeal unit in which the environment is its air-conditioned workplace, will we have justified Nature's gamble with human intelligence. Our power and influence over the natural world has passed the point of no return, and we must now choose between anarchy and order in that world.

In the end, the thing we need to focus on above all others is that we should live lives in our time that detract nothing from the Earth's hospitality towards, and enjoyment by, future generations – that we leave it no worse than we found it. This shouldn't have to be preached tiresomely from every street corner; it is simply a matter of good planetary housekeeping. This book points to Nature as holding the blueprint to achieve this.

Of course, there will be a cost to pay in sculpting the new economic ecosystem, but only a monetary one, although this can be offset by economic growth in green development with neutral cost to consumers. This cost may cause the myopic and self-interested to wriggle, squirm and cry foul, but in fact it is not so much cost as investment – the most productive and sensible investment the world could ever make. The era of take and take economics is passed. But make no mistake, the new era will be no less challenging, and no less fun – austerity need not be on the menu.

And the best of it is that when the short-term readjustment pains are over, the technology developed and deployed, the behaviour modified, and we have trained ourselves to live within our planet's capacity, we may be looked back on by future generations, not as condemned culprits for a diminished world, but as heroes who faced up to and overcame our innate weaknesses through a combination of science, sense and self-control.

If the mass of scientific evidence is to be believed, it is no exaggeration to say that we are at a critical crossroads; that unless the world gets its act together right now it faces an era of despair and decline. But I believe that it is not too late to turn it instead into one of hope and rejuvenation.

It is time to put the economic anarchy of the past behind us, take control of our destiny, and trigger a new era of global economic evolution. We need only charge up the mechanism and set the wheels in motion. By creating a sustainable, stable economic ecosystem, we have it within our grasp to put an end to the old economic order that is leading us – with all its wiles and temptations – towards decline, and replace it with science and order. What a legacy that would be.

Recognising the ubiquity of Nature's sublime paradigm, and then finding the will and the courage to grasp our fortunes before they grasp us, and then our children, is surely the overriding duty and, God willing, the destiny of our generation.

Postscript – a new perspective

"You don't need new ideas; you need a new perspective"
Oliver Burkeman

This book has been all about adopting a new perspective on our place in the world by looking at ourselves and our economic activity from an ecosystemic viewpoint.

New perspectives are not easy to come by though. For all our superior brains, we humans often find ourselves trapped in a nightmare *déjà vu* world where however hard we struggle to escape our worst problems, whatever inventive ideas we come up with to change our ways, we seem destined to repeat our mistakes endlessly. Perhaps Ramis and Rubin's classic film *Groundhog Day* struck such a chord because people recognised this feeling of being stuck in a time warp, unable to escape our fate whatever we might try, growing frustrated and angry at our repeated failure to escape it.

Our problem is that we view the world through fixed lenses that prevent us from seeing the bigger picture; we see what is happening in the room, but fail to look out of the window, so we remain trapped in that room. We do this in our personal lives and no less so in our behaviour on the big stage, particularly in behaviours that affect the health of our precious planetary ecosystem.

In the movie, escape from Groundhog Day could only be found via a reawakening and a radical change of heart. This is something that the human world needs to emulate – by rediscovering and reinventing its entire relationship with the natural world. The way the world can free itself from the cycle of environmental failure is therefore not to keep tinkering with the same old failed approaches, but instead to step back and change how we look at the problems we want to solve. *"The real act of discovery,"* wrote Marcel Proust, *"consists not in finding new lands but in seeing with new eyes."* The satirical comedian George Carlin called this trick *"vuja dé"*, a weird feeling of foreignness in the familiar that reveals previously unrecognised solutions and opportunities.

This book offers a new lens through which we can find ways to solve our environmental problems, throwing open the windows of modern life to see it anew through what Zen Buddhists call "beginners mind", that pure and expansive mindset stripped of preconceptions and prejudices that allows us to see the world as it really is. Without such a fresh perspective on ourselves and on our environmental problems we are certain to remain trapped in our Groundhog Day despite our newly avowed determination to escape it, reaching our epiphany only when it is far too late.

I suggest with humility that *Junglenomics* represents the voice of Nature, encompassing all the different strands of environmental decline in the one corrective formula that has served Nature so well for billions of years. For those of us who do not wish the human species to live in this destructive way any more, it could perhaps become our voice, and a focus for long-overdue change.

We are the problem, yet within us lies the solution – if only we have the understanding, the will, and the imagination to find it.

"I am only one, but still I am one. I cannot do everything, but still I can do something; and because I cannot do everything, I will not refuse to do something I can do."
Edward Everett Hale

Index